DATE DUE

GAYLORD			PRINTED IN U.S.A.

The
MOFFATT
NEW TESTAMENT COMMENTARY
Based on *The New Translation* by the late
REV. PROFESSOR JAMES MOFFATT, D.D.
and under his Editorship

THE JOHANNINE EPISTLES

The
Moffatt
New Testament Commentary
Based on '*The New Translation*' by the late
REV. PROFESSOR JAMES MOFFATT
D.D., LL.D., D.Litt.

and under his Editorship

Volumes already published

THE GOSPEL OF MATTHEW
by THEODORE H. ROBINSON, M.A., D.D.

THE GOSPEL OF MARK
by B. HARVIE BRANSCOMBE, M.A., PH.D.

THE GOSPEL OF LUKE
by WILLIAM MANSON, D.D.

THE GOSPEL OF JOHN
by G. H. C. MACGREGOR, D.D., D.LITT.

THE ACTS OF THE APOSTLES
by F. J. FOAKES-JACKSON, D.D.

THE EPISTLE OF PAUL TO THE ROMANS
by C. H. DODD, M.A., D.D.

THE FIRST EPISTLE OF PAUL TO THE CORINTHIANS
by JAMES MOFFATT, D.D., LL.D., D.LITT.

THE SECOND EPISTLE OF PAUL TO THE CORINTHIANS
by R. H. STRACHAN, D.D.

THE EPISTLE OF PAUL TO THE GALATIANS
by GEORGE S. DUNCAN, D.D.

THE EPISTLE OF PAUL TO THE PHILIPPIANS
by J. HUGH MICHAEL, D.D.

THE EPISTLES OF PAUL
TO THE COLOSSIANS, TO PHILEMON AND TO THE EPHESIANS
by E. F. SCOTT, D.D.

THE PASTORAL EPISTLES
by E. F. SCOTT, D.D.

THE EPISTLE TO THE HEBREWS
by THEODORE H. ROBINSON, M.A., D.D.

THE GENERAL EPISTLES: JAMES, PETER AND JUDAS
by JAMES MOFFATT, D.D., LL.D., D.LITT.

THE JOHANNINE EPISTLES
by C. H. DODD, M.A., D.D.

THE REVELATION OF ST. JOHN
by MARTIN KIDDLE, M.A., assisted by M. K. ROSS

In preparation
THE EPISTLES TO THE THESSALONIANS
by J. S. BEZZANT

THE JOHANNINE EPISTLES

BY

C. H. DODD, M.A., D.D.

*Norris-Hulse Professor of Divinity
in the University of Cambridge*

HARPER & ROW, PUBLISHERS

New York, Evanston, and London

THE JOHANNINE EPISTLES

Copyright, 1946, *by* C. H. Dodd

Printed in the United States of America

IN PIAM MEMORIAM

PRAECLARI SCRIPTVRARVM SACRARVM INTERPRETIS

QVI COMMENTARIORVM HANC SERIEM

CONSILIO INSTITVIT

IVDICIO DIREXIT

NOMINE ORNAVIT

IACOBI MOFFATT

INTER LABORES DEFVNCTI

HOC OPVSCVLVM

IPSIVS NVTV INCEPTVM

TANDEM ABSOLVTVM DICAT AVCTOR

PREFACE

In studying the Johannine Epistles I have consulted various current commentaries, notably those of Rothe, Westcott, B. Weiss, Holtzmann, R. Law (*The Tests of Life*), Windisch, and A. E. Brooke, to whose admirable Introduction I am much indebted, although I sometimes come to different conclusions. The interpretation, however, which I offer here has in large measure emerged from studies primarily directed towards the understanding of the Fourth Gospel in its contemporary setting.

CAMBRIDGE,
   January, 1945

CONTENTS

INTRODUCTION

COMMENTARY

THE FIRST EPISTLE OF JOHN

CONTENTS

INTRODUCTION

I. THE JOHANNINE EPISTLES IN THE EARLY CHURCH

THE first clear evidence of the existence of any of these writings is afforded by Polycarp, Bishop of Smyrna, who died as a martyr at the age of eighty-six, A.D. 155–6. Apparent echoes of the language of 1 John are fairly numerous in his work. Many of these however might be due simply to acquaintance with 'Johannine' ways of thought and speech, such as might be expected in one with Polycarp's background. We are credibly informed by Irenaeus (who knew him) that Polycarp had been acquainted with 'John' (Eusebius, *Ecclesiastical History*, V. 20. 6). But there is at least one passage which seems to go beyond this. It is in the seventh chapter of Polycarp's *Epistle to the Philippians*. The parallel passages are here given in a literal translation for the purpose of comparison.

<table>
<tr><td align="center">*Polycarp vii*</td><td align="center">1 *John*</td></tr>
<tr><td>1. 'Everyone who does not acknowledge that Jesus Christ has come in the flesh, is antichrist; and whoever does not acknowledge the witness of the cross, is of the devil. . . . 2. Wherefore, leaving the futility of the many, and their false teachings, let us return to the word handed down to us from the beginning.'</td><td>iv. 2–3. 'Every spirit which acknowledges that Jesus Christ has come in the flesh is of God; and every spirit which does not acknowledge Jesus is not of God; and this is the (spirit) of antichrist.' (Cf. ii. 22, 'this is antichrist.')

iii. 8. 'He who commits sin is of the devil.'

ii. 24. 'Let that which you heard from the beginning remain in you.'</td></tr>
</table>

Here Polycarp is saying the same thing as 1 John, and saying it in almost the same language, though somewhat more succinctly. It seems most natural to conclude that Polycarp was acquainted with our First Epistle. For the two lesser epistles Polycarp offers no similarly clear evidence. (See the careful display and assessment of the evidence in P. N. Harrison, *Polycarp's Two Epistles to the Philippians*, pp. 300–1.)

The date of Polycarp's work is unfortunately not precisely determined. There have been many attempts to interpret the apparently contradictory internal evidence. The solution of the problem offered by Dr. P. N. Harrison (in the work cited above) is that the so-called Epistle to the Philippians consists of two epistles of Polycarp to the same church, written at different times. One of them was apparently written within a fortnight or so of Ignatius's visit to him, which was in all probability A.D. 115. The other, in which our crucial passage occurs, must have been written later; but how much later, it is difficult to say. Dr. Harrison dates it about 135-7; but his arguments for so late a date are not conclusive. It might well be ten or fifteen years earlier. Indeed, there seems no cogent reason why the interval between the first letter and the second may not have been measured in months rather than years.

Next, Papias, Bishop of Hierapolis in the second century, made more than one quotation from 'the former epistle of John.' So Eusebius informs us (*Ecclesiastical History*, III. 39. 17), and we may accept the statement, since Eusebius had before him the complete text of Papias's work, which is now extant only in fragments. The expression 'the former epistle' would in a classical Greek writer imply the existence of only two epistles of John; but in the Hellenistic and Roman periods the comparative and superlative were frequently confused, and Eusebius has exactly the same expression in a context where he speaks explicitly of three Johannine epistles (*op. cit.*, III. 25. 2). We may take it that this is Eusebius's way of saying '1 John.' It implies nothing about Papias's acquaintance with either or both of the lesser epistles. It has been thought that the following passage of Papias contains a reminiscence of 3 John: 'I did not take pleasure, like most people, in those who . . . report alien commandments, but in those who report the commandments given to faith by the Lord, and proceeding *from the Truth itself*' (Eusebius, *op. cit.*, III. 39. 3); cf. 3 John 12: 'Testimony is borne to Demetrius by all, and *by the Truth itself*.' This is no very striking parallel; and as it occurs in a passage where Papias is glorifying oral tradition over against written documents, it might be naturally explained (so far as it can be said to echo specifically Johannine language) as the result of Papias's association with Johannine circles. For so much we may safely affirm about him, though Eusebius showed that there is no sufficient ground for accepting Irenaeus's statement that he was a 'hearer of John.' In sum, we may conclude that Papias cited our 1 John, and assume (*e silentio*) that he did not cite either 2 or 3 John, though that does not necessarily mean that he did not know them.

The date of Papias's work is again uncertain. Some would date it between 120 and 140: some between 140 and 160.

Thus our two earliest witnesses are less valuable than might have been hoped. We may say with certainty that 1 John was known in the province of Asia (to which both Smyrna and Hierapolis belonged) before the middle of the second century; and we may say with great probability that this date might safely be brought up to about A.D. 120–5 at latest, since there is no need to date any part of Polycarp's work later than this.

There are in other writers, some of them earlier than these, passages which have been adduced as echoes of the language of our epistles; but on examination they prove to be of a kind which could be sufficiently explained by the generally diffused tradition of apostolic teaching, or, it may be, by the specially 'Johannine' form of that tradition. They fall far short of pre-supposing an acquaintance with these particular writings.

It is only in the last quarter of the second century that evidence becomes really satisfactory. Irenaeus, Bishop of Lyons (died about A.D. 202), quotes freely from 1 John, and also from 2 John, attributing both writings to 'John the disciple of the Lord,' to whom he also attributes the Fourth Gospel (*Adversus Haereses* [ed. Harvey], I. 9. 3, III. 17. 5, 8). Clement of Alexandria (head of the catechetical school at Alexandria about 180–202) frequently quotes 1 John and attributes it to the Apostle John (*Stromateis*, III. 5. 45). In the Latin *Adumbrationes* (supposed to represent extracts from the Greek *Hypotyposes* of the same author) there is a short summary of 'the Second Epistle of John' (expressly so-called), with the scarcely consistent statements that it was written (*a*) 'to Virgins,' and (*b*) 'to a Babylonian woman named Electa who signifies the Catholic Church.' We may suppose that the Latin translator (or adaptor) has been guilty of some confusion.

However this may be, it is certain that Clement did know at least one epistle beside the First, since in one of his quotations from that work he cites it as 'the greater epistle' (*Stromateis*, II. 15. 66). In a correct Greek writer this would imply that Clement knew only two; and that is probably the case; but we cannot be sure that even Clement was immune from the common Hellenistic confusion of comparative and superlative to which allusion was made above.

The first known list of New Testament books is the so-called Muratorian Canon, which was made at Rome about A.D. 200, probably by the learned scholar and theologian, Hippolytus, dissenting Bishop of Rome about that time. The references to the Johannine epistles in this document are as follows.

> (After giving an account of the composition of the Fourth Gospel, Hippolytus proceeds:) 'What wonder, then, that John so emphatically brings out the several points in his epistles also, saying in his own person, "What we saw with our eyes and heard with our ears, and our hands handled, these things we have written to you." Thus he describes himself not only as an eyewitness, but also as a hearer and writer of all the wonders of the Lord in order.' (Then, after dealing with the Acts and the Pauline epistles, he proceeds:) 'The epistle of Jude and two of the above mentioned John are reckoned among the catholic writings.'

The meaning of this surely is that Hippolytus recognizes as canonical two epistles of John, one of which is identified by his quotation as our 1 John. Some critics indeed have tried to secure his attestation for all three Johannine epistles, by assuming that after dealing with the First Epistle in connection with the Fourth Gospel, he then means to say 'there are two *more* epistles of John which are reckoned canonical.' That is a quite unnatural forcing of language. There are (he makes it quite explicit) two 'catholic' or canonical epistles of John. One of them he has already quoted for its bearing on the Fourth Gospel. Whether the other is our 2 John or 3 John remains uncertain. Since, however, Irenaeus, whose relations with Rome about this time were intimate, recognizes 1 and 2 John, but ignores 3 John, we may probably take it that these same two were acknowledged as canonical at Rome at the close of the second century. From that time on 1 John has a secure place in the Canon of the New Testament.

It is otherwise with the two lesser epistles. As we have seen, there is evidence of the existence of more than one Johannine epistle during the second century, and 2 John is definitely attested. Of 3 John there is no explicit mention until we reach the third century, and there is no clear citation from it until the fourth century. Origen of Alexandria and Caesarea (A.D. 185–254), who includes 1 John among canonical writings, and quotes from it, attests the existence of two other epistles, whose authenticity is doubtful (Eusebius, *Eccl. Hist.*, VI. 25. 10). This doubt long remained. Eusebius himself, in the early fourth century, while placing 1 John among the 'unquestioned' books of the Canon, relegates 2 and 3 John to the category of 'disputed' books (*op. cit.*, III. 25. 3). Later still Jerome, who himself accepted all three epistles as the work of the Apostle John, records that many attributed 2 and 3 John to a different author, John the Presbyter (*De Viris Illustribus*, 9, 18). By his time, however, all three were generally recognized as canonical in Greek and Latin Christianity, thanks largely to the authority of Athanasius. In the Syriac New Testament, on the other hand, none of them appear before A.D. 500.

As a curiosity of criticism, it may be mentioned that in the fourth century it was widely held that the First Epistle at least, and perhaps all three, were addressed to Parthia, and the title '*To the Parthians*' actually occurs in a handful of late MSS. This theory, though supported by so great an authority as Augustine, has no probability. It is difficult to conjecture how it arose. It is possible that it has some connection with the statement in the Clementine *Adumbrationes* (see p. xiii) that 2 John was addressed to a Babylonian lady (Babylon being within the territory of the Parthian Empire). But was Clement (or his Latin adaptor) thinking of 1 Pet. v. 13: 'She in Babylon elect together with you'? And is this perhaps the source of the whole 'Parthian' theory?

To sum up: 1 John has an established place in Christian tradition at least from the second quarter of the second century.

It first emerges in the province of Asia, and is first quoted extensively, and attributed to John, by Irenaeus, a native of the same province. It is already included in the Roman New Testament of about A.D. 200. 2 John first appears in the last quarter of the second century, attributed to the author of 1 John, and is probably included in the Roman Canon of about A.D. 200. Elsewhere both its authorship and its canonicity were widely disputed down to the fourth or (in some places) fifth century. 3 John is first mentioned, as a writing of dubious authenticity, in the first half of the third century, and is not definitely admitted to the New Testament until about the middle of the fourth century—later still outside Greek and Latin Christianity.

The external evidence, therefore, for the two lesser epistles is late, meagre and unsatisfactory, especially for the Third. It should however be borne in mind that both are extremely short, and contain very little material for quotation. Critical questions fall to be determined largely upon the ground of internal evidence, and cannot profitably be discussed until we have examined the character and contents of the writings themselves (see, further, pp. lxvi *sqq.*).

For a full account of the patristic evidence the reader may be referred to A. E. Brooke's Introduction to his Commentary on 1-3 John (*International Critical Commentary*), pp. lii – lxii.

II. BACKGROUND AND SETTING OF THE FIRST EPISTLE

At the beginning of the Christian era there was a movement or tendency within paganism towards a purer, more reasonable and more inward piety. Its representatives often patronized traditional cults, particularly those known as 'mysteries,' and they invented or developed others; but its underlying assumption was that all religions come to much the same thing, if they are rationally understood. Its exponents offered ways of rationalizing most of the current rituals and myths. The movement covered a wide range. Near the bottom of the scale it was little more than a way of making superstition respectable for the minor *intelligentsia*. Near the top, it took form in a high religion of mystical communion with the Divine. Certain general assumptions can be recognized. The material world is evil. The rational part of man is a prisoner in it, and an exile from the world of light; in fact, in some way a separated part of the supernal world, an effluence, or radiation, of that eternal Light which is Reason, or pure Being, or God. By knowledge of the world of light, communicated in esoteric revelations or initiations of one kind or another, the rational spirit of man can liberate itself from its prison of matter and rise to the supernal world. It is then united or identified with, or absorbed in, the Divine.

Many variations were played upon this theme, all of them controlled by the central dogmas: the distinction between the realm of light and the realm of darkness which is the material world, and deification through supernatural knowledge (*gnosis*). The movement undoubtedly attracted many charlatans, but it also had exponents (like those writers who are responsible for the tractates of the *Corpus Hermeticum*) who display a pure and genuine mystical piety. In general, we may recognize in it the traits of a type of religion which recurs in many periods; laying stress upon 'enlightenment'; usually individualist and esoteric in temper; jealous of its 'spirituality' and disdainful of the material world, and of history.

When Christianity appeared in the Graeco-Roman world, it early came into contact with this higher paganism; naturally enough, for it too was a missionary faith aiming at the conversion and salvation of mankind through the revelation of God and communion with Him. On the one side, believers in a generalized religion, expressing itself in various mythologies and cults, readily welcomed one more cult, one more mythology, which could be added to the ingredients of the theosophical hotch-potch. They prepared to adopt Christianity as they had already tried to adopt Judaism. On the other side, enthusiastic but ill-informed converts to Christianity were eager to reinterpret the faith 'in terms of modern thought,' as we say. There are hints of attempts at assimilation already in the Epistle to the Colossians and the Pastoral Epistles; and the Fourth Gospel can best be understood as a brilliant attempt to undercut the whole process by a genuine and thoroughgoing reinterpretation, in which alien categories are completely mastered and transformed by the Gospel, and constrained to express the central truth of Christianity in universal terms. It was along the lines laid down in the Fourth Gospel that the problem was in the end successfully solved. But that is to anticipate.

At the end of the apostolic age, church history, it has been said, enters a tunnel. When it emerges, in the middle of the second century, we discover a central body which is the Catholic Church, surrounded by a medley of sects claiming in some sense the Christian name, and varying from recognizable though somewhat eccentric presentations of the Gospel, through various half-Christian or near-Christian systems of belief, to downright caricatures. Their names, and some account of their peculiar tenets, can be read in the pages of Irenaeus, Hippolytus and Epiphanius. To some of them ancient writers apply the term 'Gnostic,' and this has been adopted by modern writers as a general designation for all these would-be Christian heresies. Others apply the term to all systems of thought, with or without a tinge of Christianity, which teach salvation through *gnosis* or supernatural knowledge. It is equally appropriate to them all, and there are advantages in using in its widest denotation a term which brings out the common element in a great variety of religious beliefs. We need not however dispute over names. The facts are clear. What is not altogether clear is the process by which this situation came about, for the rise of heretical Gnostic sects took place during the 'tunnel' period.

The First Epistle of John appears to reflect a critical moment at an early stage in the process. It speaks of a group of Christian teachers who had gone wrong. They were not only teachers: they were prophets—'false prophets' our author calls them. He does not deny that they spoke by inspiration; only he is sure that their inspiration was not divine. As prophets, they must have been persons commanding respect and exercising authority in the Church. They began to teach new doctrines, and, presumably after failing to carry the Church with them, seceded, and continued their missionary activity in the pagan world. Their mission was successful. They

xviii

found a wide hearing—indeed, a wider than the orthodox teachers could command. All this is told us in plain terms in 1 John ii. 18–19, iv. 1–6. The secession clearly gave the Church a harsh shock. We may conjecture that it may have been the first case, at least in this province, of a deliberate secession on doctrinal grounds, and the fact that it was led by prophetic men, respected and influential, to whom the laity had been accustomed to look as leaders, made the situation very dangerous. The fellowship of the Church was rent; the unity of belief and teaching was broken; the rank and file might well be disturbed and perplexed. It is to this situation that the epistle is addressed.

What then did these dissenters teach? All that we are told directly is that they denied the reality of the Incarnation. This denial was characteristic, we are told, of the 'Docetists.' But in fact any 'Gnostic' was bound to find some way to avoid the scandalous idea that the Son of God, the Revealer, the Intermediary between the Divine and the human, suffered the degradation of direct contact with matter, the embodiment of all evil; and above all he was bound to deny that the Divine could suffer. The false prophets therefore were certainly on the track which led to later Gnostic heresies. For their further tenets we can only proceed by inference. Our author attacks people who use (unworthily and untruly as he thinks) such language as, 'we are born of God,' 'we are in the light,' 'we have no sin,' 'we dwell in God,' 'we know God.' He is prepared to use such expressions, properly defined, in a fully Christian sense. It is their false and unworthy use that he reprobates. All the same, it is noteworthy that if such expressions cannot in all cases be exactly cited from Gnostic sources, they are certainly closely analogous to Gnostic language, and taken together describe well enough the best type of Gnostic piety (in the widest sense), with its intense spirituality and its claim to mystical experience—above all to that 'knowledge' of God which is the way to salvation and deification.

Our author also finds in his adversaries a neglect of Christian morality. Is this neglect to be called 'Gnostic'? Christian apologists of the second century charge the Gnostics with all manner of moral enormities. The pagans, we may recall, made similar charges against Christians, and Christians have been known to retort them upon the Jews. There seems however no reason to doubt that some of the heretics believed themselves to be so far above good and evil that their conduct scandalized even the easy-going censors of Roman society. Yet it would certainly be unjust to tar all Gnostics with that brush. In some Gnostic circles there is evidence of ascetic personal morals. When our author urges that those who cherish the Christian hope should 'purify themselves as Christ is pure,' some of his opponents might have applauded the sentiment, while adding that they could not understand how the Son of God could be described as 'pure' if He was involved in matter. It is, however, to be noted that our author, with a sure instinct, thinks of Christian morality as being from first to last a matter of obedience to the divine command of love or charity. It does not appear that charity plays any considerable part in the ethical ideals of Gnosticism, pagan or Christian. That type of piety went along with an individualism which had usually little sense of social obligations.

On the whole, then, there is good ground for concluding that the errors with which this epistle is concerned are associated with that tendency in the religious life of the time which is known as 'Hellenistic mysticism,' or 'the higher paganism,' or especially in its near-Christian dress, as 'Gnosticism.' Reference to writings in the Gnostic tradition will often illuminate passages in the epistle (as this commentary will attempt to show). In common with the Fourth Gospel, the First Epistle of John shows the influence of Gnostic ways of thought. It was not without reason that the Gospel according to John was welcomed in some heretical circles, and at first looked at askance by some ultra-conservatives in the Church. But both parties were wrong. The use of current religious phraseology and thought-forms serves only to bring out more clearly a radical divergence.

The religious quest of the Hellenistic world was not in vain. It attained some genuine religious insight; and it provided early Christian thinkers with an intellectual apparatus for interpreting Christianity to the wider world, and, in doing so, penetrating more deeply into the meaning of the Gospel. But the more openly the religious discussion was conducted upon ground common to Christianity and the best non-Christian thought, the more clearly did the specific *differentia* of the Christian faith emerge. Augustine, himself trained in a philosophy which was the fine flowering of the Hellenistic spirit, put his finger upon the point when he said that most of the statements made in the Prologue to the Fourth Gospel were already familiar to him from the writings of the Neo-Platonists; but one thing he could not find there: 'The Word was made flesh" (*Confessions* vii. 9). It was there that the issue was joined between two rival philosophies of life. And it was this issue that our author saw to be raised by the disturbing propaganda of 'false prophets' in the churches which he knew and for which he felt responsible. In all that he writes he has this problem in mind.

III. CHARACTER AND CONTENTS OF THE FIRST EPISTLE

The First Epistle of John (unlike the Second and Third) has no epistolary introduction or conclusion, such as we find in Pauline and other New Testament epistles, after the regular models of contemporary correspondence. It is not so much a letter as a somewhat informal tract or homily. It seems, however, to have been addressed, in the first instance, to a particular circle, rather than written for general publication. The situation in view is apparently local, and there is evident a certain warmth of intimacy between writer and readers. The tone of the work is that of a pastor addressing his flock. Yet no names or other particulars are given, to connect the work with this or that local church. It may perhaps be best understood as a circular letter, like 1 Peter and (probably) Ephesians, addressed to the churches of a whole region.

The argument is not closely articulated. There is little direct progression. The writer 'thinks around' a succession of related topics. The movement of thought has not inaptly been described as 'spiral,' for the development of a theme often brings us back almost to the starting-point; almost, but not quite, for there is a slight shift which provides a transition to a fresh theme; or it may be to a theme which had apparently been dismissed at an earlier point, and now comes up for consideration from a slightly different angle. The striking aphorisms which are the most memorable things in the epistle do not usually emerge as the conclusion of a line of argument. They come in flashes, and their connection with the general line of thought is sometimes only hinted at.

Any attempt to divide the work into orderly paragraphs and sections must be largely arbitrary, and will indicate only in a broad way the succession of topics. After separating off the exordium (i. 1–4) and the postscript (v. 14–21), we may regard the epistle as falling into three main divisions, to which the following headings may be supplied:

I. What is Christianity? i. 5 – ii. 28.
II. Life in the Family of God. ii. 29 – iv. 12.
III. The Certainty of the Faith. iv. 13 – v. 13.

Within this framework the argument may be summarized as follows, square brackets marking words inserted to bring out implied connections of thought, and round brackets the author's own parentheses.

'I am writing about that which is the theme of all Christian preaching and teaching—the Gospel, God's life-giving Word to man. Since the life of eternity was manifested in time by the incarnation of the Son of God, we can speak of it with an assurance based upon direct testimony to historical facts.

'My object in writing is to promote the threatened unity of the Church in this crisis of schism and apostasy (i. 1–4).

I

1. 'The main purport of the Christian revelation may be summed up in the familiar maxim, "God is light." Since light is an absolute, excluding darkness, fellowship with God must show itself in a life radiant with goodness, and free from all dark ways: in other words, a good life, free from sin. Only in such a life can Christian fellowship be realized.

'(Free from sin, however, not in the sense of a personal achievement of moral perfection—the claim to sinlessness made by some is a delusion—but free from sin by divine forgiveness and renewal mediated through the sacrifice and the intercession of Christ.)

'Again Christianity offers [in the familiar phrase] knowledge of God; but it recognizes no such knowledge as genuine unless it shows itself in obedience to God's commands.

'And again, Christianity means union with God; but insists that such union involves moral conformity with His character as revealed in Christ (i. 5 – ii. 6).

2. '[To return to our starting-point—"light" and "darkness"; how fittingly the terms describe the contrast between the new order of life revealed in Christ and the old order which is doomed.] The new order is marked by Christ's own "new commandment" of love, or charity. There is no genuine "enlightenment" apart from obedience to this commandment.

'As Christians you are actually living within the new order, in which you possess forgiveness of sins, knowledge of God, and victory over all evil powers.

'Over against this new order stands the pagan world-order, in irreconcilable opposition to God, and doomed to destruction. The Christian who loves God and obeys His will has no attachment to this doomed world, but belongs to the immortal order (ii. 7–17).

3. 'The end of this world is at hand. We have been taught that it will be immediately preceded by the appearance of "Antichrist"—and Antichrist is here! For what else is this appalling apostasy, this denial of Christ and of the Father He reveals? The false teachers claim superior "enlightenment"; but there is enlightenment enough for every Christian in the simple Gospel which you received. If you remain stedfastly, and intelligently, loyal to the Gospel, you are secure in the truth, and can face the impending Day of Judgment with confidence (ii. 18–28).

II

1. '[Loyalty to the Gospel includes right conduct; and] right conduct is the sign that by God's grace we have been born

again as His children. Consider how much is implied in the Gospel assurance that God is our Father. It is, first, a proof of God's love for us. Secondly, it is a promise that we shall hereafter see God and be like Him. Thirdly [and this is the point I wish to emphasize here], it lays upon us the obligation to imitate the divine character as revealed in Christ.

'There is a stark contrast between righteousness (or right conduct) and sin (or wrong-doing), a contrast which no sophistry should be allowed to obscure. The Son of God, Himself sinless, came to abolish sin. The children of God, by virtue of a divine heredity, live a life over which sin has no power (ii. 29 – iii. 10).

2. 'I remind you again of Christ's own commandment: "Love one another." Hatred among brothers is a monstrous thing. It is pilloried in the bible story of Cain, the first murderer—for hatred is murder. Cain stands for the pagan world-order, which is the realm of hatred, and of death. We are living in the new order which is a realm of life; and the token is, that we love one another.

'What love, or charity, is, we learn from Christ's action in laying down His life for us. We are bound to imitate His sacrifice—even if it be only in the humble way of giving up what we have, to relieve a brother's need. In any case, charity is action (iii. 11–18).

3. 'It is only in the exercise of charity that we have solid assurance of our Christian standing before God; and if conscience is still uneasy, we may take confidence from the thought that God knows us better than we know ourselves. If our conscience is clear [as the conscience of a Christian should be], then we may live in frank and open intercourse with God, asking Him for what we need, and doing what He wills. To live thus is what is meant by union with God; and a token of this union is the gift of the Spirit (iii. 19–24).

'(The gift of the Spirit, however, may be counterfeited. There is false inspiration as well as true. The test lies in the confession of Christ as the incarnate Son of God. The false teaching which denies the incarnation is [as I said before] the mark of Antichrist. As the world-power of evil is already overcome by those in whom God dwells, so also is the false teaching, whose very success in the pagan world sufficiently indicates its pagan origin. The Church is God's family: its testimony is received by those who know God, rejected by those who are none of His. The former show the true inspiration, the latter the counterfeit) (iv. 1–6).

4. '[To resume:] love, or charity, is of divine origin, and those who practise it are children of God, and know God. In fact, God *is* love. His love is disclosed to us in the coming of Christ and His work of redemption; and that loving action of God's is the one ground of all love, or charity, among men. Clearly, then, the command to love one another is an inseparable consequence of the Gospel of God's love. There is no "vision of God" in this life; but there *is* real union with God: we have it when His love is freely active in our love for one another (iv. 7–12).

III

1. 'We have assurance of this union, [as I said before,] in the gift of the Spirit. But moreover, [though man cannot see God in His eternal being,] there is one thing we *have* seen— the coming of Christ, the Son of God incarnate, as Saviour of the world. To hold that conviction is to have union with God, for it is to be aware of His love. [I repeat:] God is love; to live in union with God is—to live in love. And living in love we need have no fear of the impending Day of Judgment; for we are already at one with our Judge; and love excludes fear (iv. 13–18).

2. '[To sum up:] we love, because He loved us first. The test for the reality of our love is simply practical charity towards our brothers. Unless a man loves his fellow (whom he has seen), it is idle to assert that he loves God (whom he cannot see). It is moreover God's own command [through the teaching of Jesus Christ] that in loving Him we should love our fellows, and love without obedience is meaningless. Through faith in Christ we are all children of God, ''Love me, love my child,'' is a maxim applicable here as in ordinary

human relations: if we love God, we must needs love our brother, who is His child.

'To love God is to obey His commands. [But surely, you will say, that is too hard for us. No:] it is not hard to obey God, because we are His children, having within us that divine quality of life which is victorious over the world. Our faith assures us victory over God's enemy, without us and within: the faith, I mean, which affirms that Jesus is the Son of God incarnate (iv. 19 – v. 5).

3. 'This faith we must hold in its fulness. Christ came, not only by the water of His baptism, [as the first great initiate,] but also by the blood of His cross, [as Saviour of the world]. In evidence, we have the testimony both of the Spirit [in the earthly ministry of Christ, and in the Church], and of the water [of His baptism, and ours], and the blood [of His cross, and of the sacramental chalice]. The witness is consentient, and it is the testimony of God Himself. It is, however, only in the act of faith in Christ that we appropriate the testimony to ourselves. To reject it is to give the lie to God.

'The sum of the testimony is this: that God has given us eternal life, in His Son: to have Christ is to live; to be without Christ is to be dead. I have written to you who believe, to assure you that you possess eternal life' (v. 6–13).

POSTSCRIPT

1. 'The Christian assurance of which I have spoken has an especial bearing on prayer. Prayer which conforms to the will of God is assured of an answer; and in particular prayer for a fellow-Christian who has fallen into sin (provided it is not mortal sin) (v. 14-17).

2. 'There are three things of which we can be quite certain: (i) the child of God is preserved from sin; (ii) we are God's children, in an evil world; (iii) through the incarnate Son we know the God who is utterly real, and being in union with Him we live the life of eternity. Knowing this, have nothing to do with unreal substitutes for God' (v. 18-21).

The immediate aim of this epistle, as we have seen, is to meet a critical situation arising out of the preaching of a distorted form of Christianity. By way of meeting it, the author recalls his readers to the original springs of Christian belief; to **that which you learned from the very beginning** (ii. 24), **the message you have learned from the very beginning** (iii. 11), **the old command which you have had from the very beginning . . . the word you have heard** (ii. 7), in short, the 'word of life,' embodied in the primitive, apostolic Gospel (i. 1–3). That recall is a note that sounds all through, whatever may be the particular topic discussed in any passage.

It is not at first sight obvious to the reader that what the author is giving is in fact the common, original Gospel of primitive Christianity. His forms of expression certainly differ from those of most of the New Testament, and have a close resemblance only to those of the Fourth Gospel, which is admittedly a relatively late work, and one with a highly individual cast of thought and language. It will therefore be of interest to confront the teaching of the epistle with what we know of the early presentation of the Christian faith to the world.

About the character and contents of the primitive Gospel, at least in its broad lines, the New Testament leaves us in no doubt. The briefest possible formulation is that which Mark gives as a summary of the preaching of Jesus: 'The time is fulfilled and the Kingdom of God has drawn near. Repent and believe the Gospel' (Mark i. 15). How the Apostles proclaimed this Gospel in the earliest days we may learn from a comparison of *data* in the Pauline Epistles (the earliest surviving Christian documents) with the apostolic speeches in the Acts of the Apostles (which though written down much later agree so remarkably with the Pauline *data* that we must conclude they rest upon good and early tradition). The *kerygma*, or proclamation of the Gospel by the earliest preachers, may be summarized somewhat as follows:[1]

[1] For the evidence, see my book *The Apostolic Preaching and its Developments*, Chapter I.

xxvii

The crisis of history has arrived; the prophecies are fulfilled; and the 'Age to Come' has begun.

Jesus of Nazareth, of the line of David, came as God's Son, the Messiah.

He did mighty works;

gave a new and authoritative teaching or law;

was crucified, dead and buried (died for our sins);

rose again the third day;

was exalted to 'the right hand of God,' victorious over 'principalities and powers';

will come again as Judge of quick and dead.

The apostles and those who are in fellowship with them constitute the Church, the New Israel of God, marked out as such by the outpouring of the Spirit.

Therefore repent, believe in Christ, and you will receive forgiveness of sins and a share in the life of the Age to Come (or eternal life).

The setting of this apostolic preaching is eschatological; that is to say, it presupposes the general scheme of Jewish belief in the providential ordering of history towards a final crisis in which God's purpose will be fulfilled, and His sovereign rule over the world will be demonstrated in judgment upon evil and in the redemption of men. The essential point in the *kerygma* is that the decisive step in this culminating act of history has already been taken. In the coming of Christ the Kingdom of God has come upon men for judgment and redemption; and consequently, in the Church, the new Israel of God, there exists a divine community enjoying within time and space the 'life of the Age to Come'; and the final consummation is impending, in which Christ will be manifested in glory as Judge and Redeemer to wind up the historical process.

It is clear that the author of this epistle lives fully within this eschatological faith, even though in many respects his expression of it differs from that of the primitive Church. He is aware of living at the moment of history in which, so to

speak, the two 'ages' overlap. **It is the last hour** of this age.
The world is passing away. It is true that he never relates this
conviction, as earlier writers do, to the Hebrew conception of
history as the working out of a divine plan interpreted by the
prophets. He never alludes to the fulfilment of prophecy, as he
betrays virtually no interest in the Old Testament, and no
acquaintance with the contemporary thought of Judaism.
For him the two 'ages' of Jewish-Christian thought are
the realms of light and darkness which figure in Hellenistic
theology. **The darkness is passing away and the true light is
already shining** (ii. 8). That is his charactertistic way of
restating the evangelical proclamation of the new age. The
epithet **true**—more properly 'real,' as in John i. 9—in itself
betrays the philosophical background of his thought. He
speaks of the 'real' light in a quasi-Platonic sense; that is to
say, the eternal or archetypal light ('the light that never was
on sea or land'); the light of which all visible lights are only
suggestive symbols; the **real light** which in John i. 9 is identified
with the Logos, the eternal Principle of creation and revelation. But the realms of 'light' and 'darkness' do not here
represent, as for Hellenistic thinkers in general, a static map
of the universe in its several planes. The darkness fades, the
light dawns: there is movement and change; something is
happening. What our author means is that a divine action has
taken place which profoundly alters the character of human
existence in this world: a new dispensation, a new order, has
been constituted by act of God; and *this* is the realm of light,
within which Christians live, even while the pagan world
continues (not for very long) to live in the old order of darkness.

If he is indifferent to the historical antecedents of the act of
God as expressed in prophecy and its fulfilment, he is very
much alive to the historical actuality of the events in which
that act of God was manifested. As in the primitive Preaching,
so here, the passage from the age of darkness to the age of
light was effected by the coming of Christ. In the simplest
terms he affirms, **We know that the Son of God has come**
(v. 20). In eschatological prediction the Messiah (or God Himself as Judge on the Last Day) is 'the *Coming One*' (see Heb.

x. 37, citing the Greek of Hab. ii. 3; Matt. iii. 11). In the apostolic Preaching Christ is He who *has come*. The change of verbal form is significant. Another way of stating the same fact is to say that Christ was 'sent' (iv. 9, 14). This is a form of expression especially congenial to 'Johannine' circles, but it has primitive origins, as may be seen from the coincidence of Pauline language with that of the Gospels (cf. Gal. iv. 4; Rom. viii. 3; Mark ix. 37). He adds statements of the purpose or effect of the coming of Christ expressed in distinctively 'Johannine' language (iii. 5, 8, iv. 9). The form of expression nevertheless recalls several statements in the Synoptic Gospels about the coming of Christ and its purpose (e.g. Luke xix. 10; Matt. xx. 28; cf. also Matt. v. 17, ix. 13, etc.). Again, in ii. 22 we have a clear echo of a very primitive confession of faith: Jesus is the Christ (cf. Mark viii. 20). In iv. 15 this takes the alternative form, Jesus is the Son of God, which is also primitive (cf. Mark iii. 11, v. 7, xiv. 61–62, xv. 39; Matt. vii. 29, xiv. 33, xvi. 16; Rom. i. 3–4, etc.).

In all this our author keeps closely to the forms of the primitive Preaching. But the development of Christian theology, and the emergence of 'Gnostic' versions of Christianity, made it necessary to elaborate this clause of the *kerygma* so as to preclude erroneous interpretations. Some teachers asserted that the Son of God, the eternal Christ, had indeed 'come,' in a sense, but only by taking on the temporary appearance of a man (much after the fashion of the 'theophanies' which Jews and Gentiles alike believed in). The actuality of the events on which the Gospel rested was thus denied, and the unique connection of the eternal with history, which was the presupposition of the proclamation of a new order, was destroyed. Hence the simpler confessions of faith needed to be restated in the form 'Jesus Christ has come in the flesh' (such is the literal translation of iv. 2). To deny this is to deny the Gospel (iv. 3). It is because of the vital importance of this conviction of the actuality of Christ's human life that the writer appeals so emphatically to the evidence of the senses in i. 1–3.

Of the mighty works of Christ, 'in the flesh,' to which the

kerygma seems to have alluded (Acts ii. 22, x. 38), our author has nothing to say: it was hardly germane to his purpose. On the other hand, he is insistent upon the authority of His teaching. It is doubtful how far this point was generally included in the *kerygma*. Only the form given in Acts iii. 22 expressly indicates Christ as the second and greater Moses, prophet, teacher and lawgiver. This comparative silence, however, must not be misunderstood to mean that the primitive Church was not interested in the teaching of Jesus. It is evident from the whole New Testament that the message of the Church was conceived as having two main aspects: the Gospel of Christ, the theme of preaching (*kerygma*), and the Law or Commandment of Christ, the theme of teaching (*didaché*). (The distinction was partly a matter of method and of ministerial organization.) The Gospel of Christ is essentially a declaration of what God, in His grace towards man, has done through Christ; the Law of Christ is a statement of what God requires of those who are the objects of His gracious action. The two are intimately united, though distinguishable. The distinction and the relation between the two appear in the structure both of the Gospels, which interweave the story of Jesus and the record of His teaching, and of the Epistles, several of which are divided into a 'theological' part, expounding the implications of *kerygma*, and an 'ethical' part, developing and applying the Law of Christ (so Romans, Galatians, Ephesians, Colossians, 1 and 2 Thessalonians, Hebrews—with an attenuated 'ethical' section—and 1 Peter).

In the First Epistle of John there is a thorough integration of the Commandment and the Gospel. Whether one says that the teaching of Jesus is a part of the Gospel, or that the 'word of life' (i. 1) includes inseparably both Gospel and Commandment, the unity of the two elements in the Christian message is complete (see ii. 7–11). To have stated this with the utmost clearness and emphasis is a distinctive service to Christian thought, and one to which the author was provoked by propaganda which seemed to deny it. When something hitherto taken for granted is challenged, it must be made perfectly explicit. Hence the reiteration in this epistle of what might

xxxi

almost seem a Christian truism. Nowhere else in the New Testament is it made more clear that the evangelical proclamation of the love of God in sending the Saviour (iv. 9, 14), and the commandment 'Love one another' (iv. 11, 21), are aspects of a single and indivisible divine revelation by which the Christian religion is constituted; and nowhere is there less excuse for the reader to suppose that Christian theology can stand apart from Christian ethics, or Christian ethics apart from theology.

Upon the relation of this epistle to the tradition of the teaching of Jesus more must be said presently. We now take up again the main thread of the *kerygma*.

In all our accounts of the apostolic preaching the death of Christ has a prominent place. **I passed on to you,** writes Paul, **what I had myself received, namely, that Christ died for our sins, as the scriptures had said,** and he appeals confidently to the consensus of apostolic testimony. (1 Cor. xv. 3, 11). The Old Testament 'scriptures' to which this highly compressed statement refers can, at least in part, be identified by comparison with other passages in the New Testament. It seems that the most important of them is the prophecy of the Suffering Servant of the Lord in Isa. lii. 13 – liii. 12. The opening words of this prophecy are cited (freely) in the Petrine speech, Acts iii. 13; and in Acts viii. 26–38 it is made the text of the preaching of the Gospel to an Ethiopian (which we may take as typical of the earliest 'foreign missions'). The implication is that from an extremely early period, if not from the very first, the preaching of the apostles interpreted the death of Christ through the prophetic conception of the Servant of the Lord, whose vicarious sufferings bring salvation to 'many.' The reference to the Isaianic prophecy is incorporated in the Synoptic Gospels (Mark x. 45, ix. 12, Luke xxii. 37, etc.), and there is no good reason to reject their evidence that it was already made in the sayings of Jesus Himself. Our author therefore is keeping closely to the primitive *kerygma* when he says, **The blood of Jesus His Son cleanses us from every sin** (i. 7); or, in language which is the 'Johannine' equivalent for Mark xv. 45, **He laid down His life for us** (iii. 16; cf. also

Gal. ii. 20). There is so far no attempt to go further theo-
logically than the simple statements of the early *kerygma*; and
even in ii. 2, iv. 10, where Christ is said to be the 'expiation'
for our sins (cf. Rom. iii. 25), there is nothing that goes
beyond the implications of the Isaianic prophecy.

In the Preaching of the Apostles, the announcement of the
death of Christ is regularly followed by the announcement of
His resurrection. Indeed the double proclamation that Christ
died and rose again is the core of the *kerygma* in all its forms.
It is surprising to find that in this epistle there is no direct
allusion to the resurrection. One other New Testament writing
resembles it in this respect. In the Epistle to the Hebrews the
only direct reference is in the liturgical language of the closing
Benediction and Doxology (xiii. 20–1). In practically every
other book of the New Testament the resurrection has a
dominant place.

It seems possible, however, to distinguish two slightly
different ways of regarding it. Some, it would seem, thought
chiefly of the appearances of the risen Christ to His followers,
and especially of their evidential value for faith. Others (or the
same persons in a different context) thought chiefly of the
risen Christ as exalted 'at the right hand of God,' ready to
come again in glory. The difference is reflected in various forms
of the *kerygma*: compare, for instance, Acts ii. 32–6, iii. 13–21,
where the emphasis is entirely on the latter aspect, with Acts x.
40–1, xiii. 30–1, where the emphasis is on the former aspect.
(See also R. H. Lightfoot, *Locality and Doctrine in the Gospels*,
where a somewhat similar distinction is drawn between the
outlook of the Gospels according to Mark and Luke). If the
foreground of one's mind were occupied with the thought of
Christ's eternal power and glory in the heavenly places, the
fact of His resurrection might be taken to be implied in this
larger and more inclusive truth. To put it in terms of the
kerygma, the affirmation of Christ's resurrection might be
taken as implicit in the clause affirming His victory over 'principalities and powers,' and His eternal session 'at the right hand
of God.' Perhaps this is true of our author.

For the clause just referred to, that which affirms Christ's exaltation, the earliest forms of the *kerygma* appear to look back to Psalm cx. 1 (Acts ii. 34-5, Rom. viii. 34, 1 Pet. iii. 22, etc.) to which (according to an entirely credible statement in Mark xii. 35-7) Jesus Himself had drawn attention. This passage was understood to indicate (i) that the risen Christ is 'Lord of all' (Acts x. 36; cf. Phil. ii. 9-11), and (ii) that He is victorious over all cosmic powers (cf. 1 Pet. iii. 22). This double theme is elaborated in a great variety of ways in the New Testament writings. In the Fourth Gospel His victory is won over the Prince of this world (xii. 31; cf. xiv. 30, xvi. 11), and consequently over the world itself (xvi. 33). It is this line of thought that is followed by our author. The world, that is, human society organized in hostility to God (or in plain terms, pagan society as he knew it), lies in the power of the evil One (v. 19), or the devil. It was to destroy the deeds of the devil that the Son of God appeared (iii. 8). He is greater than he who is in the world (iv. 4)—more powerful, that is, than the Prince of this world—and consequently He is the conqueror of 'the world' as a power hostile to man's salvation. And from this follows the further consequence, which the writer draws for his readers' encouragement, that to have faith in Christ is to share His victory; our faith, that is the conquest which conquers the world; for he who believes that Jesus is the Son of God is the world's conqueror (v. 4-5). We shall certainly be within the author's intention if we understand that for the confirmation of his readers' faith he is appealing once more to the most certain testimony of that which you learned from the very beginning; in other words, the Gospel itself as declared in the Preaching of the Apostles and handed down in the Church. The Gospel, rightly understood, is a proclamation of Christ's victory; and to accept the Gospel heartily, in its fulness, is to share that victory. He would have allowed no other ground for confidence or optimism in the great war against the powers of evil and of the lie.

The testimony of the apostolic preaching to Christ ends with a clause affirming the certain expectation of His second coming which brings the 'end of the age' (Matt. xxviii. 20), the 'restoration of all things' (Acts iii. 21), and the last judgment

(Acts x. 42, Rom. ii. 16, etc.). It would appear that in the earliest days the second advent was proclaimed as the immediately impending completion of a process set in motion by the entry of Christ into the world, and carried forward in His ministry, death, resurrection and ascension. As time went on, and the Lord did not return in the way He was expected, the continuity of the process was broken. The new situation was met by various Christian thinkers in different ways. In the Fourth Gospel, although the belief in a judgment on the 'last day' is retained, its significance is attenuated; for the whole episode of Christ's incarnation, including His passion and death, is shown to be the world's Day of Judgment; and the promise of His return is held to have been fulfilled by His resurrection and the coming of the Paraclete (John iii. 17–21, ix. 39–41, xii. 31–32, xiv. 15–23). The author of the First Epistle knows nothing of this reinterpretation of the Advent hope. He holds to the belief that the great Day of Judgment is at hand; and although he must have seen the repeated disappointment of that belief, he thinks he now has definite grounds for confidence that the delay will not be prolonged (ii. 18). Once again the expectation proved illusory. But this belief, persisting all through the first century of Christianity, that the consummation of all things lay 'round the corner,' had its value. It served to keep alive, through a period of intense trial, a sense of the inconceivable nearness and reality of the unseen world, and of the Lord 'whom having not seen ye love'; and it evoked a sense of moral urgency corresponding to the incalculable significance of the present moment, which (for all one knew) might in strict truth be the last moment before the great Day dawned.

It is instructive to observe the ideas which in this epistle are associated with the thought of the Lord's advent. First, the thought of coming judgment, here as elsewhere in the New Testament, sharpens the sense of moral responsibility. But this sense of responsibility is not to be associated with any craven fear; for our Judge is Christ, and Christ is the expression of the divine love, and if we dwell in love there is nothing to frighten us in the thought of meeting Christ (iv. 14–18, ii. 28). For, secondly, the main thing is, after all, that Jesus Christ Himself is to appear: **we are to see Him as He is** (iii. 2). The writer has here put in the simplest possible words, not indeed the whole content of Christian eschatology, but the controlling conviction which gives character to any eschatology which is to be distinctively Christian. From it he proceeds to draw consequences directly relevant to the ethical life of a Christian man: we cannot see Christ as He is without being like Him; and this prospect must powerfully stimulate moral endeavour (iii. 2–3).

It is clear that while our author shares the popular belief of early Christianity in an almost immediate end of the world, he avoids the crude and even fanatical forms which that belief could take (as it does, for example, in parts of the Book of Revelation), and emphasizes aspects of it which are of permanent relevance to Christian faith and life.

In addition to the affirmations about Christ and His work, the *kerygma* seems to have included, in one form or another, a testimony to the Church as the People of God under the new covenant, distinguished as such notably by the gift of the Spirit (as foretold in prophecy), and enjoying forgiveness of sins and the assurance of salvation. In the examples of apostolic preaching given in the Acts, the proclamation of the Gospel normally issues in an appeal to the hearers for faith and repentance, accompanied by the offer of initiation (by baptism) into the life of the true 'Israel of God' with all its distinctive privileges (Acts ii. 38–9, iv. 11–12, xiii. 38).

In our epistle the word 'church' does not occur (as it is also absent from the Fourth Gospel); but the author is acutely conscious of the Church as a community called into being by the act of God in Christ and sustained by **fellowship with the Father and with His Son Jesus Christ** (i. 3). Like the earliest preachers, he appeals to the witness of the Spirit (v. 6; cf. Acts ii. 33, v. 32, etc.). He does not allude to more developed doctrines such as the Pauline conception of the 'Spirit of Christ' as the animating and unifying principle of the Body of Christ and the ground of moral achievement, or the Johannine conception of the Paraclete as Christ's representative dwelling in

His Church and mediating His judgment upon the world (John xvi. 7–11). He stands upon the ground of the simpler early Preaching: that the manifest presence and activity of the Spirit is the evidence of the truth of the Gospel and the reality of Christian experience.

Fully in line, again, with the earliest tradition is the contrast drawn in ii. 7–17 between the Church and the world. 'The world' is here human society organized in hostility to the will of God; but it is also the embodiment of an order of life belonging to the evil age which has in principle been brought to an end by the coming of Christ, and is now manifestly in process of dissolution. Over against this dying order is a new order of life, also embodied (it is implied) in a society, the Church, which possesses the marks of the people of the new covenant (cf. Jer. xxxi. 31–4; Heb. viii. 8–12)—forgiveness of sins and knowledge of God; and is, by virtue of Christ's conquest of 'principalities and powers', victorious over the world.

In contrast to the dying world, the divine community, being united with the will of God, remains for ever (ii. 17). For our author the supreme divine gift is life eternal (v. 11), and it is this which is proclaimed in the Gospel, which accordingly is called 'the word of life' (i. 1). It is likely that in 'Johannine' circles the idea of 'eternal life' was in some measure affected by Hellenistic philosophy; but the idea itself is rooted in the earliest Preaching. In the Acts, although the complete expression occurs only in a passage with a Pauline colouring (Acts xiii. 46–8), yet elsewhere the effect of the Preaching upon the Gentiles is described as 'repentance unto life' (xi. 18); the Gospel itself is called 'the words of this life' (v. 20); and Christ Himself, 'the Prince of life' (iii. 15). In the Synoptic Gospels the expression 'life ' or 'eternal life,' is used as an alternative for 'the Kingdom of God' in certain connections. To 'enter into the Kingdom of God,' to 'enter into life,' to 'inherit eternal life,' and to 'be saved' are synonyms (Mark ix. 43–7, x. 17, 23–6). In the eschatological setting of the earliest preaching 'eternal life' is 'the life of the Age to Come,' now inaugurated by the coming of Christ. That is what it essentially is (and not any philosophical conception of immortality) in this epistle.

Of its character and quality the author has important things to say, to which we shall turn presently.

So much for the *kerygma*, or proclamation of the Gospel. We now turn to the other side of the tradition, that which preserved the Sayings of Jesus, chiefly for the purpose of instruction in Christian morals, individual and social. We have already seen that our author insists with particular emphasis upon the inseparable unity of the Gospel and the Commandment of Christ. He often echoes the teaching of the Lord as reported in the Fourth Gospel. It will, however, be of some interest to enquire whether he shows acquaintance with a tradition of the Sayings over and above the tradition embodied in the Fourth Gospel; and here our standard of comparison must be the Synoptic Gospels. There is no verbal similarity close enough to suggest that the author was acquainted with any of these Gospels in their existing forms. Nevertheless there are some striking resemblances which strongly suggest that he was acquainted with an oral tradition of the Sayings similar to that which underlies the Synoptic record.

We have already observed that for him the Law of Christ is summed up in what he calls (as does the Fourth Gospel) the New Commandment: 'Love one another.' That form of the precept is Johannine. But in iv. 21 he seems to betray knowledge of a formulation similar to that which we have in Mark xii. 28–31 and parallels.[1]

Mark xii. 29–31	1 *John iv.* 21
The first commandment is: . . . Thou shalt love the Lord thy God. . . . And the second is this: Thou shalt love thy neighbour as thyself.	This commandment we have from Him: that he who loves God shall love his brother also.

This combination of the commandments of love to God and love to man is not made in the Fourth Gospel.

In 1 John iv. 11 the precept is put in another way: 'If God so loved us we ought also to love one another.' The principle is similar (though the language is different) to that which is

[1] In the following citations, a literal translation is offered, the degree of identity in language being sometimes disguised in the Moffatt rendering.

expressed in Matt. xviii. 33, 'Ought you not to have had mercy on your fellow-servants as I had mercy on you?' Again, in iv. 7 we have (in distinctively 'Johannine' language) the doctrine that 'he who loves is born of God'; but the same idea is present in Matt. v. 44–5: 'Love your enemies . . . that you may become sons of your Father in heaven.' On the converse side, our author says that hatred is murder, and the murderer is excluded from eternal life (iii. 15). There is sufficient authority for this in Matt. v. 21–2 (though once again there is no verbal parallel). 'It was said to the ancients: Thou shalt not kill; whoever kills is liable to the Judgment. But I say to you: Whoever is angry with his brother is liable to the Judgment.'

In these fundamental matters of Christian ethics we might perhaps have assumed, even without direct evidence, that any type of Christian tradition would preserve the essentials of the teaching of Jesus in one form or another. But there are many other passages where, though there is no extensive identity of language with the Synoptic Gospels, there are nevertheless significant echoes.

In ii. 22, 23, 28, iv. 2, 3, we have pronouncements upon the general theme of 'confessing' and 'disowning' Christ, which seem to be the result of reflection upon such sayings as those which are preserved in Mark viii. 37–8, Matt. x. 32–3, Luke ix. 26, xii. 8–9 (the keywords 'confess,' 'disown,' 'shame' are common to the Gospels and the Epistle). It appears that these sayings were present in more than one of the sources of the Synoptic Gospels, and there is no reason why our author should not have been acquainted with yet another version of them, in the oral tradition which he received (see also notes, pp. 56–7, 64).

Compare again the following passages:

Matt. vii. 21	1 *John ii.* 17
Not everyone who says to me 'Lord, Lord!' will enter the Kingdom of Heaven, but he who does the will of my Father in heaven.	He who does the will of God remains for ever.

We recall that to 'enter the Kingdom of heaven' and to 'inherit eternal life' are synonyms in the Synoptic Gospels.

Matt. v. 8–9
Blessed are the pure in heart, for they shall see God. Blessed are the peacemakers, for they shall be called sons of God.

1 *John iii.* 1–3
See what love the Father has given us, to be called children of God . . . we shall see Him as He is. . . . He who has this hope cleanses himself.

It certainly looks as if our author were acquainted with the Beatitudes in one form or another. He has put together the blessings of seeing God and being called God's children, which in Matthew are kept distinct, and associated them both with the idea of purity.

Matt. xxiv. 11
Many pseudo-prophets will arise and lead many astray.

1 *John iv.* 1
Test the spirits . . . because many pseudo-prophets have gone out into the world.

Matt. vii. 15, 20
Beware of pseudo-prophets. . . . From their fruits you shall recognize them.

Matt. xxiv. 24
Pseudo-christs and pseudo-prophets will arise . . . so as to lead even the elect astray, if possible.

1 *John ii.* 18
As you have heard that Antichrist is coming, so now many antichrists have come.

'Antichrist' is not identical with 'pseudo-christ,' but it may be that the author of the epistle had in mind some such saying as this, and combined it with other current predictions.

Mark xiii. 5
Beware that no one leads you astray.

1 *John iii.* 7
Children, let no one lead you astray.

Matt. v. 48
You shall be perfect, as your Father in heaven is perfect.

1 *John iii.* 7
He who performs righteousness is righteous as He is righteous.

Luke vi. 36
Be merciful, as your Father is merciful.

(Here, as so often, it is not very clear whether 'He' is the Father or the Son; but for this author the difference is negligible.)

'Perfect,' 'merciful,' 'righteous': these might well represent variants of one saying.

Luke vi. 22	1 *John iii.* 13
Blessed are you when men hate you.	Do not be surprised if the world hates you.

Matt. vii. 8 = *Luke xi.* 10	1 *John iii.* 22
Everyone who asks receives.	Whatever we ask for we receive from Him.

Mark xi. 24	1 *John v.* 15
Whatever you pray and ask for, believe you have received it, and you shall have it.	If we know that He hears us whatever we ask for, we know that we possess those things we have asked of Him.

Matt. x. 25 (*cf. Luke vi.* 40)	1 *John iv.* 17
It is enough for the disciple to be as his teacher, and the slave as his master.	As He is, so are we in this world.

Matt. xi. 30	1 *John v.* 3
My yoke is kindly and my burden light.	His commandments are not heavy.

If it be allowed that these examples cumulatively build up a probability that our author is referring to a body of traditional Sayings of Jesus similar to that which we have in the Synoptic Gospels, then we may perhaps trace reminiscences of such a tradition in other places where the resemblance is not so obvious.

In the notes on i. 5–6 it is suggested that the teaching about 'walking in the light,' there and in ii. 9–11, though it has immediate antecedents in the Fourth Gospel, nevertheless fairly represents the purport of such passages as Matt. vi. 22–3, Luke xi. 34–6, where the keywords are 'light' and 'darkness.' The figurative use of the term 'blindness' in ii. 11 is consonant with the language of the Synoptic Sayings (cf. Luke vi. 39), and the term translated **pitfall**—*skandalon* in the original—is one that has a significant place in the vocabulary of the Synoptics (Matt. xiii. 41, xvi. 23, xviii. 7). It is not found in the Fourth

Gospel, and it is not a word that a Hellenistic writer would ordinarily be likely to use (see Moffatt Commentary, *Romans*, xiv. 13).

Again, while the language used about 'the world' in ii. 15–17 has a distinctively 'Johannine' ring, the contemptuous dismissal of the desires of a transient world is implicit in Luke xii. 29–30: 'You are not to seek after things to eat and drink, for all that is what the nations of the world seek after,' and Mark viii. 36: 'What advantage is it to a man to gain the whole world and forfeit his soul?'

Finally, when our author declares the content of the 'word of life' to be 'what we have heard, what we have seen with our eyes,' can we exclude an allusion to the great 'beatitude' of Matt. xiii. 16–17 (Luke x. 23–4)?

> 'Blessed are your eyes because they see, and your ears, because they hear. In truth I tell you, many prophets and saints desired to see what you see, and did not see it; to hear what you hear, and did not hear it.'

To sum up: while the First Epistle of John is written in a peculiar idiom both of thought and of speech, showing the undeniable influence of the Hellenistic environment, its author is justified in claiming that the substance of his message to his readers is neither more nor less than the original and unchanging content of the Church's common faith, embodied in the Gospel and the Commandment, and attested by primary witnesses. It is this that gives his work its universal, catholic, significance. He might have spent his time in discussing and refuting the errors of the heretical propaganda. If he had done so, the epistle would now have had little more than antiquarian interest. But the 'word of life,' that is the Gospel and the Commandment of Christ as delivered by the apostles, commands the prime interest of Christians everywhere and at all times. Fidelity to it, under all changes of theological climate, remains the test *stantis vel cadentis ecclesiae.*

It is clear that the theological climate prevailing at the time and place of writing differs appreciably from that of most of the New Testament. The author is free to reinterpret and apply fundamental articles of faith in relation to a new situation: a task to which Christian teachers are called at every period. He writes as a pastor to his people, rather with the practical aim of recalling them to fundamental loyalties than with the intention of developing theological doctrines. His interest in the building up of Christian dogma is limited. It is not here, but in the Fourth Gospel, that we must look for the distinctively 'Johannine' contribution to the clarification of Christology and of the doctrine of the Atonement, and for that profound insight into the Christian experience of God as Father, Son and Paraclete which both enforced and made possible the formulation of the doctrine of the Trinity. Our author is little concerned about precise theological definition. He often writes in terms which leave it uncertain whether the reference is to God the Father or to Christ. It seems as if he were almost indifferent to that distinction of Persons which is drawn with such clearness and subtlety in the discourses of the Fourth Gospel; and his allusions to the Holy Spirit follow the usage of popular Christianity without apparent interest in any deeper theological implications.

The especial emphasis, however, which he places upon certain aspects of the Church's tradition issues in a distinctive and consistent presentation of the Christian life and faith which is of high importance to theology in the wider sense.

First we may place his emphasis upon the realization of eternal life here and now. As we have seen, our author shares the eschatological expectations of early Christianity. When he speaks of eternal life, he includes in it the idea of continuance after death (or, rather, after the dissolution of this world, ii. 17), and he holds out the prospect of a future glory at present inconceivable. Yet he makes it perfectly clear that eternal life is a present possession and experience of believers (v. 12–13). The Christian is *now* a child of God: the divine 'seed' (the germ of divinity, may we say?) resides in him; he knows God, dwells in God and is indwelt by God; he has fellowship with the Father and the Son; he is in the light; he possesses an 'unction' or initiation which confers supernatural knowledge;

he has within him the divine Spirit witnessing to the truth of that which he believes, and to the reality of his experience of God. These modes of expression (with two exceptions) echo more or less clearly the language of contemporary Hellenistic mysticism. There they refer to the initiate who by knowledge of God has become immortal like the gods. Here they are used to describe the believer as the possessor of eternal life; and they bring into full light the truth (implied all through the New Testament) that the eternal life which is offered through the Gospel is by no means simply a prolongation of existence beyond the grave, but life of a particular quality, lived in union with God, and accessible to present experience, while it waits for its perfection upon a change yet to come.

Secondly, he insists that all such language is misleading or meaningless unless it is capable of being translated into ethical terms. To be in the light is to be cleansed from evil; to know God is to obey His commands; to be a child of God is to to be pure and righteous like Him (or at least to be getting purified, iii. 3). And at this point we begin to see the relevance of our author's repeated insistence upon the actuality of Christ's life 'in the flesh.' It proceeds from no theoretical interest in dogma. As we have seen, our author is not distinguished by any such interest. He does not insist upon the Incarnation because this doctrine is necessary to a complete theological scheme; but because the incarnate life of Christ fills the concept of eternal life with human, personal, ethical meaning. What is it to dwell in God? It is to live after the example of Christ (ii. 6). What is it to walk in the light? It is to obey the commands of Christ (ii. 7–11). In other words, all this 'mystical' language about eternal life is false and pernicious if it is used in a merely 'mystical' sense; even in a merely religious sense; it is true only if religion and ethics interpenetrate; and the religious ethics, or ethical religion, of Christians is defined by reference to the remembered and recorded life and teaching of Jesus Christ, who suffered under Pontius Pilate.

Thirdly, when once it is recognized that real religion is ethical religion, and that it falls to be judged by the standards of the life and teaching of Jesus Christ, it is seen to demand as its essential mark one overriding ethical principle, of which Christ is the supreme exponent; that which our author, like all New Testament writers, calls by the untranslatable Greek term, *agapé*. We are bound to render it, in general, by the English word 'love,' though our older religious speech took a word from the Latin and called it 'charity.' In common English usage, neither word is a complete equivalent to the Greek. In this commentary 'charity' is frequently used as an alternative rendering, to remind the reader that if he reads 'love' he must understand it in a distinctive sense. Whichever word we use, however, it requires to be filled with meaning from the source which originally supplied the colourless Greek term with its Christian connotation—the source to which our author continually refers us: the life and teaching of Jesus Christ. If we have the Gospel record in mind, we need not be at a loss about the meaning of 'love,' or 'charity,' as the word is used in this epistle. And if we understand this, then, as our author constantly affirms, we know what eternal life really means.

It is clear that the life of eternity, so conceived, can be lived only in community. *Agapé* is of such a nature that we simply cannot love God to the exclusion of our fellow men. Whatever religious emotion may be aroused in the soul by the contemplation of the divine Being, it is not worthy to be called *agapé* unless it issues in a concern for some fellow human being, which will lead us to serve him at our cost (iii. 16–17). That is to state the principle in its lowest and simplest terms. But such mutual service by self-sacrifice is a property of community life: indeed, it alone is capable of creating a real community out of an aggregation of people. Thus the kind of religion recommended in this epistle has little in common with the mysticism which is described as a 'flight of the alone to the Alone.' The fatherhood of God implies a family of God in which His children live as brothers. This is the basis of the 'fellowship' which is the essential mark of the Church (i. 3).

The author is so acutely aware of the intimacy of the family tie within the Church that he sometimes speaks as if the

Christian fellowship alone offered the proper field for the exercise of charity. He speaks of love either for 'one another' or for our 'brothers,' and the context shows that he is thinking of fellow Christians (see iii. 14, v. 1–2), of whom alone it can be said, strictly, that they are 'children of God' (iii. 2) and consequently 'brothers' of all others who have been similarly regenerate by His Word (iii. 9 and note). (The doctrine that all men, as such, are by nature the offspring of God has little biblical support. It is found explicitly in the New Testament only in a quotation from a pagan poet (Acts xvii. 28); and it is implied in Luke iii. 38, and possibly, though not probably, in Jas. i. 18, but nowhere else. See Moffatt Commentary, *Romans*, pp. 130–1.)

In justice to the author, it must be remembered that he is dealing with a particular situation which has arisen within the Church. It is not the attitude of Christians towards mankind at large that is in question, but their attitude towards one another in the Church. The author therefore is primarily concerned with charity in its particular aspect (to employ Paul's precise terminology) of love for the brotherhood (*philadelphia*, Rom. xii. 10; see note in Moffatt Commentary). He certainly does not intend to deny that *agapé* has also a wider application; and in many places his expressions are quite unrestricted (e.g. iv. 16, 19). It is further to be observed that the Church in the New Testament is represented as the nucleus (or 'firstfruits'; cf. Rom. xi. 16, Jas. i. 18, Rev. xiv. 4) of a redeemed humanity; as the trustee (so to speak) of God's benefits towards all mankind; and that in fact a great deal of what is said about the Church is fully true only if its ultimate limits are set nowhere short of the frontiers of the human race (or even of the whole creation; see Rom. viii. 20–3, Eph. i. 3–14). Our author is aware of this, in spite of his severe insistence upon the opposition between the Church and the world (see ii. 2, iv. 14). As he says that Christ is the expiation for our sins, and hastens to add, 'not ours only, but those of the whole world'; so we may read his maxim, 'We know that we have passed from death to life, because we love our (Christian) brothers,' with the addition—'and not them only, but all our fellow men.' The Church, like the family, should be a school of charity whose lessons may be applied abroad.

If we put these three points together, we arrive at a picture of what is most distinctive in this epistle. There are always cropping up two misconceptions of what religion is. For some minds, it is a matter of exalted 'spiritual' states; for others, it is 'morality tinged with emotion.' To minds of the former cast this epistle may at times smack of 'moralism' or even 'legalism'; to minds of the latter cast, its exalted language about religious experience as a foretaste of eternal life may seem almost highfalutin. The writer, however, insists that while glib talk about religious experience is a snare and a delusion in the absence of a serious attention to daily conduct, a truly virtuous life can spring only out of a unique relation to God, which is not achieved by us, but granted by His grace. He is able to maintain this position persuasively because he construes both religious experience and morality in terms of *agapé*, which is at once the only valid basis of communion with God, and the only spring of true virtue.

Finally, this reading of the Christian life as one of union with God, upon ethical conditions, these conditions determined by the overriding principle of love, or charity, culminates in our author's outstanding contribution to Christian theology: the doctrine that 'God is love.' For a discussion of its meaning and implications, the reader must be referred to the notes on iv. 8. Starting without any aim at dogmatic definition, the author of the epistle has found himself led, through reflection upon the content of the tradition and of Christian experience, to formulate the most profound, as well as the simplest, summing up of the Christian revelation of God: a maxim which, once enunciated, becomes the touchstone of Christian faith and life, and a signpost to the direction which must be taken by all sound theological thinking.

IV. RELATION OF THE FIRST EPISTLE TO THE FOURTH GOSPEL

That very judicious critic, Bishop Dionysius of Alexandria, about the middle of the third century, wrote as follows about the Fourth Gospel and the First Epistle of John:

THE JOHANNINE EPISTLES

'The Gospel and the Epistle agree with one another. They begin alike . . . [John i. 1. 14; 1 John i. 1–3] . . . and he deals with his whole matter by way of the same topics and terms, some of which I will briefly enumerate. Anyone who reads attentively will find in each writing, life largely, light largely, and the repudiation of darkness; truth continually, grace, joy, the flesh and blood of the Lord, judgment, the forgiveness of sins, God's love for us, and the mutual love enjoined upon us; that we must keep all the commandments; the condemnation of the world, the devil, and Antichrist; the promise of the Holy Spirit; God's adoption of us as sons; the absolute faith demanded of us; the Father and the Son everywhere. To characterize them generally all through, one may observe one and the same complexion in the Gospel and the Epistle' (Eusebius, *Ecclesiastical History*, VII. 25. 18–21).

The good bishop is quite right; most of the themes treated in the Epistle have a place also in the Gospel, and there is a general affinity of theological outlook, at least in comparison with any other part of the New Testament.

Not only the ideas of the two writings, but also their ways of expressing them, are similar. It would be easy to compile a list of fifty or more phrases in the Epistle which have close parallels in the Gospel. The reader, however, can best form an impression of the extent of the similarity, if he goes through the text of the Epistle (perhaps with the help of a concordance or a good reference Bible), and underlines all those expressions which echo the language of the Gospel more or less exactly. A glance at the result will show how few and short are those passages of the Epistle which are free from such echoes.

We seem bound to conclude, either that the two writings are from one hand, or that the writer of the one was strongly influenced by the writer of the other, whether that influence was due to personal discipleship, or to a deep and prolonged study of his work, or to both.

The unvarying tradition from early times, which is upheld by many modern scholars, is that the First Epistle and the

Gospel are the work of one author. There are, however, some difficulties about this view. When we have fully recognized the close kinship of the two writings, we must also observe that there are differences between them, both in form and in content, which are by no means negligible.

First, there are differences of style, in spite of the general similarity which we have noted. These differences could be fully set out only in a detailed study of the Greek text;[1] but in a measure they can be appreciated in an English translation.

There is surely to be felt in the Fourth Gospel a richness, a subtlety, a penetrating quality of style to which the Epistle cannot pretend. While the rhythm of both is slow and regular, in the Gospel it is subtly varied, within the limits imposed by its general character; but in the Epistle regularity often descends to monotony. The language of the Gospel has an intensity, a kind of inward glow, a controlled excitement, which the reader does not feel, or seldom feels, in the Epistle. The language of the Epistle is generally correct Greek, though not always as lucid as might be wished; it is sometimes forcible and epigrammatic; but it does not suggest the pen of a ready writer. It does not persuade the reader (as does the Fourth Gospel) that here is a man who, with a relatively small vocabulary and a narrow range of grammatical idiom, has genuine power of style.

Such impressions of style are apt to be subjective; but in certain respects they are open to be tested by detailed study of the linguistic phenomena in the Greek. Thus, the impression of a certain monotony is confirmed by the observation that the writer of the Epistle greatly overworks a few favourite grammatical constructions; and that he uses a much smaller variety of compound verbs (little more than one-tenth of the number

---

[1] For such a detailed study the reader may be referred to my paper, *The First Epistle of John and the Fourth Gospel* (Manchester University Press), reprinted from the *Bulletin of the John Rylands Library*, Vol. 21, No. 1, April, 1937. Subsequent revision has shown that the word-lists and statistics given there need minor corrections. These do not, however, affect the general conclusion; on a balance, they slightly strengthen the evidence for a significant difference of style between the two writings.

used in the Gospel), and of those 'grammatical words' (particles, conjunctions, and the like) which, especially in Greek, give variety and individual colour to a writer's style.

On the other hand, he has forms of speech which are lacking in the Gospel. Like many popular writers on philosophical subjects in the Hellenistic period, he is fond of the figure known as the rhetorical question (see ii. 22, iii. 12. 17, v. 5), which probably does not occur in the Gospel (for Pilate's 'What is truth?' is at any rate not that kind of rhetorical question). Again, the conditional sentence (to which he is immoderately addicted, having an average of just under five per page, against just over one per page in the Gospel) is used in a variety of rhetorical figures unparalleled in the Gospel (see i. 6, 8, 9, ii. 1, 29, v. 9, 15, and perhaps iii. 20).

Among the idioms present in the Gospel, but absent from the Epistle, the most interesting and significant are a group which have been held to betray Semitic influence. In some of these the Semitic character is not sure, but there are at least five notable idioms, characteristic of the Gospel, where the case for Aramaism is very strong. Of these, four are entirely unknown to the Epistle, and the fifth occurs doubtfully in one passage where the manuscript evidence leaves the true text uncertain. Indeed, a careful scrutiny of the language of the Epistle fails to disclose any evidence of definable Semitism, apart from two quite doubtful examples. The language of the Gospel, on the other hand, undoubtedly shows a definite Semitic colouring, whether this is due to translation from an Aramaic original (which is unlikely), or to the use of Aramaic sources, or (which seems most probable) to bilingualism in the writer.

The vocabulary of the Gospel is larger than that of the Epistle, as we might expect, in view of its much greater length and the greater variety of its themes. Yet the Epistle, short as it is, has nearly forty words and expressions which do not occur in the Gospel. There is so far nothing very remarkable. It is a different matter when we observe that out of the numerous words present in the Gospel but absent from the Epistle, a list of over thirty can be compiled which are either so frequent in the Gospel, or so closely related to its central ideas, that their absence from a writing claiming Johannine authorship is significant. It is surely strange that the author of the Gospel should have written a second work upon some of the central Christian themes—themes which have a prominent place in his major work—without using (for example) the words which came so readily to him for the ideas of being saved and lost, for grace and peace, for the divine necessity ('it must needs be'), for 'bearing fruit' in Christian living, without referring to Christ as 'Lord,' to His glory, His descent from heaven and ascent to heaven again, or His resurrection. No one can say it is impossible; but it makes one wonder.

The weight to be given to considerations of style and language will be estimated differently by different minds. We turn now from form to content, and enquire how far the ideas of the Epistle, and its religious or theological outlook, are identical with those of the Gospel, or differ from them significantly.

That the two writings, as compared with the rest of the New Testament, show a decided affinity of thought and standpoint is, as we have observed, obvious to any attentive reader. That there are certain differences is equally obvious, and not surprising. A writer who exactly repeats himself in two separate works betrays an infertile mind. Moreover, it is natural enough that some of the themes treated in the Gospel should be lacking in the Epistle, a short work with a restricted aim.

There are, however, some divergences which seem to go beyond what we should naturally expect in two works from the same hand.

In the first place, the Epistle is unique among New Testament writings (if we except its two short companions) in having no quotation from the Old Testament, only one explicit reference to the Old Testament (iii. 12), and few if any direct echoes of Old Testament language. The Fourth Gospel, like the other Gospels, has numerous quotations, and still more numerous implicit (but quite definite) allusions, and its language frequently recalls that of the Greek Old Testament. This difference might be accounted for by the difference in aim between the two writings, or by the Evangelist's use of sources which contained Old Testament material. (It may be noted that some parts of the Gospel, for instance the Farewell Discourses, have fewer Old Testament quotations or allusions than some other parts, though in no part are they absent.) But there is a further point. Not only has the Fourth Gospel an extensive Old Testament background; it also betrays close acquaintance with contemporary Jewish ideas and practices, and a strong interest in the doctrines, not only of Hellenistic Judaism, but of the Rabbinic Judaism of Palestine. A great Jewish scholar, the late Israel Abrahams, once said that the Fourth Gospel struck him as the most Jewish of the four. Whether or not that is an overstatement, no one would be tempted to any such statement with reference to the First Epistle. We have already noted that its language shows no clear trace of Semitism; and while all the literature of early Christianity carries over something from its Jewish antecedents, there is no other New Testament writing in which the Jewish colouring is so little significant as in the Johannine Epistles. Here then is a formidable difference between our two writings: the Gospel according to John has a stamp derived from the influence of the Old Testament, from interest in Judaism as a living religion, and from knowledge of a Semitic tongue: the Epistle is free from any such stamp.

In contrast, the Hellenistic element, which in the Fourth Gospel is fused with the Hebraic after a unique fashion, has in some respects freer play in the First Epistle.

The maxim, for instance, 'God is light' (i. 4), belongs properly to a circle of ideas neither Christian nor Jewish in origin, though it is here filled with definitely Christian meaning. The Fourth Evangelist, like Philo the Jew, stops short of enunciating it without qualification. The writer of the Epistle is less guarded (see notes, pp. 18–19).

It is argued in the notes that the ideas of the divine 'seed' (iii. 9), and of the 'unction' or 'chrism' which confers supernatural knowledge (ii. 20, 27), are best understood as derived (with a profound change of meaning) from 'Gnostic' sources. Neither of these ideas occurs in the Fourth Gospel.

Again, the argument implied in the statement, 'We know

that if He is manifested we shall be like Him, because we shall see Him as He is' (iii. 2), is shown in the notes (p. 71) to rest upon presuppositions characteristic of 'Hellenistic mysticism.' The Fourth Gospel promises the vision of Christ in His glory (xvii. 24), but does not draw the inference that we shall bear His likeness.

Most significant of all, the weightiest theological pronouncement in the Epistle—the maxim, 'God is love'—while its inspiration is wholly Christian, appears to have been moulded upon lines traceable directly to ideas of Hellenistic thinkers about the divine nature (see notes, pp. 107–10). The maxim is so familiar to us, and the idea so deeply rooted in Christian thought, that the reader of the Epistle is hardly aware how strange it is to find such a statement in the New Testament. In form, it equates the Deity with a purely abstract idea—purely abstract in a sense not applicable to such Old Testament maxims as 'The Lord is my salvation.' The sense intended is far from abstract; but the fact remains that the author of the Epistle has followed a mode of thought and expression avoided in all other New Testament writings, including the Fourth Gospel. (It should perhaps be added that the term 'Spirit' in the Johannine definition, 'God is Spirit,' is for any ancient thinker, Hebraic or Hellenistic, anything but abstract, whatever it may be for moderns.)

Here then we have evidence which enables us to carry a step farther our definition of the difference between the outlook of the Epistle and that of the Fourth Gospel: the Epistle is not only less Hebraic and Jewish; it is also more free in its adoption of Hellenistic modes of thought and expression.

Thirdly, there are various points, and those by no means unimportant, where the Epistle represents a theological outlook nearer than that of the Gospel to primitive, or popular, Christianity. These have already been referred to (pp. xxvii–xlii) and receive full treatment in the notes. They need only be summarized here.

(i) The Epistle holds out the prospect of a near Advent of Christ and end of the world, quite in the primitive way, taking no account of the profound reinterpretation of eschatology which is one of the distinguishing marks of the thought of the Fourth Gospel—a reinterpretation, it should be added, which appears to do fuller justice to the teaching of Jesus Christ than the naïve thinking of the primitive Church.

(ii) The statements made in the Epistle about the redemptive efficacy of the death of Christ scarcely go beyond the terms of the primitive apostolic Preaching. Only one technical term of theology is used, the word which should be translated 'expiation' (ii. 2, iv. 10; see notes, pp. 25–7). This term, which is little more than an index to the doctrine of the Suffering Servant of the Lord in the prophecy of the Second Isaiah, is avoided in the Fourth Gospel. Though the Evangelist, like most other New Testament writers, alludes to the classical prophecy, he never develops the idea of expiation. His distinctive doctrine (to put it with impossible brevity) is that in dying Christ both accomplished the final 'descent' of the Son of God from heaven, and was 'lifted up' in glory, thereby frustrating the powers of evil, releasing the life that was in Him to dwell in believers, and drawing all men into the unity of the divine love (see John iii. 13–17, vi. 48–51, xii. 23–4, 31–3, xvii. 19–23). Of all this there is nothing in the Epistle.

(iii) The conception of the Spirit in the Epistle remains within the limits of primitive or popular belief (iii. 24, iv. 6, iv. 13, v. 6–8; see notes, pp. 95–9, 128). There is no trace of the high 'Johannine'· doctrine which is found in the Gospel. (John iii. 5–8, iv. 23–4, vi. 63, and especially xiv. 15–17, 25–6, xv. 26, xvi. 7–15). It is particularly remarkable that although one of the leading ideas of the Epistle is the divine generation of believers (iii. 1–2, 9, v. 1, etc., see notes), it has no allusion —at any rate no direct allusion—to the function of the Spirit in regeneration as set forth in John iii. 5–8.

Eschatology, the Atonement, the Holy Spirit: these are certainly no minor themes in Christian theology. In all three the First Epistle of John represents an outlook widely different from that of the Fourth Gospel. When this difference is added to those previously noted, the question arises acutely: Is it likely that these two works are the product of a single mind?

It is, of course, true that authors change their style with the passage of years, or even in response to changes of circumstance; it is also true that an active mind continues to modify its ideas, often quite substantially, while retaining certain fundamental characteristics. It may be that the differences we have been considering can be so accounted for. It is however not very easy to frame a plausible hypothesis. It is often suggested that the inferior mental powers manifest in the Epistle are due to increasing years. In that case we should have to suppose that the Evangelist not only declined in powers of thought and expression (though still capable of flashes of creative insight), but also reverted in various respects to a stage of religious thought which at the time of his major work he had left behind. On the other hand, if we have regard to the relatively primitive character of some of the ideas in the Epistle, it might be suggested that it was the product of its author's 'prentice hand, and the Gospel of his maturity. We should then think of the massive theology of the Fourth Gospel as having its starting point in the simpler ideas of the Epistle; and of the somewhat unguarded concessions to Hellenistic thought which we have noted in the Epistle as having been corrected by the author's more mature mind. It is, however, difficult to take this view, since there are places where the argument of the Epistle is hardly to be understood without reference to fuller statements in the Gospel (see especially ii. 7–8, iii. 8–15, v. 9–10, and notes). It is in fact difficult to set aside the impression, which is confirmed by a very wide consensus of scholars, that the Gospel is the earlier work and is presupposed in the Epistle. (Reference may be made to the full discussion in Brooke's Introduction in the *International Critical Commentary*, pp. xix–xxvii; which seems conclusive on this point.)

If the Fourth Gospel is regarded, with a whole school of critics, as the work of several hands, it might be suggested that the author of the Epistle had a part in its composition; and such an hypothesis might account for some of the facts. But the tide of criticism seems to be setting away from separatist theories. It seems almost certain that the Gospel bears all through (apart from possible minor and occasional editorial touches, and in spite of the possible use of various sources) the stamp of a single mind; and in view of the facts we have noted, it is difficult to find the same mind at work in the Epistle. Again, if the theory won its way, that the Fourth Gospel was written originally in Aramaic, a place might be found for the author of the Epistle as translator. But this theory is improbable, and the hypothesis based upon it has difficulties of its own. It may prove possible to frame some other hypothesis, which will admit identity of authorship and yet account convincingly for the deep-lying differences. In such matters strict proof is seldom attainable.

The simplest hypothesis, however, seems to be that the author of the Epistle was a disciple of the Evangelist and a student of his work. He is not a mere imitator, but he has become possessed by certain of his master's ideas, though not going the whole way with him; and he has caught something of his style and manner, though with a difference. The phenomenon is not unfamiliar. In our own time there is an influential school of theologians who draw their inspiration from one great teacher, Dr. Karl Barth (*quem honoris causa nomino*). They are not all slavish followers, by any means. Some of them disagree with their master on some points, or develop his ideas in ways which he would not acknowledge. But the stamp of his mind is upon them. One may observe, sometimes not without amusement, how they repeat his characteristic expressions, and overwork his favourite turns of phrase. They do not set out to imitate, but apparently they cannot help themselves. It may be that the relation of the author of the Epistle to the Evangelist was similar.

The question of authorship is not of the first importance. The present commentary, however, is written upon the assumption that the First Epistle of John best reveals its character and significance when it is not treated as a great author's second thoughts, but allowed to speak for itself. It is in any case not merely derivative. It represents a definite stage towards that central or normal Christianity which emerged from the New Testament period.

V. CHARACTER AND CONTENTS OF THE SECOND AND THIRD EPISTLES

The Second Epistle has the form of a private letter. This form however seems to be a thin disguise for a pastoral epistle addressed to a Christian congregation by a person of weight and authority who describes himself as 'The Presbyter' (see notes on verse 1).

After a general exhortation to the congregation to maintain right belief and Christian charity, the writer warns his readers specifically against certain persons who are carrying on propaganda on behalf of an 'advanced' or progressive type of Christian theology (as they call it), which, however, involves the denial of the reality of Christ's incarnation. The recipients of the letter are assumed to be instructed in the orthodox 'doctrine of Christ.' They are to stand firmly by this doctrine, which alone provides the basis for a genuinely Christian life and experience. Any professedly 'advanced' doctrines are to be tested by this norm. If any wandering missionary appears, whose teaching fails to stand this test, he is to be excluded from Church fellowship, and even from the most elementary social intercourse.

The verses which prescribe this rigorous boycott of heretics (10-11) are the only portion of the epistle (except the epistolary introduction and conclusion) which adds anything of substance to what is contained in 1 John. For the rest, it simply echoes the teaching of that epistle in brief, repeating both its emphasis upon the 'commandment' of love, or charity, and its characterization of the heretical teachers and their doctrine. The situation contemplated in the two writings is similar, but apparently not identical. The Second Epistle appears to announce the existence of a widespread movement of heretical propaganda as if it were something quite new to the church addressed. It is not certain that the propagandists have yet reached this church, but *if* any heretical teacher should appear, the letter will tell them how to proceed (verses 7, 10). In the First Epistle, on the other hand, we have the impression (though there is no unequivocal statement) that the recipients of the letter are already in the thick of the controversy. It does not, however, seem plausible to explain the difference on the ground that 1 John is later than 2 John, because the ideas briefly indicated in 2 John need for their understanding the fuller exposition given in the longer writing. In particular, the term 'antichrist' is thrown out without any explanation (verse 7), and we could hardly understand what lies behind it without the exposition in 1 John ii. 18, iv. 1–6; and the play upon the idea of the 'new commandment' (verse 5) gains point if it is referred back to 1 John ii. 7–8. The relation of the two writings remains enigmatic.

The Third Epistle has an entirely different character. It is, quite obviously, a genuine piece of personal correspondence. How closely it follows the conventions of first-century letter-writing is illustrated in the notes. The Presbyter, his friend Gaius, his opponent Diotrephes, and even the briefly mentioned Demetrius, stand before us as individuals, acting their parts in a dramatic situation. The letter gives us a vivid glimpse of a moment in the life of the Church full of human interest, and possibly of historical importance. Unfortunately the glimpse is so brief, the letter so isolated, that we cannot define precisely the issues at stake in the conflict between Diotrephes and the Presbyter. Clearly enough, the Presbyter is in a position of authority and responsibility, with a group of churches (it would appear) under his charge. Travelling agents commissioned by him move among the churches and carry the Gospel to the pagan population with the financial and moral support of the Christian communities of the neighbourhood. In one church, however, they have met with a rebuff. Some of its members wished to welcome them, but others were strongly opposed to their reception.. The opposition was led by Diotrephes, whom we see, through the eyes of the Presbyter, as an ambitious demagogue with a turn for vituperative rhetoric. The occasion became a trial of strength between Diotrephes and the Presbyter; and Diotrephes won. The party which wished to welcome the missionaries was overborne, and its members driven from the church, whether by formal excommunication or by mere mob violence. The travellers, thus turned adrift, seem to have postponed their further missionary journeys and returned to the Presbyter to report.

This brings us to the situation in which 3 John was written. The Presbyter, perturbed by what he hears from the missionaries, and incensed by the discourtesy they (and he as their sponsor) have received from Diotrephes, plans to visit the offending church as soon as possible, to deal with the disturbances. Meanwhile, he writes a letter to the congregation, but, suspecting that Diotrephes will either prevent the letter from reaching its members, or induce them to ignore it, he writes at the same time the letter now before us. It is addressed to a loyal supporter named Gaius, and entrusted (apparently) to Demetrius, a man of unquestioned integrity, universally respected, and completely in the Presbyter's confidence. With him travel the rejected missionaries (of whom indeed Demetrius may have been one). They had previously been generously entertained by Gaius (whether before their ill-starred encounter with Diotrephes, or after he had persuaded the church to turn them adrift, is not clear). They are now to resume their interrupted mission, and the Presbyter appeals to Gaius, as his most trustworthy adherent in those parts, to take responsibility for their needs; and at the same time apprises him of the deplorable development of Diotrephes' opposition.

The letter, which is written under the stress of strong emotion, undesignedly gives us a portrait of Gaius: a consistent Christian, generous and loyal, but, just possibly, a little susceptible to influence, since the Presbyter, after describing Diotrephes' outrageous conduct, feels it necessary to add: **Beloved, do not imitate evil, but good.**

Such is the background, and the purport, of the letter. It is tantalizing to have this sudden vivid glimpse, and to learn nothing of what preceded or followed. For lack of such information many points must remain uncertain. There is nothing to indicate any connection with the problem of heretical teaching towards which the other two epistles are directed. There is no hint that Diotrephes was unorthodox, though the Presbyter (we must suppose) would hardly have failed to mention a fact, if it had been a fact, so much to his opponent's discredit. The conflict, to all appearance, does not turn upon doctrine, but upon the question of authority. It is probably an episode (as suggested in the notes) in the process through which (not without tensions and difficulties) the Church passed out of the 'missionary' phase, in which the authority of the apostles and their immediate representatives was paramount, to the phase of local episcopacy which we find established in the course of the second century.

In the absence of anything like cross-references (for the similarities between the epistolary introduction and conclusion of 2 and 3 John are merely a matter of a writer's idiosyncrasy modifying current epistolary conventions) it is not profitable to attempt any connection between 3 John and the other Johannine epistles. It remains an isolated item in a correspondence of which the ecclesiastical historian would gladly have had more.

VI. CRITICAL PROBLEMS OF THE SECOND AND THIRD EPISTLES

The external evidence, as we have seen, shows that in ancient times there was no unanimous or consistent tradition of the lesser Johannine epistles (pp. xv–xvi). The judgment that they were all three from one hand, and canonical, did not prevail until a late period. In some quarters 1 and 2 John formed a pair, and 3 John was ignored. In other quarters 2 and 3 John formed a pair, and were attributed to an author different from the writer of 1 John. We have now to enquire what evidence can be gleaned from the epistles themselves regarding their relations with one another and with the major Johannine writings.

The Second Epistle, as we have seen, is largely made up of material parallel with the First. Thus, verse 5 is parallel with 1 John ii. 7, verse 6 with 1 John v. 3; in verse 9 the peculiar expression, **possesses both the Father and the Son,** recalls 1 John ii. 23, and in verse 12 the concluding phrase recalls 1 John i. 4, as well as John xv. 11, xvi. 24.

At the same time there are some striking parallels with passages in the Fourth Gospel which have no parallel in 1 John. In the following list, the Greek has been translated literally, since the Moffatt translation tends to disguise similarities by variant renderings.

2 *John*	*John*
1. 'who know the truth.'	viii. 32, 'you will know the truth' (the same verb: 1 John ii. 21 has a different verb).
2. 'the truth which . . . will be with us for ever.'	xiv. 16–17, 'He will give you another Paraclete to be with you for ever, the Spirit of truth.'
4. 'as we received commandment from the Father.'	x. 18, 'this commandment I received from my Father' (the expression 'to receive a commandment' does not occur in 1 John).
8. 'that you may receive a full reward.'	iv. 36, 'the reaper is receiving a reward' (the verb in 2 John is a compound form of the verb in John. The idea of 'reward' does not appear in 1 John).
9. 'everyone who . . . does not remain in the doctrine of Christ.'	viii. 31, 'if you remain in my word, you will really be my disciples.'

If now we examine the actual vocabulary of 2 John, we arrive at the following results. The total number of different words used in this brief writing is 84. Some 20 of these we may ignore, as too commonplace to call for notice ('the,' 'and,' 'not,' and the like). Of the remaining 64 significant words, there are 4 which are not found in the New Testament except in Johannine writings. Of these, two are peculiar to 2 John ('lady' and 'paper'); one is common to 2 and 3 John ('ink'), and one is common to 1 and 2 John ('antichrist'). Only one of these peculiar words has any theological significance. Of the remaining 60 words, 9 are not found either in 1 John or in the Fourth Gospel (according to the best text), though 3 of them occur in 3 John; and 16 are found in the Fourth Gospel, but not in 1 John.

Leaving these figures for the moment, we turn to 3 John. Here parallels to the other Johannine writings are less striking.

The greeting in verse 1 is similar to 2 John 1, and the epistolary conclusion in 13–14 is similar to 2 John 12–13. The substance of verse 11 might be regarded as a brief summary of the teaching of 1 John iii. 4–10, but apart from this there is little that recalls the First Epistle. The repeated emphasis on 'truth' and 'love' is broadly Johannine, but not characteristic of any one writing. The most striking parallel with the Fourth Gospel is in verse 12: its first clause is shaped like John xv. 27a, and its second clause recalls the editorial note in John xxi. 24, which is in any case not by the Evangelist, but in turn recalls, though more remotely, John xix. 35. To these we may add the not very striking similarity of 3 John 3 to John xviii. 37, and of 3 John 4 to John xv. 13 (which, however, uses a different, and more correct, grammatical form of the word 'greater'). These parallels do not go very far, but so far as they go, they suggest certain habits of speech rather than deliberate imitation of the Fourth Gospel.

Analysis of the vocabulary of 3 John shows the following results. The total number of words used is 99, or 78 significant words. Of these, 23 are not found either in 1 John or in the Fourth Gospel, 4 of them being peculiar to 3 John, 1 common to 2 and 3 John, and 2 common to both these epistles and other New Testament writings. Of the rest, there are 5 words which are found in the Fourth Gospel but not in 1 John, and one which is found in 1 John, but not in the Fourth Gospel.

In dealing with such extremely short writings, linguistic *data* must be used with caution, but so far as they go, they do not, *prima facie*, suggest a very close relation between 2 and 3 John over against 1 John. The 'non-Johannine' words (i.e. words not found either in John or in 1 John) which they have in common are practically confined to the epistolary introductions and conclusions, where there is, naturally, no basis of comparison with the First Epistle or the Fourth Gospel. The total number of significant 'non-Johannine' words in 2 John amounts to just under 20 per cent.; in 3 John, to almost exactly 30 per cent. 3 John is therefore appreciably less 'Johannine' in its vocabulary than 2 John. The Third Epistle again has only one passage substantially parallel with 1 John, over against a whole series of parallels in the Second Epistle. Apart from these close echoes of 1 John, the Second Epistle has a vocabulary nearer to that of the Fourth Gospel than to that of 1 John, and so has 3 John, though in a lesser degree. All three may fairly be said to have a recognizably Johannine colouring, but the linguistic phenomena would not be inconsistent with either of the critical views held in ancient times, which separate one or both of the lesser epistles from the major Johannine writings, though they do not lend decisive support to either of them.

Some modern critics, following those ancients who separated the Second and Third Epistles from the First, and attributed them to a different author, have suggested the theory that the 'Presbyter' who wrote these two short letters is no other than the 'John' who wrote the Revelation (see Moffatt, *Introduction to the New Testament*, 1912, pp. 479–82, 513–14). It is true that the Apocalyptist describes himself not as a 'presbyter,' but (by implication) as a 'prophet' (Rev. 1. 3, xxii. 9). There is, however, no reason why the Presbyter may not have had the gift and repute of prophecy; and in any case both works proceed from someone who, in whatever capacity, was conscious of pastoral responsibility and authority over a group of churches, and probably a group of churches in the same province. But this theory is no longer tenable after R. H. Charles's study of the language of the Revelation in the Introduction to his Commentary on that work (*International Critical Commentary*), Vol. I. pp. xxix–xlv, which shows conclusively that, whatever differences of style and language there may be among the Johannine Epistles and Gospel, they form a definite group in contrast to the Revelation, and that it is in the highest degree improbable (not to say impossible) that the Apocalyptist could have written any of them.

Let us then attempt to estimate probabilities. We may start with 3 John, which is unquestionably a genuine private letter. Although it is not attested, probably, before the third century, there is no likelihood that it is a late fiction. It is so brief, and so unimportant in content, that we can well understand that there were few occasions for quoting it, but we could not understand why anyone should have taken the trouble to fabricate it. It is a writing with a distinctive vocabulary of its own, largely independent of that of the First Epistle and the Fourth Gospel, and yet with certain turns of expression sufficiently marked and numerous to indicate its affinity with the Johannine group of writings. There is little to suggest direct dependance upon either the Gospel or the First Epistle. There is, in fact, only one verse (11) which directly recalls the teaching of either; and that is far from being a quotation or repetition. The epistle is the spontaneous composition of a writer who, even in the unconstrained self-expression of private correspondence, slipped naturally into 'Johannine' turns of speech from time to time. Such a writer might be either (a) the Fourth Evangelist, or (b) the author of 1 John, or (c) a member of the Johannine school, influenced by one or both of these writers. In any case, however, he bore high authority and responsibility in the Church. He commissioned missionaries and planned for their support, and he expected to have his directions carried out by the various congregations in his region. He was in fact (if the interpretation given in the commentary is correct) one of the 'elders' or 'presbyters' who in the sub-apostolic age carried on the tradition of apostolic authority. Such a figure can hardly be identified with a subordinate member of a Johannine school.

The Second Epistle professes to be the work of the same author, and we must choose between accepting this claim, on the one hand, and, on the other hand, regarding the work as a deliberate fiction. Certainly 2 John does not make the same impression of spontaneity as 3 John. A large part of its contents (verses 5–7) is a sort of résumé of teaching given in 1 John, largely in the same phrases, and in a form which seems to presuppose the longer writing. At the same time the description of the false teaching in verse 7 (see commentary) differs curiously in one word from the corresponding description in 1 John. Either it is a different heresy, which seems scarcely credible, or the author of 2 John has used the Greek verb loosely, although in 1 John it is used with perfect idiomatic correctness. The epistolary opening and close are so very like those of 3 John that we should naturally suppose them the work of the same author, unless it is a case of deliberate fabrication. But what is the purpose of the mystification about the 'elect Lady,' her 'sister' and her 'children'? If the Presbyter could be so frank and downright in 3 John, why must he beat about the bush in the companion epistle? If it is a genuine letter from the Presbyter to a church for which he felt a special affection (as verse 1 implies), it is strange that the individuality of the church does not emerge in a single syllable. The precepts (apart from the *ad hoc* regulations about heretics) are such as might be addressed by any Christian minister to any group of Christians at any time, whether he knew them personally or not.

There is here much to suggest the possibility that 2 John is an imitation composed by a writer who had both 1 John and 3 John before him. His motive might have been to claim the authority of the Presbyter for the boycott of heretics, which is his sole substantial addition to material present also in the other two epistles.

If, however, we assume an imitator, we must confess that he has done his work with rare skill. As the foregoing analysis of the language shows, he keeps well within the limits of 'Johannine' vocabulary, with only the modicum of 'non-Johannine' words which we should expect in a free composition. In verses 5–7 this would be sufficiently accounted for by direct imitation of 1 John, but elsewhere the choice of words is nearer to that of the Fourth Gospel, and there are several distinct echoes of phrases in the Gospel, which appear on examination more like unconscious habits of speech than deliberate imitation.

Upon internal grounds, therefore, the hypothesis of fiction falls short of complete plausibility. The external evidence confronts it with a more serious difficulty. Slight as this evidence is, it makes it clear that 2 John obtained relatively early recognition, at least in some quarters, while the reception of 3 John was late and doubtful in any area covered by our evidence. It would indeed be paradoxical if a genuine letter of the Presbyter failed of recognition while a fictitious imitation was canonized.

The simplest hypothesis seems to be that 2 John is, in spite of differences, a genuine work of the author of 3 John. But it is also closely related to 1 John, much more closely than is 3 John, and forms in some sort a link between these two writings. The internal evidence left it open whether the author of 3 John was the Fourth Evangelist, or the author of 1 John, or a disciple of one or both of these. If, however, we were right in distinguishing the author of 1 John from the Fourth Evangelist, we must now eliminate the Evangelist from the list of possible authors of the two lesser epistles, since 2 John seems to be, in some sense, dependent on 1 John, and the Evangelist cannot be thought to have followed so closely the work of one who (on our theory) was his disciple. Of the remaining two possibilities, it seems that we must prefer the identification of the Presbyter with the author of 1 John, on the ground that his dignity and authority appear to be in no way inferior.

The evidence is far from satisfactory, but on the whole the best tentative conclusion would seem to be that all three Johannine epistles are the work of the 'Presbyter,' who is to be distinguished from the Fourth Evangelist. 1 John may be supposed to have the character of a circular epistle, addressed to a fairly wide Christian public; 2 John is addressed to some particular local congregation; and 3 John is a private letter to a friend, albeit on church affairs. 1 and 2 John may have been written within a very short time, and deal with successive stages of a single situation. 3 John deals with an entirely different situation, and may have been separated from the others by a considerable lapse of time. These considerations may suffice to account for the differences which have led some ancient and some modern critics to separate one or both of the lesser epistles from 1 John.

VII. PLACE, DATE AND AUTHORSHIP OF THE JOHANNINE EPISTLES

The writer is not named in the text of the epistles; nor do they indicate either the place from which, or the place to which, they were sent.

The first evidence of the existence of Johannine epistles comes, as we have seen, from the province of Asia, in the writings of Polycarp and Papias, to whom we may add Irenaeus, a native of the same province (pp. xi–xiii). This suggests *prima facie* that they belonged originally to that province, and this view is confirmed by the peculiar use of the title 'Presbyter,' which again appears to be associated with the province of Asia (see notes on 2 John 1). There is nothing which conflicts with the conclusion that these writings originated in that province; and indeed few would question this conclusion, even if they would place the origin of the Fourth Gospel elsewhere.

The dating of the epistles depends too largely upon some unsolved problems in the chronology of early Christian literature to admit of certain or precise determination. We need not indeed assume that all three are strictly contemporary. If one were to trust mere impressions, the Third Epistle might be thought to betray a more vigorous, the First Epistle a riper age. But in any case the difference of time cannot be great. The following points may be noted:

(*a*) The external evidence gives us, in Polycarp and Papias, a *terminus ante quem* which is in no case later than A.D. 140, and may be some twenty years earlier.

(*b*) The 'Presbyters,' representing the sub-apostolic generation, seem to belong to the period round about the reign of Trajan (A.D. 98–117), though some of them must have survived later.

(*c*) The ecclesiastical situation in the province of Asia, as represented in these epistles, seems to be earlier than the situation represented in the Epistles of Ignatius, A.D. 115 (see notes on 3 John). The Pastoral Epistles, which reflect conditions in the same provinces some time before Ignatius (since he seems to quote them), are of uncertain date. The Epistle of Clement to the Corinthians (about A.D. 96) seems to reflect a situation at Corinth comparable with that presupposed in our epistles.

(*d*) The First Epistle is probably later than the Fourth Gospel; but again this is a writing of uncertain date. If the date of 1 John could be fixed, it would help towards the dating of the Gospel.

(*e*) Little can be said of the probable date of the particular doctrinal controversy with which 1 and 2 John are concerned. If these epistles could be dated, we should have a much-needed fixed point in tracing the development of Gnosticism.

(*f*) The epistles do not seem to belong to a period of persecution. The Church indeed is unpopular (1 John iii. 13), though it is implied that travelling missionaries might, if they would, look for subscriptions from friendly pagans (3 John 7). The danger which the Presbyter fears is that of a too ready accommodation with pagan thought and ways. The general tone of the epistles offers the strongest contrast to that of the Revelation, which shows us a Church enduring severe persecution and looking forward to yet worse. If we reflect that these epistles were written in the same province of Asia, and very likely addressed in part to the same churches, it is impossible to believe that they belong to the same period. We may take it for granted that the Revelation belongs to the reign of Domitian. The extreme tension which it reflects was relieved by his death and the accession of Nerva in 96, which began a period of relative toleration. The Epistle of Clement to the Corinthians is thought to have been written immediately after the close of the persecution. We might perhaps imagine that the disturbances at Corinth with which Clement deals, and the recalcitrance of Diotrephes at the unnamed Asian church, were both symptoms of a certain spirit of unrest in a society which had recently suffered under acute repression, and now emerged to face a new set of conditions. On the other hand, a date before Domitian's persecution is not excluded for the Johannine epistles. Only it is not clear that the Church was ever free from the immediate menace of persecution all through the Flavian period. The Epistle to the Hebrews, which is certainly pre-Domitianic (since it is quoted by Clement), is aimed at strengthening its readers to endure a fresh attack. On the whole, a post-Domitianic date seems to fit the other indications better, slight and inconclusive as they are.

Our tentative conclusion, therefore, is that the three

Johannine Epistles were written in the Province of Asia, between A.D. 96 and 110 (or thereabouts), by one of the 'Presbyters' who are known to have lived in that province at that period.

This conclusion rests upon probable arguments from internal and external evidence. If we attempt to go further, and to identify the anonymous author of these epistles with some known individual, we have little but surmise to go upon. It is unlikely that he is to be identified with John the Apostle, the son of Zebedee. The very use of the title 'presbyter' is against it. It is true that Papias (who, whether or not he merited Eusebius's verdict, 'a person of quite small intelligence,' was an uncommonly clumsy writer) expresses himself so loosely in the crucial passage that it would be possible to hold that he intended to include apostles in the wider class of presbyters; but we should probably be right in understanding him to distinguish them. Irenaeus's formula, 'the Presbyters, disciples of the Apostles,' is clear (see note on 3 John 1). The use of the term 'fellow-presbyter' by an apostle (or by a writer who impersonates an apostle, if that view is preferred) in 1 Pet. v. 1 belongs to a different context, and cannot usefully be cited as a parallel. The argument of 3 John turns altogether upon the question of the writer's authority. Can we doubt that if he had possessed the apostolic dignity, he would have flung out a defiant 'John, apostle of Jesus Christ by the will of God,' and reduced Diotrephes to silence?

The Presbyters are for us scarcely individual figures. Papias names only one explicitly, the Presbyter John. Since Irenaeus (who derives from the Asian tradition of Polycarp and Papias) cites both 1 John and 2 John under the name of 'John' (though he meant the Apostle), it is an easy conjecture that the true author is John the Presbyter (upon whom see G. N. C. Macgregor in Moffatt Commentary on *John*, pp. l–lxii). Of this John we know singularly little. He is understood to have resided at Ephesus in the province of Asia, where his tomb (along with that of John the Apostle) was shown in the third century. Papias calls him a 'disciple of the Lord,' meaning apparently that he was a survivor of the group who had heard and followed Jesus in His lifetime. If so, he would have been a very old man at the date we have assigned to the epistles. It is perhaps significant that Irenaeus says that 'John the disciple of the Lord' survived to the time of Trajan, and was known to 'the Presbyters' in Asia (*Adversus Haereses*, II. 33. 3, III. 3. 4). Since we are now indulging in conjecture, there is no harm in the suggestion (which has often been made) that there may be some confusion here. Irenaeus, no doubt, meant John the Apostle, but it is not impossible that the long-lived disciple was actually not an apostolic associate of the Presbyters of Asia, but one of them—namely, John the Presbyter. If so, it is also possible that the 'John' of whom Irenaeus remembered hearing Polycarp speak was, once again, not the Apostle, but the Presbyter; and that it is the Presbyter, not the Apostle, who appears in tradition as the organizer of the episcopate in Asia. To pile conjecture upon conjecture, it may be that some of the anecdotes told of John of Ephesus refer to the Presbyter. It has been pointed out in the notes on 2 John 10-11 that the story of Cerinthus at the baths would at least fit the character of the author of that epistle; and it certainly looks as if it was the author of 1 John who, when in extreme old age he was carried to church, had only one sermon to preach: 'Little children, love one another' (Jerome, *Commentary on Galatians*, vi. 10).

We are here, it must be repeated, in the realm of pure conjecture. It is quite possible that the shadowy figure of John the Presbyter may be brought to life along these lines, and recognized as the author of these epistles, but evidence is lacking to turn the possibility into a probability. Two observations should be made. First, if the author is John the Presbyter, and if he was (as Papias seems to say) a personal disciple of the Lord, he cannot have been much less than twenty years of age in A.D. 30, and was therefore not far short of ninety in the early years of Trajan (assuming that he is the John who survived till that Emperor's reign). The First Epistle, even if it be thought to show something less than the vigour of a man in the prime of life, would be an astonishing performance for one of nearly ninety; and the journeys contemplated in

2 and 3 John would probably be beyond his powers. If therefore the epistles are attributed to John the Presbyter, the pre-Domitianic date must be preferred. Secondly, if the arguments adduced above (pp. xlvii–lvi) are accepted as leading to a distinction between the author of 1 John and the Fourth Evangelist, then, obviously, the epistles can be attributed to the Presbyter John only at the cost of withdrawing his candidature for the authorship of the Fourth Gospel, which at the present time is widely favoured, and is approved in the Commentary on the Gospel according to John in this series.

We must confess that we do not know who our Presbyter was. It does not greatly matter. He has left us a recognizable self-portrait in his three epistles. If we cannot affix a famous name to the portrait, we know what manner of man he was, what he taught about faith and duty, and what part he played at a critical moment in the history of the Church.

THE FIRST EPISTLE OF JOHN

EXORDIUM
(i. 1–4)

It is of what existed from the very beginning, of what we 1
heard with our ears,[1] of what we saw with our eyes, of
what we witnessed and touched with our own hands, it is
of the Logos of Life (the Life has appeared; we saw it, 2
we testify to it, we bring you word of that eternal Life
which existed with the Father and was disclosed to us)—
it is of what we saw and heard that we bring you word, 3
so that you may share our fellowship; and our fellowship
is with the Father and with His Son Jesus Christ. We are 4
writing this to you that our joy may be complete.

The opening sentence of the Epistle, extending to the end
of verse 3, is exceedingly complex. The writer has tried to
pack into it more than a single sentence can well contain, at
the cost of clarity. The Moffatt version smoothes over some
difficulties of construction (as one must do if the translation
is to be readable), and gives a fairly clear sense, which may
be that intended by the author.

According to this way of taking the sentence, **what existed
from the very beginning, what we heard, what we saw with
our eyes, what we witnessed and touched with our own hands,
is** identical with the **Logos of Life.** The Greek word **Logos** is
retained untranslated because it is taken to be a technical
term, as in the Prologue to the Fourth Gospel, where it is
said that **the Logos existed in the very beginning,** and that
in him life lay; that **he became flesh,** and that **we beheld his
glory.** If our present passage is held to be moulded on the
lines of the Prologue, the first clause of verse 1 may be referred
to the pre-incarnate Logos, and the following three clauses to

---

[1] The words 'with our ears' are not found in the MSS. and seem to
have been interpolated here by inadvertence.

the incarnate Logos, that is to say, 'the Jesus of history,' who, as a Man among men, could be seen, heard and touched. So much for verse 1. In verse 2 there is a certain shift of expression. The Fourth Gospel says that the Logos was **with God in the very beginning**, and implies that He **was disclosed to us** in the Incarnation (though the actual verb here rendered 'disclosed' is not used in the Fourth Gospel in this context). In our present passage it is not the Logos, but the Life, that **existed with the Father and was disclosed to us**. The difference may be more apparent than real. In John i. 9–13 it is not easy to say which clauses have the Logos for their formal subject, and which, the Light that was in the Logos. It seems clear that since for the Evangelist the Logos has the aspects (as we might put it) of life and light, it makes little difference to the sense whether we speak, on the one hand, of the Light, or the Life, or on the other hand of the Logos in His aspect of light or of life. And so here, when the writer says that the Life was with God and was disclosed to us, we need not suppose that he means anything substantially different from what is said in the Prologue to the Fourth Gospel.

According to the Moffatt rendering, then, our author starts by saying that it is his intention to speak of Christ as the eternal Logos, in whom was life—indeed, who is Himself the Life—and who as such existed in union with God the Father before all time, and was incarnate in time and so became the Object of sensible experience.

It is, however, not certain that this is precisely what the author means, or, in particular, that he is following so closely the tenor of the Prologue to the Fourth Gospel. It will be well to make a fresh start with a literal translation of verses 1–3a. The sentence is not good Greek, and it is only by paraphrase that it can be rendered into good English. Word for word it reads as follows:

'That which was from the beginning; that which we have heard; that which we have seen with our eyes; that which we observed and our hands felt—concerning the word of life— and the life was manifested, and we have seen and bear witness and announce to you the eternal life which was with the Father and was manifested to us—that which we have seen and heard we announce to you also.'

In this grammatical tangle one thing is clear which the Moffatt version has disguised in the interest of smoothness— namely, that the clause 'concerning the word of life' is not in the same construction as the preceding clauses. It is of course possible that the author changed the construction merely for the sake of variety. But *prima facie* the clause 'concerning the word of life' indicates the *theme* of the announcement, and the clauses 'that which was from the beginning . . . our hands felt' state the *contents* of the announcement. 'That which we have heard concerning the word of life' would be a perfectly straight- forward and perspicuous expression, and although the author has expanded the relative clause by various additions, the fundamental structure of the sentence is not altered by them, though the meaning is significantly enlarged. He is announcing (he says) to his readers what is known from direct evidence to be true about the word of life; what has always ('from the beginning') been true about the word of life. By thus dis- tinguishing the expression 'the word of life' (as giving the theme of the announcement) from the clauses beginning 'that which . . .' (as giving the contents of the announcement) we avoid the awkward necessity of taking the neuter pronouns (neuter in Greek and in English) in reference to Christ as the Logos. The Greek word *logos* is masculine, and if Christ is meant, masculine pronouns would be required in either lan- guage.

This leads to the question whether the term *logos* is here to be taken in the technical sense which it is supposed to bear in John i. 1, 14, or whether some less specialized sense of *logos* is intended. In the former case, it would be well to preserve the Greek term in translation (as Moffatt has done); in the latter case, an English equivalent should be used.

The Greek word *logos* has several meanings, but the two meanings which come into question here are (*a*) 'word,' and (*b*) 'reason' or 'thought.' For the Greek these two were not so distinct as they are for us. *Logos* as 'word' is in any case not mere speech, but rational speech; not mere utterance, but the utterance of a meaning; and *logos* as 'reason' is not the reasoning faculty, but a rational content of thought, articulate and fit for utterance; the meaning which a word expresses. The Stoics used *logos* also for the rational principle immanent in the universe, conceived as the sum of a plurality of *logoi*, by virtue of which things are what they are. Very many thinkers, of different schools, came under the influence of Stoic metaphysics. Among them was Philo the Jew, whose Logos-doctrine has so greatly influenced Christian theology. But Philo is always aware that *logos* also means 'word,' and that the Word of the Lord in the Old Testament is the medium both of creation and of revelation. In the New Testament (apart from our present passage) the prologue to the Fourth Gospel is the only place where it is plausible to recognize the 'metaphysical' use of the term *logos*. It seems, however, probable that the immediate background of the Prologue is the biblical concept of the Word of the Lord by which the heavens were made (John i. 3; Gen. i. *passim*; Ps. xxxiii. 6; Wisd. ix. 1), and which came to God's people through the prophets (John i. 11; cf. O.T. *passim*); the Word of God which is also His Law (Isa. ii. 3, etc.; Ps. cxix.); which in turn is equated with the creative, immanent and revealing Wisdom of God (Prov. viii. 22–31; Wisd. vii. 22–viii. 1; Ecclus. xxiv. 23). More remotely in the background is the Stoic *logos* as the immanent principle, or meaning, of the universe, a conception (not altogether unlike that of Wisdom) which no doubt reached the Evangelist through Hellenistic Judaism, in a form similar to that which is familiar to us from Philo. The translation 'word,' though it is narrower in meaning than the Greek *logos*, is justified, even in John i. 1–14, because it recalls the all-important Old Testament background, and here it is the natural rendering. We may read 'the word of life,' leaving open for the moment the question of the precise connotation of the term in this context.

Now the expression 'word of life' occurs in Phil. ii. 16: **Hold fast the word of life.** The definite article is not expressed in the original, but this need not be significant, and the Moffatt translation (which conforms to the A.V. and R.V.) is probably justified. If we insisted on the absence of the article, the meaning would be a message or announcement of life, or a promise of life (cf. 2 Tim. i. 1); and in any case *the* word of life (*par excellence*) could be no other than the Gospel, by which life and immortality are brought to light (2 Tim. i. 10). Similarly in Acts v. 20, 'the words of this life' means 'this Gospel.' Pauline and Lucan usage is not decisive for a Johannine passage, but in this case we have grounds for saying that Johannine usage agrees. In John vi. 68 the words of Christ are **words of eternal life**. These words (*rhēmata*) it is elsewhere explained, are derived from God, and are collectively the Word (*logos*) of God, which is truth, and which Christ gives to men (John xvii. 6-8, 14, 17). In view of this, it may appear almost accidental that the expression 'the word of life' does not occur in the Fourth Gospel. If it had appeared, it is fairly clear what its meaning would have been. It would be in accord with Johannine ideas to understand 'the word of life' in our present passage as the life-giving Word of God which came to men through Christ and is embodied in the Gospel.

Following this line of interpretation, we should understand the author to mean that his theme is the Gospel, and that he is stating, in the first place, what has always[1] been true about it (and not any innovation or afterthought), and, in the second place, what can be attested upon the immediate evidence of the senses (and not some airy speculation or **fabricated fable**; cf. 2 Pet. i. 16).

Having defined the Gospel as the Word of Life, he now adds, in parenthesis, that by 'life' he does not mean any abstract idea, but the divine reality disclosed to men in the incarnate Christ, whose appearance on earth is a fact attested by eyewitnesses. It is in this sense (he proceeds) that he announces eternal life—namely, by bearing witness to Christ, in whom the

[1] 'From the very beginning.' If the passage is understood in this way it is not necessary to determine whether 'the beginning' here is the absolute Beginning of the universe (as in ii. 13-14) or the beginning of the preaching of the Gospel (as in ii. 7, 24, iii. 11). The Gospel is by its nature, as the Word of God, an 'eternal Gospel' (Rev. xiv. 6). The emphasis is upon the unchanged, original content of the Gospel, over against novel forms of doctrine.

divine life which existed from all eternity was made accessible
to human knowledge.

3*a*   Having made this explanation, the author resumes his interrupted sentence with a repetition of some words from the
opening clause, and brings it to a conclusion: **it is of what we
saw and heard that we bring you word.** Whatever may be the
uncertainties regarding the precise construction of the involved
sentence, its general purport is now clear. Faced with novel
doctrines of a speculative cast, the author recalls his readers
to the unchanging apostolic Gospel, which is the Word of God,
and to its attestation by eyewitnesses of the historical facts
about Jesus Christ. We shall find that this appeal to the
primitive Gospel and this insistence upon the historical reality
of the Incarnation, recur all through the Epistle.

3*b*   He now passes on to a statement of his purpose in writing.
Why is he thus recalling them to the Gospel and its factual
truth? **So that you may share our fellowship.** The word **fellowship** renders a scarcely translateable Greek word, *koinōnia*,
which is often rendered 'communion.' Neither English word
is wholly adequate to convey the meaning of the Greek. 'Communion' is etymologically the nearest, but in English usage it
is too specialized; 'fellowship,' on the other hand has been
overworked in recent years, and has been flattened and
reduced in significance. Fundamentally, the meaning of the
Greek term is simple. *Koinōnoi* are persons who hold property
in common, partners or shareholders in a common concern,
like the fishermen disciples in Luke v. 10, who (it is implied)
were joint owners of the little fishing fleet. Thus *koinōnia* is
properly 'partnership,' 'joint ownership,' or the like. Even
where property is not concerned, the word carries this idea of
partnership or sharing through a wide range of usage. Now, if
the blessings of Christianity are thought of as an 'inheritance,'
of which believers are 'joint-heirs' (Rom. vii. 17; Eph. iii. 6;
1 Pet. iii. 7), then the Christian may be described as a 'partner'
or 'joint-shareholder' (*synkoinōnos*, Phil. i. 7; Rev. i. 9) with
his fellow Christians. They hold shares together, in the Gospel
(1 Cor. ix. 23), in faith (Philem. 6), in sufferings (Phil. iii. 10)

and consolation (2 Cor. i. 7), in the distress and realm and patient endurance which Jesus brings (Rev. i. 9), in the Holy Spirit (2 Cor. xiii. 13; Phil. ii. 1), in the future glory (1 Pet. v. 1). The same 'partnership' finds expression when Christians share their money or goods with one another (Rom. xv. 26, 2 Cor. viii. 4–5, ix. 13, Phil. iv. 15; the principle is clearly laid down in Rom. xv. 27). In all these passages the original has *koinōnos* or one of its cognates or derivatives, though the translation necessarily varies. The *koinōnia* has a special embodiment in the service which Paul calls the Lord's Supper, and which among ourselves is often called the Communion *par excellence*, as being a 'sharing' of the Body and Blood of Christ under the forms of bread and wine partaken in common (1 Cor. x. 16–17). It seems likely that the fellowship or 'Communion' of Acts ii. 42 is in fact the primitive Eucharist or Holy Communion, there described as 'breaking bread and praying together,' an apt enough summary of the minimum essentials of the Liturgy.

The nature of the *koinōnia* is set forth in the New Testament under two especial figures, that of a tree and that of a human body. As the branches of a vine (John xv. 1–6), or olive tree (Rom. xi. 16–24), draw their life from the root and parent stem, and so are 'joint-shareholders in the richness of the olive,' as Rom. xi. 17 has it, so Christians share a common life drawn from Christ through His Spirit. Similarly the constitution of the Church reproduces the organic unity of a human body (1 Cor. xii; Rom. xii. 4–5). When one member suffers the others suffer with it; and as when the mouth speaks, or the ear hears, it is the whole body that speaks or hears through its members, so all the experiences and activities of the whole Church are in some sort communicated to the individual believer; and in turn the due activity of each part enables the Body to grow and build itself up (Eph. iv. 16). These metaphors make it clear that the 'partnership' of Christians is not a mere pooling of their own individual resources, whether material or spiritual; for neither tree nor body is constituted by an association of separately living parts; the life that is shared exists only as shared; and in the application of the metaphors it is made

7

clear that the life of the Church is the divine life disclosed (as our author has it) in the incarnate Christ and communicated through His Spirit. Thus it matters little whether we say that **we participate in Jesus Christ our Lord** (as 1 Cor. i. 9), or that Christ is the Vine and we the branches (as John xv. 5) or that as the body is one and has many members, so also is Christ (as 1 Cor. xii. 12), or that **we form one Body in Christ** (as Rom. xii. 5), or that Christ is the Head of the Body (as Eph. i. 22, iv. 15; Col. i. 18): the implication is the same in each case. Again, the services that individual members render to the Body are not contributions out of their own resources; they are gifts bestowed upon the Body by Christ through His Spirit, and held for its benefit by the individual as a 'shareholder' (Rom. xii. 4–5; 1 Cor. xii. 4–12). According to Paul's teaching, the supreme gift of the Spirit is love or charity, by which the body is held in unity and built up (1 Cor. xii. 31 – xiii. 3, Eph. iv. 16, Col. iii. 14). Since love is the characteristic activity of God—since, indeed, according to the teaching of this Epistle, **God is love,** and to remain in love is to remain in God—we are shareholders in the divine nature (2 Pet. i. 4) according as **we** receive and exercise the gift of charity.

The author's purpose, then, is to promote this **fellowship** in the face of disruptive tendencies. False teaching and bitter antagonisms threaten a dissolution of partnership in the common faith and a breach of the common bond of charity. To counter the menace he would recall his readers to the 'word of life,' to the Gospel, without which there is no Christianity at all. The Gospel is grounded upon most sure testimony, and it provides a searching test for all teaching offered as Christian. And the 'word of life' includes the commandment of charity (ii. 7, iii. 11), which is inseparable from the Gospel proclamation of God's redemptive act in Christ. A return to the Gospel and the Commandment will restore and confirm the threatened fellowship of the Church. Nothing else will. For the Church is not a human association (such as a club or party, which might get over difficulties by a little politic give-and-take); it exists by sharing the divine life embodied in Christ: **our fellowship is with the Father and with His Son Jesus Christ.** And that life is

3c

8

disclosed in the 'word of life,' in the Gospel which proclaims the facts of Christ's coming, and the Commandment which declares what that coming means in terms of personal relations among men.

The remoter aim of such a restoration of fellowship is stated 4 in the words **that our joy may be complete.** It cannot be doubted that there is a reference to the words of the Lord in the Fourth Gospel. In John xv. 1-10 we have the great exposition of the *koinōnia* of the Church under the figure of the Vine, leading to the definition of love as the mode of **fellowship with the Father and the Son,** and concluding (xv. 11), **I have told you this that my joy may be within you and your joy complete.** The words are repeated in a different but allied context in xvi. 24. With these passages in view we can hardly take verse 4 to mean simply 'It will give me great pleasure when these divisions are healed.' (That idea is expressed in different language in 2 John 4, 3 John 3.) It means that with the restoration of the threatened fellowship the Church will enter into the joy of its Lord, according to His word.

This last verse raises a question which must be discussed before we dismiss the exordium—the question, namely, of the sense in which the writer uses the pronoun 'we.' On the face of them, the opening verses taken together seem to imply a distinction between those who had direct experience of the historical facts of the Gospel, and those who knew of them only at second hand, the writer being included in the former class ('we'), and his readers in the latter ('you'). The first person plural might be the familiar epistolary use, in which 'we' means 'I' (like our editorial 'we'), or it might stand for a group to which the writer belongs, and in whose name he writes.

Elsewhere throughout the epistle he commonly uses the first person singular when he is addressing his readers in the capacity of their pastor and teacher (ii. 1, 7, 12-14, 21, 26, v. 13, 16). The first person plural, on the contrary, is very frequently used in a way which includes author and readers in one class. It is what we might call the preacher's 'we.' This form of speech is common in homilies of all periods, and might appear no more than a matter of tact, particularly appropriate where censure has to be passed or error corrected. But it has deeper roots. It belongs to the language of the Church as a fellowship, in the sense explained above. When a preacher addresses his fellow Christians, he must indeed speak 'as the oracles of God' (1 Pet. iv. 11), but he remains one member of the body among others, sharing not only in its corporate faith and experience, but also in its liability to faults and errors which, speaking 'as the oracles of God,' he must reprobate. Similarly, the congregation, as belonging to the body of Christ, implicitly possesses the truth which the preacher communicates. He must always say in effect what our author says to his readers (ii. 21): **I am not writing to you because you do not know the truth, but because you do know it** (and consequently may be expected to recognize and assent to it when it is spoken). The first person plural therefore is an appropriate construction to use. Our author frequently employs it to mean (in effect) 'all Christians,' or 'any Christian.' The contrast to 'we' in this sense is not 'you,' but 'the world' or some equivalent expression (ii. 2, v. 19). The writer freely uses this 'we' even where he is hypothetically contemplating Christians falling into error (**If we say we have fellowship with Him when we live and move in darkness, then we are lying**), as well as when he is affirming the great common realities of Christian faith and experience (**We are children of God; We know we have crossed from death to life**).

Where 'we' and 'you' occur in the same context, it is often difficult to establish the precise difference in meaning. (There are in fact several places where some manuscripts read 'we' and others 'you,' and the true reading could not be determined from the sense of the passage alone.) In ii. 28 for example, we have an alternation of 'you' and 'we' without any apparent change of meaning. It can hardly be supposed that our author intended to say, 'Do you remain in Him so that I (or my colleagues and I) may have confidence.' The meaning of the sentence would not have been different if it had read, 'Let *us* remain in Him so that *we* may have confidence,' or 'Remain in Him so that *you* may have confidence.' In ii. 18–21 the first person singular, the first person plural and the second person plural all occur. In verse 21 (already quoted) we have 'I' and 'you': I do not write to you because you do not know the truth but because you do know it. The writer and his readers are clearly contrasted, yet in such terms as point to the overcoming of the contrast in a fellowship of mutual understanding, for which an inclusive 'we' is the appropriate pronoun. In 18–20 'we' and 'you' alternate: *You* have learned . . . which makes *us* sure . . . They withdrew from *us* . . . *You* have been anointed by the holy One. It does not seem possible that 'we' is either the epistolary plural (meaning 'I') or the true plural of the 'I' in 21 (meaning 'my colleagues and myself'). The 'anointed' Christian community is the same community from which the heretics have seceded; and when the author says that an observation of the present situation makes us sure that it is the last hour, it is not likely that he means either 'I am sure' or 'My colleagues and I are sure': he means that it is a Christian certainty shared by all who have the 'anointing' through which true knowledge comes (compare similar expressions in ii. 3, 5, iii. 2, 14, iv. 13, v. 18–20). In other words, the relation of 'we' and 'you' is not antithetical. If there is any distinction, 'we' is the wider and more inclusive expression, standing for the Christian community as such.

A somewhat more difficult case is iv. 4–6. The words of verse 6*a*, We belong to God, he who knows God listens to us, he who does not belong to God does not listen to us, might very naturally be understood to refer to authorized teachers of the Church among whom the writer reckons himself—but for the illegitimate implications it would seem to carry: namely, (*a*) that when he says we belong to God he means 'my colleagues and I belong to God,' and (*b*) that this 'we' is to be distinguished from the 'you' of verse 4: Dear children, you belong to God. But 'We belong to God' and 'You belong to God' cannot be distinguished in that way. We can only conclude that when the writer says, He who knows God listens to us, the first personal pronoun really stands for the Church as such, proclaiming the Gospel which becomes the touchstone to test its hearers, whether or not they belong to God and know God. That this proclamation may actually be carried out by a particular group within the Church is true, but if 'we' stands for such a special group, it does not contrast them with the laity, but identifies them with the whole Church, their words being its utterance, and as such heard by those who belong to God, and rejected by the world.

With this in view, consider the meaning of the first person plural in iv. 14: **We have seen, we do testify, that the Father has sent the Son as Saviour of the world.** Does this imply that the author (or the author and his colleagues, if the 'we' is a strict plural) stands as an actual eyewitness of the Gospel facts, over against his readers, who can only accept his testimony? If so, does that hold good also for the preceding verse? Does the author mean, 'My colleagues and I know that we are in intimate communion with God, because we (unlike you) possess the divine Spirit'? Surely not. We have here an example of a type of argument which recurs all through the epistle, in which the validity of certain propositions is tested by reference to the common Christian faith and experience. The writer here affirms the reality of a mutual indwelling of God and the believer on the ground that all true believers have a share in the divine Spirit; only, instead of 'all true believers,' he says, 'we.' This generalizing 'we' persists throughout the whole context, iv. 7-19, which contains some of the most important general propositions about the Christian life. At no point should we for a moment suspect any restriction of the scope of 'we,' except in the phrase 'we have seen.' It is difficult to accept a sudden shift of meaning so radical that whereas all through the passage 'we' has meant Christians in general, it now means a group of eyewitnesses sharply distinguished from Christians in general.

It might be suggested that the expression 'we have seen' refers here not to eyewitness, but to inward or spiritual vision, which might be predicated of any Christian who (in terms of verse 13) has a share of the divine Spirit. The author, however, has guarded against such an understanding in the first verse of the epistle (at which we must glance for a moment before returning to it for more detailed investigation). He is writing, he says, about what we saw with our eyes and touched with our hands. He could not have made it clearer that he is speaking of sensible experience and not of spiritual vision. But if it is not inward vision, but actual sensible experience that is in question, can the 'we' of verse 14 be given the wide reference which belongs to the pronoun in the context? Must not the pronoun, here at least, stand for a closed group of eyewitnesses?

It may be observed that the same difficulty about the first person plural arises in some passages of the Fourth Gospel. Particularly in John i. 14 we have an expression which recalls our present text: **The Logos became flesh and tarried among us; we have seen his glory**; which in turn can hardly be separated from i. 16: **We have all been receiving grace after grace from his fulness.** Does 'we' mean the apostolic witnesses or Christians in general? It may be that the solution of the problem in both writings is the same.

It is possible that the way to a solution may be found through the doctrine of the 'fellowship' of the Church which is so important to our author. The English word 'fellowship' as we have seen, is weaker than the original word *koinōnia*, which connotes a sharing of life and experience so deep and thoroughgoing that what is predicated of the whole community can in some real sense be predicated of each member, and *vice versa*. The background of this is the sense of solidarity which was so intense in ancient societies. It is a commonplace to students of the Old Testament. The 'I' of the Psalms, for example, seems to expand and contract between the individual, a group, and the entire nation. It expresses the solidarity of the Psalmist with the Israel of God. The experiences he describes are not less his own for being also those of his people, and not less corporate for being personal. And as there is solidarity among all members of God's people who are contemporary with one another, so there is solidarity among the successive generations of Israel. Thus Amos writes in the eighth century B.C.: 'Thus saith the Lord . . . I brought *you*

13

up out of the land of Egypt, and led *you* forty years in the wilderness' (Amos ii. 10), although the Exodus lay at least five hundred years behind him; and Joshua, addressing the elders of Israel after the conquest of Canaan, can even be represented as saying, 'Thus saith the Lord . . . *Your eyes saw* what I did in Egypt' (Joshua xxiv. 7), although, according to the tradition, the whole generation of the Exodus died in the wilderness.

This sense of solidarity is not peculiarly 'Semitic.' Similar examples can be quoted from Greek and Latin authors. Indeed, it might be said that a faint shadow of it persists among ourselves, and sometimes colours our speech; as when an undergraduate says, 'We went head of the river in 1870'! But it needs an effort for us, born into the individualism of the modern world, to realize in imagination the strength and spontaneity of the sentiment of solidarity in ancient societies. The Old Testament usages, however, to which we have referred, are of more direct significance for our present purpose, because in Israel the natural solidarity of blood and soil was increasingly transcended by the sense of a unity based on the divine calling and covenant.

In the New Testament the conception of the *koinōnia* of the Church represents a perfect sublimation of natural solidarity, or its re-creation upon a higher level. Bearing this in mind, we may freely illustrate the language of Christian fellowship from the established forms of speech developed out of the social solidarity of antiquity, and especially from Old Testament language. It is noteworthy that both Amos and Joshua (in the passages cited above) are speaking of the 'mighty acts of the Lord' by which Israel was redeemed and became a holy people. It is of these events that both speak as if their hearers had personal experience of them. If Joshua could say, 'Your eyes saw what I did in Egypt,' to an audience who could not have been actual eyewitnesses, because he did not distinguish the experience of individuals from that of the society in which they lived and moved, so our author (referring also to the 'mighty acts of the Lord,' by which the Church was redeemed and became a holy people) may be conceived as saying, 'We have seen,' even though the 'we' might include

14

many who had not been individually eyewitnesses of the Gospel facts. The Church, through its solidarity with the apostles and eyewitnesses, possesses their testimony, and therefore can bear witness before the world to the reality of the Incarnation, saying, 'We have seen'; and any member, speaking in the name of the Church, may repeat that affirmation, without necessarily making an individual claim to sensible experience of the facts. This does not preclude an alternate expansion and contraction of the 'we,' analogous to the expansion and contraction of the 'I' of the Psalms. But neither this passage nor any other of those we have examined seems to afford any solid ground for the supposition that the author is thinking in terms of a closed group of eyewitnesses (such as the Apostles) over against the general membership of the Church, or that the pronouns 'we' and 'you' distinguish this closed group from the readers of the Epistle.

In the exordium, to which we now return, the position is somewhat different. Here certainly a distinction is made (as is natural) between the author and his readers, and this distinction is expressed by 'we' and 'you' in verse 4: 'We are writing this to you,' and similarly in verse 3. 'We bring you word, so that you may share our fellowship.' Yet this 'we' of authorship is in each case at once swallowed up in a 'we' which can be no narrower in scope than the whole membership of the Church. In verse 3, 'Our fellowship is with the Father and with His Son Jesus Christ' can hardly mean, 'My colleagues and I enjoy communion with God, which we should like you to share.' 'Our fellowship' is surely the *koinōnia* which belongs to all members of the Church as such; the fellowship which they have one with another (i. 7). And 'Our joy,' as we have seen, is the joy of the whole Church in realizing its *koinōnia* (for although in the dramatic setting of John xv. 1–11 the promise is addressed to the eleven Apostles, its intended application is as wide as that of the allegory of the Vine to which it is appended). The question is whether the 'we' of verses 1 and 2 is the 'we' of authorship, referring to the writer's own experience (which is not that of his readers), or the wider 'we' which includes the whole Church united in fellowship. On the one hand, this kind of language would be very natural from the Apostle John, or the Presbyter John ('the disciple of the Lord'), or some other eyewitness to whom the authorship of the epistle might be ascribed. On the other hand, it is not in itself sufficient to prove authorship by an eyewitness. We have seen that the author can say, **We have seen; we do testify,** where 'we' includes all Christians who, as such, 'remain in' Christ and 'have a share in His Spirit' (iv. 13–14); and his language here—**we saw with our eyes** (cf. Joshua's 'Your eyes saw'), **touched with our own hands**—differs only in the emphasis with which he insists that it is actual seeing, hearing and touching that he means, and not anything like inward vision. It is there that the emphasis lies, and not upon the direct knowledge of some Christians over against the second-hand knowledge of others. Even if the language is that of an eyewitness, his 'we' is like the 'I' of the Psalms, which can stand both for the individual Psalmist and for the Israel of God. He speaks not exclusively for himself or for a restricted group, but for the whole Church to which the apostolic witness belongs by virtue of its *koinōnia*, over against the world which being outside the *koinōnia* has no knowledge of the incarnate Son, and therefore no knowledge of the Real God (v. 20). He has already in mind those who break the fellowship of the Church, and who, by rejecting the evidence of eye, ear and hand to the reality of the Incarnation (iv. 2–3), range themselves with the unenlightened world (iv. 5–6).

I. WHAT IS CHRISTIANITY?
(i. 5 – ii. 28)

The general intention of this section of the Epistle is to set forth the distinctive marks of Christianity as a way of life and belief, over against current misunderstandings or misrepresentations.

First, various expressions for forms of 'religious experience' are passed in review, and subjected to searching criticism in the light of the fundamental axioms of Christianity, emphasis

being laid upon the evangelical doctrine of forgiveness
(i. 5–ii. 6).

Secondly, Christ's 'new commandment' of love is shown to
be of the essence of the Christian religion, which is the disclosure of a new order of life, in contrast to the doomed order
of a pagan world (ii. 7–17).

Thirdly, a direct attack is made upon the false doctrines
which are being propagated in the Church, and the readers are
recalled to the certainties of the divine revelation in the
Gospel of Christ (ii. 18–28).

I. A CRITICISM OF 'RELIGIOUS EXPERIENCE,' WITH AN EXCURSUS UPON SIN AND FORGIVENESS (i. 5–ii. 6)

Here is the message we learned from him and announce to you: 5
    'God is light and in Him there is no darkness, none.' If we 6
    say, 'We have fellowship with Him,' when we live and move
    in darkness, then we are lying, we are not practising the
    truth; but if we live and move within the light, as He is 7
    within the light, then we have fellowship with one another,
    and the blood of Jesus His Son cleanses us from every sin.
    If we say, 'We are not guilty,' we are deceiving ourselves 8
    and the truth is not in us; if we confess our sins, He is 9
    faithful and just, He forgives our sins and cleanses us from
    all iniquity; if we say, 'We have not sinned,' we make Him 10
    a liar and His word is not within us.   ii.
    My dear children, I am writing this to you that you may not 1
    sin; but if anyone does sin, we have an advocate with the
    Father in Jesus Christ the just; He is Himself the propitia- 2
    tion for our sins, though not for ours alone but also for the
    whole world.
    This is how we may be sure we know Him, by obeying His 3
    commands. He who says, 'I know Him,' but does not obey 4
    His commands, is a liar and the truth is not in him; but 5
    whoever obeys His word, in Him love to God is really
    complete.
    This is how we may be sure we are in Him: he who says 6
    he 'remains in Him' ought to live as He lived.

We shall find a clue to the meaning of this section of the epistle if we understand the writer to be alluding all through to certain maxims which were used as watchwords by heretical teachers. Some of them he would accept himself, but in a different sense, or with different implications. 'We are sinless'; 'we know Him'; 'we are in Him': this is the kind of language used by those who claimed superior enlightment, and were leading the Church away from the simplicity of the Gospel. None of these maxims could be directly repudiated by one who took the 'Johannine' view of Christianity. Yet they could be so applied as to destroy the distinctive character of the faith. The writer is concerned to expose the fallacy underlying their use by the heretics.

i.

5   He begins with a maxim acceptable alike to himself and his opponents: **God is light and in Him there is no darkness.** Anyone who speaks in this way is at home in the religious world of first-century Hellenism. There is indeed something natural, and almost universal, in the symbolism of light. In primitive religion the light of the sun, apparently the source of life and well-being to the earth and all its denizens, is an object of worship. When a people has passed beyond crude nature-worship, light is still the symbol of well-being as well for the body as the soul, which is referred in thankful adoration to its source in the high God. 'The Lord is my light and my salvation,' says the Hebrew Psalmist (Ps. xxvii. 1). In Greek philosophy Plato had sanctioned the description of the ultimate reality, the Eternal Goodness (or 'Idea of the Good') in terms of light. The influence of Platonism combined with that of Zoroastrianism, with its conception of the universe as the scene of an agelong conflict between light and darkness, to provide the religious mind of the Near East with an imaginative metaphysic. A Greek writer of a period not far from that of our author gives a vision of creation. First there was boundless light; then an ocean of darkness. A holy word out of the light descended upon the darkness, and the creation of the world began. That light, he says, is Mind, or God (*Corpus Hermeticum*, I. 4–6). Philo is half a Greek and half a Hebrew when he says, referring to the

18

verse of the Psalm quoted above, 'God is light, and not light only, but the archetype of every other light; or rather, more ancient and higher than any archetype' (*De Somniis*, I. 75). In the Fourth Gospel the Logos (that is to say, God as revealed in creation and in man) is equated with 'the real Light' (which is equivalent to Philo's 'archetypal Light'), and Christ as the incarnate Logos is described as the Light of the world. In fact, the teaching of this Gospel is pervaded by light-symbolism. Like Philo, however, the Evangelist stops short of the statement that the eternal God is to be defined as Light. Both these great theologians, the Jewish and the Christian, apparently felt that to go the whole length in adopting the language of current religious philosophy might endanger the conviction of the personal transcendence of God which is fundamental to Judaism and Christianity alike. Our present author is less guarded. Perhaps he was hardly aware that in summarizing the purport of Christian teaching as given in the Fourth Gospel he is giving it a turn which brings it nearer to current forms of expression, and nearer, no doubt, to the language of the heretics whom he is criticizing.

Where then does he differ from them? Not in emphasizing the truth that the being of God as light excludes any trace of darkness. They, like their compeers outside Christianity, would have affirmed that as strongly as he. It is in the corollary that he immediately draws, **If we say, 'We have fellowship with 6 Him,' when we live and move in darkness, we are lying.** That is to say, he is not interested in any metaphysical implications of the idea that God is light, but in its ethical implications. Light is for him primarily the symbol of sheer goodness; darkness, of moral evil. If then God is altogether good, without any trace of evil, it follows that we cannot have fellowship with Him without being good in our degree. It was necessary to lay stress upon this point. The age was a religious age, and many religions and philosophical systems offered communion with the divine. But religious fervour did not always go with moral seriousness. According to our authorities for the next period, there were heretical forms of Christianity which fell far below the best kind of paganism in their moral standards. Our author sees that danger in the kind of teaching which is making propaganda in the Church—specious propagnada, since it uses the language of an elevated mysticism. He insists on the ethical criterion. Religion is not indeed just 'morality tinged with emotion,' but, on the other hand, there is no religion in the Christian sense of the word unless it includes moral endeavour and the criticism of conduct.

7*a*   To be within the light, then—that is to say, to be in union with God—means to lead a good life, since God is good. And this is the true basis of fellowship in the Church. It is a society of people who, believing in a God of pure goodness, accept the obligation to be good like Him (cf. Matt. v. 48). (This statement serves for the present; it must be filled out and clarified from later parts of the epistle, where it is shown that the specific character of 'light,' as a divine attribute and as a quality of human life alike, is love or charity. See pp. 34–6, 84–7.)

Down to this point, then, we have an exposition of the text, God is light. This maxim itself is offered as the message we learned from Him (that is, Christ). It is unlikely that the author supposed himself to be citing an actual saying of the Lord. We may conceive him as saying, in effect, 'The teaching of the Gospel about God may be summed up in the familiar maxim, "God is light," if you will allow to this maxim its full logical implications: that light excludes darkness, and that communion with a God who is all light without a shade of darkness must involve living a life free from the darkness of sin and radiant with the light of goodness.' For the use of the popular light-symbolism he found sufficient sanction in the Fourth Gospel, which he accepted as an authoritative exposition of the teaching of Jesus Christ. It is, however, of interest to enquire whether his doctrine is supported by the older tradition of the sayings of Jesus in the first three Gospels. The most significant passage for our purpose is the saying which both Matthew and Luke give from a tradition common to them both. In its Lucan form it reads: Your eye is the lamp of the body: when your eye is sound, then the whole of your body has light, but if your eye is diseased, then your body is darkened.

(Look! perhaps your very light is dark.) So if your whole body has light, without any corner of it in darkness, it will be lit up entirely, as when a lamp lights you with its rays (Luke xi. 34–6). Here we have a picture of single-minded integrity, under the combined figures of a space flooded with light, and of a man with perfect eyesight. It is in fact a picture of one who (as our author would put it) lives and moves in the light, contrasted with one who lives and moves in darkness. This quality of integrity is the same as the purity of heart which leads to the vision of God according to Matt. v. 8 (cf. 1 John iii. 2–3), and it is a reflection in man of the 'perfectness' of God (Matt. v. 48), who alone is 'good' without qualification (Mark x. 18). Similarly, to imitate the impartial benevolence and beneficence of God towards all men is to be a son of God (Matt. v. 43–7, Luke vi. 35–6; cf. 1 John ii. 29–iii. 1). If we apply to these sayings the symbolism of Luke xi. 34–6, we shall find ourselves very close to our author's teaching that **God is light, and in Him there is no darkness**; and that to have fellowship with Him means to **live and move within the light.**

Here a fresh point comes up. To be **within the light, to have** 7*b*. **fellowship with Him,** is to be pure from sin (for 'what fellowship has light with darkness?': 2 Cor. vi. 14). Such purity belongs to believers, not through their own moral achievement, but by virtue of the death of Christ. Here the writer is faithfully reproducing that clause of the original apostolic Preaching which declared that Christ died for our sins (1 Cor. xv. 3).

It was important to guard against misunderstanding here. 8 The heretics (if we may read between the lines, with the support of what is known about 'Gnostic' teaching) take their stand upon the belief that Christians have been given a new nature superior to that of other men. Consequently, they affirm, Christians are already sinless beings; or if not all Christians, at least those who have attained to superior enlightenment. They have no further need for moral striving: they are already perfect. Indeed, some appear to have held that if the enlightened do things which in other men would be counted sinful, they are not sinners. Their mystical communion with God in itself removes them from the category of sinful men. Now up to a point this is so like our author's own teaching that he cannot lightly pass it by. He is quite clear that if a man has really been 'born of God' he cannot live in sin (iii. 9); and in spite of anything that may be said here, it remains true that a Christian is expected not to sin. Nevertheless, to assert roundly, we are not guilty, is self-deception. Our author has a plain, straightforward view of sin which is salutary in its very crudity. Just as to be righteous is, quite simply, to do what is right, so to break the moral law is to be sinful (iii. 7, 10), and an honest man must acknowledge that he has done so. There is no place for subtlety. We have sinned, and there is no use in denying it. The true teaching of the Gospel is, not that by initiation we become automatically sinless, but that within the Church we are under a dispensation which deals effectively with our sins.

9 The basic fact is that God is a forgiving God, as the Gospel (the 'word of life') declares Him to be. He is forgiving because He is faithful and just. That God is 'faithful,' or trustworthy, is a fundamental postulate of biblical religion in Old and New Testaments (cf. Deut. vii. 9; Ps. xxxvi. 5, lxxxix. *passim*, etc.; I Cor. i. 9, x. 13; I Thess. v. 24; 2 Thess. iii. 3; I Pet. iv. 19); that is to say, unlike the fickle gods of pagan mythology, He is so entirely consistent with Himself that we can rely upon Him completely in all circumstances and through all vicissitudes. It is because God is faithful, or trustworthy, that He can be the Object of faith or trust. God is also just, or righteous: without this conviction there is no ethical religion. But it is remarkable that our author should base divine forgiveness directly upon the faithfulness and justice of God. Christian teaching has often opposed the justice of God, which demands that sin shall be punished, to His mercy, which remits the punishment; and some theories of the Atonement set out to explain how this opposition is overcome. The opposition is not recognized in the New Testament. For 'John' as for Paul (see Rom. iii. 21–6 and notes in Moffatt Commentary) the mercy or forgiveness of God is a function of His righteousness; and so

22

far from forgiveness being a kind of breach in His self-consist-
ency, it is both possible and actual only because God is completely 'faithful,' completely to be relied upon in all circumstances; or, as it is put in 2 Tim. ii. 13 (with reference to
Christ), **if we are faithless, He remains faithful—for He cannot
be untrue to Himself.** God's attitude to us, His purpose for us,
do not alter because we sin against Him. When we turn to
Him again, we find Him still the same. If we confess our sins,
and in confession repudiate them, then God forgives, not (as a
man might) because He chooses on this occasion to be indul-
gent, or considerate, or tolerant, but because no other course
would be consistent with the perfectly good will by which the
whole universe is created and sustained. It is this, and this
only, in the last resort, that justifies our confidence of being
forgiven our repeated offences against the law of God. We
believe in the forgiveness of sin, not by convincing ourselves
that our sins were excusable, or remediable, or that we
meant well, or that 'we won't do it again.' It is because the
principle of forgiveness is built into the structure of a moral
order created and determined by the character of a just and
faithful God.

In view of all this, the claim to be sinless is not only self- 10
deception (as in verse 8); it is a presumptuous denial of the
truth of the Gospel; for in proclaiming God to be a faithful,
just and forgiving God, it declares man to be a sinful creature
needing forgiveness. If on the ground of any ideas of our own
we deny this, then his word is not within us: we have heard the
Gospel, and thought we believed it; but we have not inwardly
digested it. The probability is that an effective appreciation
of our own sinful condition is in most cases not (as is often
supposed) a preliminary to the hearing of the Gospel, but a
consequence of it.   ii.

The general position having been thus laid down, we are to 1
have two outstanding evidences or instances of the way in
which, according to the Gospel, sin is effectively dealt with. But
before speaking of them the writer once more enters a *caveat*:
nothing he is about to say must be understood as conferring
any license to sin. That is in any case excluded (compare the

similar misunderstanding mentioned in Rom. vi. 1 and confuted in the verses following).

First, then, Christ not only died for our sins (as verse 7 above); He also lives to intercede for us. This also is part of the Gospel (cf. Rom. viii. 34; Heb. vii. 25, ix. 24), which contemplates us always as sinners standing before God's judgment seat, and needing the mediation of an **advocate.**

The word so translated is *parakletos*, familiarly Englished as 'paraclete.' Its etymological meaning is 'one called in' to help, and so in the most general sense it means 'helper,' 'supporter' (cf. Moffatt's translation in John xiv. 16, etc.). But it was popularly used to denote a friend 'called in' to support a party to a law-suit or the defendant in a criminal trial, an 'advocate.' It is interesting to observe that in the early Rabbinic tractate *Pirqe Aboth* (iv. 13) the Greek word, transliterated into Hebrew, is used in speaking of man as a defendant before the heavenly tribunal. 'He who fulfils one commandment has gained for himself one "paraclete"; he who commits one transgression has gained for himself one accuser.' Here it is a question of balancing merit against demerit: a man's own merits are his 'advocates' to win God's favour. The New Testament repudiates this idea. We cannot acquire merit before God. We need an 'advocate' who is other than ourselves.

The same word 'paraclete' is used by Philo where he is describing the nature of true worship, as symbolized by the liturgy of the Temple. The High Priest's vestments, he says, are emblems of the created universe in its perfection as manifesting the divine Logos. 'It was necessary for him who performs the office of priest to the Father of the universe to employ as advocate His Son, most perfect in virtue, for the amnesty of sins and the supply of unstinted blessings' (*Vita Mosis*, II. 134). It may have been language of this kind that led to the choice of the term 'paraclete' for Christ as Intercessor in 'Johannine' circles. But the belief in His heavenly intercession is no innovation (see Moffatt Commentary, *Romans*, p. 144).

The belief responds to a need deeply felt wherever religion is seriously ethical. When once the conscience of man comes to recognize a moral law conceived as the will of an entirely righteous God, then every advance in our apprehension of the character of God and of His demands upon man deepens the sense of guilt which sets a barrier between God and ourselves. Yet our need to approach God is all the greater because of our sin. How if there be within the divine Being Itself that which sympathizes with us and pleads our cause? The Christian Gospel declares that this is so; and not only so, but that this Everlasting Mercy was incarnate for us in Christ, who as Man had personal acquaintance with our moral conflict, and now represents us within the eternal Godhead (Heb. iv. 14–16). If we conceive to ourselves Christ as praying for us (as He prayed for His disciples on earth), then our prayers for forgiveness and release from sin, whether for ourselves or for others (v. 16), are taken up into His intercession, which is not, as all our prayers are, weakened or hindered by sin (for He is Jesus Christ the *just*, or righteous, as our author emphatically adds). This is what is meant by praying 'in the name of Jesus Christ.' Whatever our words, or even our thoughts, may be when we pray (and they are inevitably imperfect at best, and often mistaken), the real content of Christian prayer is that which Christ asks on our behalf, and the Father grants. To this Paul adds (Rom. viii. 26) that the Spirit (who for him is scarcely distinguishable from Christ indwelling) 'intercedes' within us, when we do not know what prayer rightly to offer, and can only utter an inarticulate sigh. This conception of the Spirit as Advocate, supplementing, as it were, the work of Christ as Advocate, is not present in this epistle, but the Fourth Gospel knows the Spirit as *'another* Paraclete' (John xiv. 16).

Secondly, the heavenly Advocate is also Himself the propitiation for our sins. The word propitiation, however, is a doubtful rendering. The word in the original (*hilasmos*), which occurs also in iv. 10, is derived from a verb which in pagan Greek usage generally means to 'placate,' 'pacify' or 'propitiate' an offended person, and in particular an offended deity. The verb, however, has another meaning, rarer in pagan writers—namely, to perform an act by which defilement (ritual or moral) is removed; to 'expiate.' The sense that evil doing brings with it a kind of taint is natural and general. It is

25

related to that 'numinous' feeling in the presence of a *mysterium tremendum* in which some see the most primitive element in religion. When the object of the 'numinous' feeling comes to be identified with the moral Absolute, or with a God who is 'of purer eyes than to behold iniquity,' the sense of defilement attaches itself more and more definitely to moral evil. In antiquity it was universally believed that the performance of prescribed rituals (which might or might not include the ritual slaughter of animals) had the value, so to speak, of a powerful disinfectant. The ritual duly performed, one could be confident that the taint was removed. For such rituals the most general term in the Greek Old Testament is the verb in question, which almost invariably bears the sense 'to cleanse from defilement,' 'to expiate.' Where priests or other men are the subject, it refers to sacrifices or lustral rites. But in Hebrew thought it is possible, as it never is in Greek paganism, for the subject of the action to be God; and then the meaning is virtually indistinguishable from 'to forgive': the defilement of sin can be removed, in the last resort, only by divine forgiveness (see Moffatt Commentary, *Romans*, pp. 54–5).

Biblical usage is not necessarily decisive for a writer who makes so few allusions to the Old Testament as our present author; and in the immediate context it might seem possible that the sense of 'propitiation' is in place: if our guilt requires an advocate before God, we might, logically, need to placate His righteous anger. But the wider context denies this interpretation. Our forgiveness rests upon the justice and faithfulness of God, not upon the possibility of averting His anger. He *forgives* our sins; He *cleanses* us from all iniquity: those two verbs express precisely the ideas principally associated with words of this family throughout the Greek Old Testament (and probably also in the few cases where they occur in the New Testament, Rom. iii. 25; Luke xviii. 13; Heb. ii. 17, and in a transferred application, Heb. ix. 5).

The reference in i. 7 to the blood of Christ suggests that the author is thinking in the first place of the death of Christ as analogous to animal sacrifices (much in the same way, perhaps, as is set forth in the Epistle to the Hebrews; see Heb. ix.–x.). The term used, however, does not in itself connote a blood-sacrifice, and the expression in ii. 2 is wide enough to cover the whole work of Christ—His death especially, no doubt, but not to the exclusion of His incarnation, His earthly ministry, and His resurrection and ascension. The entire work of Christ is an act of expiation; and God is the Author of it. It is He who sent His Son to be the expiation for our sins (iv. 10)—that is to say, as the efficacious means by which **He forgives our sins and cleanses us from all iniquity.** The originating cause of the whole action is the justice and faithfulness of God, or (as in iv. 10) the love of God. Further, this act of God affects the whole human race. Christ is the expiation for our sins, and **not for ours alone, but also for the whole world.** 'The world' is in this epistle as a rule an expression for the hostile pagan order in which human life is organized in opposition to the will of God (ii. 15-17; see notes there), and as such a realm of evil and an enemy to be overcome (v. 19, 4-5). But the author does not forget that the human beings who are thus involved in a godless order remain the objects of God's care and interest; and that the Gospel affirms that He **loved the world** (in this sense) **so dearly that He gave up His only Son** (John iii. 16). This saying is echoed in iv. 9, and its universal intention is succinctly brought out in iv. 14: **The Father has sent the Son as the Saviour of the world.**

Such is the doctrine of Christ's expiation as we gather it from this epistle. We are not told precisely how the work of Christ has this effect. Christian theology has notoriously always been in some uncertainty upon this point. But an attentive study of the Gospels will suggest that the doctrine is by no means an unsupported speculation. Jesus Christ acted within a situation representative of human history at large. He became involved in desperate conflict with sinful elements in the situation. In the conflict He acted in such a way as to mirror perfectly the attitude to men which He attributed to the Father in heaven: uncompromising towards all evil; unweariedly benevolent towards those who wrought the evil. He was finally left utterly alone, and suffered the extremity of all that human wickedness could inflict. On a particular day in history, therefore, there stood on the one side a world of men with the stain of an indelible crime upon its conscience—a stain of which none of those involved in the situation were free, not Peter nor the sons of Zebedee—and on the other side stood a Person upon whom all this concentrated wickedness had no other effect than to give Him the occasion for suffering to the end in undiminished loyalty to God and goodwill towards men. At the moment when Christ seemed defeated, and all that He stood for appeared powerless in face of the sin of the world, the power of almighty God was made manifest in bringing Him back from the dead. His return to His faithless disciples was a clear act of forgiveness; and the first message they bore from Him to the world contained the offer of forgiveness for its sins (Acts ii. 38–9). The Church made its entry into history in the newborn conviction that by what Christ had done and suffered the sin that had brought Him down was, so to speak, neutralized, and its corruption sterilized, by the love and power of God. In some such way we might briefly summarize the story. It is at least sufficient to show that our author, while using the language of pre-Christian religious observance, is not deserting his canon of historical actuality (**what we heard, what we saw with our eyes, what we witnessed and touched with our own hands**) when he says that in Christ the love of God provided an expiation for sin. For it is true that the historical episode in question, while it displays in a marked degree the corruption of our nature by sin, issues in a signal exhibition of divine forgiveness, determined entirely by what Christ was, did and suffered.

Our generation, confronted with the 'mystery of iniquity' upon so vast a scale, is perhaps more ready than our immediate predecessors to receive with some understanding the doctrine of Christ's expiation. Wicked things have been done, and are being done, which shame us all and defile our common humanity. We grope about for means of redress; but we know that whatever we may do or resolve, the shame and defilement remain, and no one of our generation can ever be clear in his own conscience. The Gospel 'speaks to our condition' when it assures us, not only that God loves the world and is ready to forgive our sin, but that His love has been expressed concretely and objectively in history to provide a means of sterilizing human wickedness and effecting a forgiveness which is not merely an amnesty or indulgence, but a radical removal of the taint. We may not be able to give a fully reasoned theology of the matter, but we are entitled to believe, in face of the degradation of our common humanity, that God has done in Christ all that needs to be done to cleanse us, and done it with the complete adequacy possible only to infinite power and love.

We now pass on to another point in which the author con- ³⁻⁵ₐ ceives the teaching of the heretics to misrepresent the authentic Christian Gospel—namely, their claim to 'knowledge' of God. We are here in touch with the central idea of that movement which is often called 'Gnosticism' because of its emphasis upon *gnosis*, knowledge. It goes back, on the one hand, to the intellectualism of the Greeks. In the classical period an almost unbounded confidence in the human reason led thinkers to believe that accurate knowledge of reality was attainable, and that in such knowledge lay the ideal for human life. Plato insisted that knowledge in the true sense, as opposed to mere 'opinion,' must be knowledge of the eternal and unchangeable essence of things, and not of variable phenomena. In his doctrine of eternal 'forms' or 'ideas,' resident in heaven and contemplated by pure reason, there is already an element which may fairly be called mystical, especially when the knowledge of the ideas is represented as the soul's 'recollection' of what it had known in a higher existence. In the Hellenistic period the self-confidence of the Greek spirit faltered. Doubtful of the competence of the un-aided intellect to attain the highest knowledge, philosophers turned to religion, which in the 'mysteries' offered a revelation or vision of God. Spiritualizing this conception (for the mysteries before they were reinterpreted by philosophers were crude enough), they arrived at a conception of a 'knowledge' of God not attained by rational thought, but given in an ineffable experience. One writer says, 'Not yet are we able to open the eyes of the mind and to behold the beauty, the imperishable, inconceivable beauty, of the Good. For you will see it when you cannot say anything about it. For the knowledge of it is divine silence and annihilation of all senses. . . . Irradiating the whole mind, it shines upon the soul and draws it up from the body, and changes it all into divine essence' (*Corp. Herm.*, X. 5–6). The attainment of such knowledge became the ideal of the religious life. 'This alone is salvation for a man—knowledge of God' (*ib.*, 15). He who in this sense knows God is a 'perfect man'; he is immortal like the gods; indeed, he has himself become a god. Such ideas were widely diffused in the Hellenistic world.

In the Hebrew Scriptures also 'knowledge of God' is the goal of human aspiration. 'Let him that glorieth,' says Jeremiah, 'glory in this, that he understandeth and knoweth Me, that I am the Lord' (Jer. ix. 24). The same prophet foretells a day when 'they shall all know Me, from the least of them to the greatest of them, saith the Lord' (xxxi. 34). For the Hebrew, however, to know God is neither (primarily) an intellectual exercise nor an ineffable mystical experience. It means rather to acknowledge God in His ways with man, to recognize His claims upon man, to understand His Law with the intention of obeying it. Nevertheless, when the Old Testament was translated into Greek, the expression 'to know God' inevitably suggested to a new circle of readers the idea of a mystical apprehension of pure reality with which they were familiar. Philo, with a foot in each camp, often uses language which is similar to that of his Greek contemporaries. 'The supreme end,' he says, is 'knowledge of Him who truly is, who is the first and most perfect Good, from whom as from a fountain all partial goods are poured upon the world and those in it' (*De Decal.*, 81).

The Fourth Evangelist boldly adopts such language: 'This is eternal life—to know Thee, the only real God' (John xvii. 3). There was sanction for it in the saying attributed to Jesus in the tradition lying behind the First and Third Gospels (Matt. xi. 27, Luke x. 22), in which, claiming a Son's knowledge of the Father, He offers to reveal Him to men. The meaning is here closer to the biblical tradition than to Hellenistic ideas. In the Fourth Gospel itself it is made perfectly plain that to know God is to experience His love in Christ, and to return that love in obedience (see John xiv. 15–24, etc.). Some, however, who claimed the Christian name went right over to extreme forms of 'Gnosticism.' 'The Gospel,' said the Gnostic Basilides, 'is knowledge of the supra-mundane.' He and other heretical teachers of the second century dissolved Christian belief into various theosophical systems which, though they sometimes command admiration for the subtlety of their speculative thought, have little obvious connection with ethical religion.

The teachers whom our author has in view would appear, as we have seen, to have been precursors of the second-century Gnostics. They claimed to be enlightened, but they did not take seriously the ethical demands which true religion makes upon men. **'I know Him,'** they said. Whether the word 'Him' here refers to God or to Christ is uncertain, as elsewhere in the Epistle. In the Fourth Gospel God is known in and through Christ, and the present writer hardly distinguishes. If we have in mind i. 8, we should naturally take **'I know Him'** as a statement parallel to **'We have fellowship with Him,'** and the reference would be to God. If we look to the immediate context, we should take it to refer to Christ. It makes little difference. In any case, it is the familiar idea of 'knowledge of God' that is in view. It is easy to say, **'I know Him,'** but how can we ³⁻ **be sure that we know** Him? The answer is, **by obeying His commands.** In such obedience **love to God** is expressed, and it 5*a* is only in such ethical love that God is 'known' in any sense that matters for religion.

It is clear that the highly elliptical statement we have here presupposes the fuller exposition of the theme in the Fourth Gospel—presupposes it, probably, as an authority acknowledged both by the writer and by his opponents. They, like him, believe, on the authority of the Fourth Gospel, that eternal life lies in the knowledge of God, but they overlook the explicit teaching of that Gospel about the true nature of such knowledge.

5b–6 There is another way of formulating the relation of man to God which constitutes eternal life: it may be spoken of as 'knowing' God, or it may be spoken of as 'remaining in' God. The latter formula is characteristic of the Fourth Gospel. It is not found (verbally) in the sources which are our authorities for Hellenistic mysticism, but analogous expressions are found, and the general idea, which is that of 'mystical union,' is wide-

5b spread. Again our author asks, how can we **be sure we are in**

6 **Him**? In this case the word 'Him' must stand for Christ; for the answer is, **He who says he 'remains in Him' ought to live as He lived.** The test for the reality of the experience of union with God in Christ is the imitation of Christ. We must take it that the heretics are not talking idly when they say, 'I know Him; I remain in Him.' They are affirming their own 'religious experience.' Only, the absence of ethical seriousness in their lives throws doubt upon the validity of the experience.

In this passage our author is not only rebutting dangerous tendencies in the Church of his time, but discussing a problem of perennial importance, that of the validity of religious experience. We may have the feeling of awareness of God, of union with Him, but how shall we know that such experience corresponds to reality? It is clear that no amount of clearness or strength in the experience itself can guarantee its validity, any more than the extreme vividness of a dream leads us to suppose that it is anything but a dream. If, however, we accept the revelation of God in Christ, then we must believe that any experience of God which is valid has an ethical quality defined by what we know of Christ. It will carry with it a renewed fidelity to His teaching and example. The writer does not mean that only those who perfectly obey Christ and follow His example can be said to have experience of God. That would be to affirm the sinlessness of Christians in a sense which he has repudiated. But unless the experience includes a setting of the affections and will in the direction of the moral principles of the Gospel, it is no true experience of God, in any Christian sense. That is, of course, not all that is to be said. There will be more to be said in the Epistle itself; but so far as it goes, this criterion of the validity of religious experience holds good.

Here ends the first section, dealing with questionable claims to exalted 'religious experience,' and with the tests by which their validity must be judged. It moves largely in the sphere of anti-Gnostic polemic, and, as we have seen, it has many allusions to 'Gnostic' ideas and forms of speech. Embedded in it, however, is a passage (i. 8 – ii. 2) which recalls the fundamental teaching of the Gospel about sin and forgiveness, and does so in the native speech of primitive Christianity, formed out of its Jewish heritage, without any 'Gnostic' colouring. This is significant.

2. THE NEW DISPENSATION (ii. 7–17)

This section falls into three well-marked divisions: (*a*) In 7–11 the difference between the world of 'light' and the world of 'darkness' is correlated with the passage from the old order to the new, which, according to the apostolic Preaching, took place with the coming of Christ; and the new order is shown to be characterized by Christ's 'new commandment' of love, or charity.

(*b*) Then, in an almost lyrical strain, the writer celebrates the blessings of the new dispensation—forgiveness, knowledge of God, and victory over evil powers (ii. 12–14).

(*c*) Finally, he emphasizes the irreconcilable opposition between the Christian, who belongs to the new dispensation, and the pagan world, which belongs to the old order, doomed to destruction (ii. 15–17).

What is particularly noteworthy here is the power with which the primitive Gospel of 'realized eschatology' reasserts itself in a Hellenistic environment, finding new forms of expression, but conserving the authentic note of the apostolic Preaching.

(*a*) THE NEW COMMANDMENT (ii. 7–11)

Beloved, I am not writing you any new command, but an old 7 command which you have had from the very beginning: the old command is the word you have heard. And yet it is 8

a new command that I am writing to you—realized in Him
and also in yourselves, because the darkness is passing away
9   and the true light is already shining. He who says he is 'in
10   the light' and hates his brother, is in darkness still. He who
loves his brother remains in the light—and in the light
11   there is no pitfall; but he who hates his brother is in darkness, he walks in darkness and does not know where he is
going, for the darkness has blinded his eyes.

The writer has spoken of the divine commands, or word, in
obeying which love to God is complete. He is now to make
explicit what the command of Christ is. He has in mind that
passage of the Fourth Gospel, where Christ says, I give you a
new command, to love one another—as I have loved you, you
are to love one another (John xiii. 34). That this 'command' is
intimately related to the union with God which is eternal life
is made clear in another passage: If you keep my commands,
you will remain within my love, just as I have kept my Father's
commands, and remain within His love. . . . This is my
command: you are to love one another as I have loved you
(John xv. 10–12).

7   This well-known precept of Christ is not, he says, a new
command, in the sense that it is something added to the
original Gospel. It is an old command which you have had from
the very beginning; it is the word you have heard, that is to
8 say, a part of the Gospel itself. In what sense then is it called
in the Fourth Gospel a new command? In the sense in which
'all things are made new' in Christianity. For to be a Christian
is to be living in a new creation, as Paul had said (2 Cor. v. 17).
The writer is echoing a thought which runs all through the
New Testament when he says, The darkness is passing away and
the true light is already shining. It is the universal assumption
of all New Testament writers that with the coming of Christ
a new age has dawned: night is yielding to day, darkness to
light; Christians are sons of the Light and sons of the day
(1 Thess. v. 4–8; cf. Eph. v. 8–14). Originally this idea was set
within the time-scheme of Jewish eschatology, with its
doctrine of the two ages, 'this age' and 'the age to come.' It

was translated, partially in Paul, more thoroughly in the Epistle to the Hebrews and the Fourth Gospel, into terms of the two orders or planes of reality recognized by contemporary philosophical thought (chiefly Platonic)—the eternal order and the temporal or phenomenal order. The frequent use of light (from Plato onwards) as a symbol for the eternal order helped the transition. To say, then, that Christians are in the light carries with it, for those who are aware of the primary purport of the Gospel, the idea that through the work of Christ they have passed into a new order of life, as He died to this world and rose again. Provided that one did not lose sight of the whole rich content of this idea in its evangelical setting, the language and categories of a philosophical mysticism could be safely and profitably used to interpret it to the wider world. But it was easy for converts from the higher paganism to miss the distinctively evangelical note, and this, our author believes is what the heretics have done. For them, to be in the light, 9 means no more than to be 'enlightened,' or to be initiated into 'knowledge of the supra-mundane.' They must be reminded that to be in the light, as Christians understand it, is to be within that 'newness of life' which Christ has brought to the world; and an aspect of that 'newness' is the new command of love or charity. It is an aspect realized in Him, because He 8 lived in the love of the Father and laid down His life in love for men (cf. John x. 14-18, xv. 12-13); and realized also in yourselves, because you are within the new order in which the darkness is passing away and the true light is already shining—or are you within it? He who says he is 'in the light' 9 and hates his brother, is in darkness still, while he who loves his 10 brother remains in the light. So there is a clear criterion. To obey the command of Christ, to follow His example, and in particular to obey and follow Him in the way of love, this is to be sure we know Him, to be sure we are in Him, and to be in the light.

As for the heretics, they have missed the way, for all their 11 claims to superior 'religious experience.' Why have they done so? In the opinion of the writer it is not a simple case of intellectual error; it is a fundamentally false attitude to life, shown

in their lack of charity. The implication is that their conten-
tiousness, their arrogance and contempt for the 'unenlightened,'
on the one hand, and on the other their neglect of the practical
obligations of Christian fellowship (see iii. 17), amount to a
flat denial of the principle of charity. Anyone who denies
that principle, who hates instead of loving his 'brothers,' is so
alienated from the true life of man that he cannot think
straight: **he walks in darkness and does not know where he is
going** (cf. John xi. 9–10, xii. 35).

(b) BLESSINGS OF THE NEW DISPENSATION (ii. 12–14)

12 **Dear children, I am writing to you,**
      because your sins are forgiven for His sake:
13 **fathers, I am writing to you,**
      because you know Him who is from the very beginning:
   young men, I am writing to you,
      because you have conquered the evil One.
   Children, I have written to you,
      because you know the Father:
14 **fathers, I have written to you,**
      because you know Him who is from the very beginning:
   young men, I have written to you,
      because you are strong, and the word of God remains
      within you, and you have conquered the evil One.

The writer now turns from the argument by which he has
been confuting false interpretations of the Christian religion,
to a direct pastoral appeal to his readers. In a series of
aphorisms he reminds them of what it means to live in an age
when **the darkness is passing away and the true light is already
shining.** What are the characteristic notes of the new age as
affirmed by prophecy and by the Gospel? They are, above all
else, forgiveness of sins, knowledge of God, and victory over
the powers of evil. Thus Isaiah (xi. 1–9) forecasts the reign of
a Messiah, upon whom rests the spirit of knowledge and of the
fear of the Lord, and who will be victorious over 'the wicked.'
Under His reign, 'the earth shall be full of the knowledge of
the Lord, as the waters cover the sea.' Similarly, the Second

Isaiah (lii. 3–6) proclaims the redemption of the people of God from the worldly powers which oppress them, and continues, 'Therefore My people shall know My name: therefore they shall know in that day that I am He that doth speak: behold, it is I.' Jeremiah (xxxi. 31–4) sums up the terms of the 'new covenant' in the words, 'They shall all know Me, from the least of them unto the greatest of them, saith the Lord: for I will forgive their iniquity, and their sin will I remember no more.' This passage is echoed in various places in the New Testament, and is quoted at length in Heb. viii. 8–12 as, so to speak, the programme of the Christian dispensation. Already in the primitive apostolic Preaching as represented in Act ii. the proclamation that Christ is 'at the right hand of God,' and this His enemies are under His feet (i.e. that He is victor over the powers of evil), leads up to the offer of forgiveness of sins in His name. In Rom. viii. 31–9 Paul plays eloquently upon the same association of ideas. We are justified through Christ, who is 'at the right hand of God' and therefore we are 'more than conquerors.' Again, in the closely argued passage 1 Cor. i. 18 – ii. 16, Christ is to us both wisdom and power. In Him the Church has been chosen to overcome 'the strong things' of the world, and in Him we have both justification and knowledge of 'the things of God.' Above all, in the Fourth Gospel (which for our author is the most authoritative exposition of Christianity), Christ both 'takes away the sin of the world,' and reveals the knowledge of God, and by His death 'the prince of this world' is 'cast out' (John i. 29, xii. 31).

Our author therefore is echoing the central tradition of the Gospel when he addresses his readers as members of the people of the new covenant, whose sins are forgiven, who know the Eternal, and who have overcome the world.

His appeal is couched in a rhetorical, almost poetical, form, consisting of two sequences of three aphorisms, with a strongly marked rhythm and parallelism (not, however, the distinctively Hebraic kind of parallelism familiar to us from the Old Testament). The three aphorisms in each sequence are addressed respectively to **children, fathers,** and **young men.** (The word for 'children' in verse 12 is *teknia,* in verse 13,

37

paidia; but at this stage of the language there was little difference in meaning.) The question is whether or not the author designs each statement specifically for one of three 'age-groups' in the Church. It is not impossible to recognize a certain appropriateness to a particular age-group in some of the privileges mentioned. Thus it is natural enough that young men should be congratulated because they are strong. It is not unnatural to congratulate men of the elder generation because they know Him who is from the very beginning—the 'Ancient of Days.' To say of children that they know their Father has at least a certain sentimental aptness, and perhaps more, since there is a saying of Jesus in which the revelation of the Father is reserved for 'babes' (Matt. xi. 25; Luke x. 21) On the other hand, there is in fact no difference between the assurance to children that they know the Father, and the assurance to fathers that they know Him who is from the very beginning. And surely it is not only to young men that the Gospel assures victory over evil, or to children, the forgiveness of sins. Moreover, the fact that elsewhere in the Epistle the author frequently addresses his readers in general as 'children' (*teknia*, ii. 1, 28, iii. 18, iv. 4, v. 21; *paidia*, ii. 18; and one or the other, iii. 7, the MSS. differing), makes it difficult to suppose that in this passage alone he seriously intends to confine the term to one class among them. The threefold arrangement is probably not much more than a rhetorical figure. All the privileges mentioned belong to all Christians, but emphasis and variety of expression are secured by distributing them into groups. Christians have the innocence of childhood—not a natural innocence, but that conferred by the forgiveness of sins—as it is written, 'Of such is the Kingdom of God.' They know God as a child knows his father, in accordance with the word of Christ. They have the strength of youth—again not merely natural strength, but the power of Christ's victory over evil, which makes us 'more than conquerors through Him that loved us.' They have that serene sense of the abiding and eternal which is naturally the fruit of age and experience, but is given to Christians, young or old, by their faith. That is to say, all Christians are (by grace, not nature) children in innocence and dependence on the heavenly Father, young men in strength, and fathers in experience. It is perhaps worth observing that in non-Christian religious writers of the period we meet with the thought that the true mystic, who has risen above the limitations of time and space into communion with the eternal, has experience of all grades and stages of existence at once. 'To be everywhere at once—in earth, in sea, in heaven; to be unborn, in the womb, young, old, dead, after death'—this is to be fit for the knowledge of God (*Corpus Hermeticum*, XI. 20; somewhat similarly, *ib.*, XIII. 11). In view of our author's manifest sympathy with some aspects of 'Hellenistic mysticism,' it is in character that he should think of the Christian life as combining the characteristic experiences of childhood, youth and age.

(c) THE CHRISTIAN AND THE OLD WORLD

Love not the world, nor yet what is in the world; if anyone loves 15 the world, love for the Father is not in him. For all that is 16 in the world, the desire of the flesh and the desire of the eyes and the proud glory of life, belongs not to the Father but to the world; and the world is passing away with its desire, 17 while he who does the will of God remains for ever.

From assurance the writer passes to exhortation. The connection of thought is clear when we bear in mind that the forgiveness, knowledge and victory of which he has spoken are the notes of the new order of life inaugurated by Christ. The old order is here called **the world,** the term being used not for the created universe, nor for the human race as such (for in this sense, as we have seen, Christ is the **Saviour of the world,** iv. 14, and His death is an expiation for the sins of **the whole world,** ii. 2), but for the life of human society as organized under the power of evil, as it is described in v. 19: **the whole world lies in the power of the evil One.**

It was a part of the eschatological belief which Christianity inherited from Judaism that while God is the creator and ruler of all mankind, He has for reasons best known to Himself permitted to the powers of evil a limited and temporary rule over His world. This rule will be brought to an end when 'His Kingdom will appear throughout all His creation' (*Assumption of Moses*, x. 1). This view, which is first clearly and explicitly enunciated in post-exilic apocalypse, may perhaps have been influenced by the dualism of much religious thought in the pagan world, especially of the ethically elevated faith of Zoroaster, with which the Jews were brought into contact from the days when they formed part of the Persian Empire. According to this faith, the world is the scene of perpetual conflict between the power of light, Ahura-Mazda, and the power of darkness, Angro-Mainyu. Its message to the world was a bracing call to stand on the side of Ahura-Mazda. Zoroastrianism exercised a far-reaching influence upon the religious thought of the Hellenistic world, strengthening tendencies to dualism already present from other sources. Much of this thought has an ascetic bias against the world of matter and sense. That apocalyptic Judaism was wholly unaffected by this tendency cannot be affirmed, and Christian thought was always in danger of falling under it. But Judaism never really succumbed to dualism. It was not for nothing that at the beginning of the Persian period the Second Isaiah had formulated Jewish monotheism in absolute terms over against the dualism of Persia (see Isa. xlv. 5–7). The Jews never doubted that 'the Most High ruleth in the kingdom of men' (Dan. iv. 32). Even the temporary sway of the powers of evil falls somehow within the purpose of God, and the whole meaning of that purpose will be revealed and fulfilled when His Kingdom shall appear. In the 'present age' the sovereignty of God is real but veiled; in the 'age to come' it will be manifest. Nor is the created world of matter irredeemably evil, though it was, according to an interpretation of Gen. iii. 17, 'cursed' for Adam's sake; for in the 'age to come' the whole creation will be transfigured (cf. Rom. viii. 21).

The Christian Gospel, first formulated in terms of eschatology, affirmed that with the coming of Christ the Kingdom of God was revealed, and the Age to Come inaugurated. But this did not bring with it (according to eschatological expectation) the end of history. While Christ had undoubtedly overcome the 'rulers of this age' (1 Cor. ii. 6), or the 'prince of this world' (John xii. 31), the full effect of His victory was to be observed only within the new Israel created by His redemptive work—that is, in the experience of the Church. Outside this sphere the old order appeared to survive intact. This presented a problem with which Christian thought is wrestling all through the New Testament. Our present author is not concerned with the theological or philosophical aspects of the problem. He takes a realistic view of the actual situation. Within the Church, the experience of forgiveness, victory and knowledge of God establishes the reality and finality of Christ's redemption. That this redemption is designed for **the whole world** is a matter of faith. But the author observes in the pagan world in which he lives the marks of that domination of evil powers which Christ lived and died to destroy. Thus he sees the Christian life as one which demands a clear choice between God and the 'world; that is, in practical terms, the Christian must not compromise with the principles and ways of pagan society.

The world then, for this writer, is no merely theoretical conception, but simply the pagan society in which he and his readers' necessarily moved, and which in various ways exercised pressure upon them. It would appear that in his time, and in his neighbourhood, this pressure was not exerted by persecution. Christianity was indeed unpopular (iii. 13); but of actual persecution we hear nothing in these epistles. (Contrast the position revealed in the Revelation of John). But when persecution was relaxed, the temptation was all the greater to conform as far as possible to the practices and customs of pagan neighbours. It is against this conformity that the writer is concerned to warn his readers. In a few telling phrases he **16** characterizes what seem to him the essential marks of the pagan way of life. There is **the desire of the flesh**—that is to say, the sensuality which, not on Christian testimony alone, was deeply rooted and widespread in Graeco-Roman society. There is **the desire of the eyes,** by which we may understand the tendency to be captivated by the outward show of things, without enquiring into their real values. There is **the proud**

41

glory of life. The word translated **proud glory** is one used by Greek moralists from Aristotle onwards—*alazoneia*. The *alazōn* is a conceited, pretentious humbug. He is thus described in the *Characters* of Theophrastus:

> 'The *Alazon* is the kind of person who will stand on the mole and tell perfect strangers what a lot of money he has at sea, and discourse of his investments, how large they are, and what gains and losses he has made, and as he spins his yarns he will send his boy to the bank—his balance being a shilling. If he enjoys company on the road, he is apt to tell how he served with Alexander the Great, how he got on with him, and how many jewelled cups he brought home; and to discuss the Asiatic craftsmen, how much better they are than any in Europe—never having been away from Athens. He will say that he was granted a free permit for the export of timber, but took no advantage of it, to avoid ill-natured gossip; and that during the corn-shortage he spent more than fifteen hundred pounds in gifts to needy citizens. He will be living in a rented house, and will tell anyone who does not know the facts that this is the family residence, but he is going to sell it because it is too small for his entertainments' (*Characters*, No. 23: my translation, abridged).

The vulgar 'climber' of this light-hearted but pungent caricature came to the front in the irresponsible, acquisitive, individualistic society of the Hellenistic world. Our author, looking upon contemporary society from a Christian standpoint, and judging it with a deeper seriousness, sees it as the very incarnation of this pretentious, self-glorifying spirit.

By **the world**, then, we are to understand pagan society, with its sensuality, superficiality and pretentiousness, its materialism and its egoism. These are the marks, our author means, of that old, bad order out of which the Christian has been brought into the new order inaugurated by Christ. The two orders are mutually exclusive. If a man hankers after what **the world** can offer, **love for the Father is not in him.** There must be no compromise with the false standards of paganism. It was necessary to say this because, clearly, the kind of teaching he has in view made for compromise. It may be—we do not know —that the teachers whom the author is attacking had no conscious intention of lowering the ethical standards of the Church; but their willingness (as he sees it) to accommodate Christian doctrine to current ideas went with a general desire to minimize the difference between Christianity and the ordinary life and thought of the time. And that difference is for him real, substantial and irreconcilable.

For (and here he returns to the eschatological presupposi- 17 tions of early Christian thought) **the world** (pagan society) is an order not only temporal and transient in its character, but actually passing away before one's eyes; **the darkness is passing away and the true light is already shining.** The new age has dawned, and with its coming the power and reality of the old order are broken. To belong to the new order is to have eternal life, which endures when the old order passes away. But to belong to the new order is not to lay claim to mystical experience—to say 'we know God,' or 'we are in the light,' or 'we have no sin.' It is to **do the will of God,** and this, as we have already learned, is to live by the principle of love, or charity, over against the sensuality, materialism, and self-glorification which are the marks of the old order. **He who does the will of God remains for ever,** for he belongs to the order of immortality.

This rigid separation of the Church and the world looks rather like the ascetic dualism which was common enough in the religious thought of the time. The distinction between the eternal and the temporal orders of being, the spiritual world and the world of the senses, was familiar. It was held that in order to attain to immortality it was necessary to turn away from the world of the senses and to have communion with the eternal. Many taught that for such communion it was necessary to repress bodily desires, since they are concerned with the things of sense. Such teachers would have felt themselves at one with our author in his emphatic antithesis of God and the world. 'I thank God,' writes one of them, 'who has put it into my mind, as touching knowledge of the Good, that it is impossible for it to exist in the world. For the world is the totality of evil, and God, the totality of good' (*Corp. Herm.*, VI. 4). The similarity, however, is not so close as it seems. By 'the world' such writers mean the material world as such. The body is evil because it is material, its desires evil because they are desires for material things. Our author means human society in so far as it is organized on wrong principles, and characterized by base desires, false values, egoism. The material world as such is God's creation. We have no reason to doubt that he would have agreed with Paul that in the material order nothing is in itself unclean (Rom. xiv. 14), since 'the earth is the Lord's and the fulness thereof' (1 Cor. x. 26). But an order of society based upon the primacy of material values is contrary to God's purpose for humanity. Again, the main object of these teachers of the higher paganism was the release of the individual soul from the bonds of matter, and its 'deification' through knowledge of the eternal. In their writings any allusion to social obligations is extremely rare. The Christian writer on the other hand opposes to love of 'the world' a love of God which is also love for other men, and to 'the world' as a godless and egoistic society he opposes the 'fellowship' of a community based upon mutual love. Moreover, while 'the world,' that is, godless society, lies in the power of the evil One, Christ is nevertheless the Saviour of all mankind; His sacrifice is available for the sins of the whole world. The dualism of God and the world is thus ultimately overcome through God's love for the world. It is true that the writer has not clearly drawn the logical conclusions from his premises. He speaks in the main as though mankind were rigorously, and permanently, divided into two classes, represented by the Church and 'the world.' This is partly because he is not here interested in anything but the practical needs of an immediate situation. Empirically, the the Church stood as a community based upon high ethical standards over against pagan society with its degraded moral standards. Compromise was easy; it must be resisted at all costs. Any kind of teaching which suggested that the difference between Christianity and paganism was (shall we say?) one of degree rather than of kind, was a denial of the very *raison d'être* of the Church, God's new creation.

If, therefore, the teaching of this passage is not strictly dualistic or ascetic, it does inculcate a certain detachment of Christians from the secular order. We may ask how far this is really dependent upon the writer's particular eschatological beliefs, and consequently no longer applicable to Christians of our own time.

The world, which seemed to him to be trembling on the verge of dissolution, has had a reprieve of eighteen centuries and is still running. Apart from some eccentric sects, most Christians do not now suppose that there is any urgent prospect of the 'end of the world.' Then are we to say that our author's argument falls to the ground because its premise has proved false? Since this world, though no doubt transitory, is still fairly durable, is there any reason why we should not make the best of both worlds, or why the Church should not come to favourable terms with its social environment? A more ready answer to such questions might have been given in the optimistic days before 1914, than we are now prepared to give. In those days civilization seemed at last to have arrived at security and permanence, and most of us confidently expected that progress would continue indefinitely, to the 'great, far-off, divine event.' To this state of mind there was little real meaning in such a proposition as **'the world is passing away with its desire.'** To-day, however, insecurity and impermanence are the outstanding features of the world as we see it. We may not expect the world to come to an end to-morrow, but the essential transience of the whole order of civilization is no longer a theory to be complacently entertained, but a fact—to be welcomed or resented, but in any case reckoned with. It is not a matter of faith either that our civilization should persist, or that it should perish: it is a matter, not only of faith, but of observation, that it has no inherent permanence. Not only so, but if 'the world' be defined in terms of **the desire of the flesh, and the desire of the eyes, and the proud glory of life**—in other words, if, and in so far as, civilized society has the marks of

45

sensuality, materialism and self-glorification, then it is self-destructive.[1] It is this, and not the merely natural transience of the material universe as such, that sets the world over against the will of God. Nor is the object of our faith the eternal as such, by virtue of its permanence over against a transient world, but God Himself as holy will, active for the salvation of men. To live in willing obedience to that will, while we move in the temporal sphere, is to dwell in the eternal world, to possess eternal life: **he who does the will of God remains for ever.**

How far the Church should in practice hold itself aloof from its social environment, and how far enter into alliance with the secular order to reform it, is largely a question of expediency dependent on changing conditions. Under the conditions of the first century, the Church had no choice. It could bear its witness only by separation from pagan society. We need not look far for indications that similar conditions might recur. Such separation, indeed, can never be complete. In the realm of thought, even the author of this epistle was substantially, though perhaps unconsciously, indebted to the higher paganism, and those early thinkers who naturalized within Christian theology the best thought of the Hellenistic world did good service to the faith. A certain spiritual tact led them to draw the line beyond which a sympathetic appreciation and co-operation would lead to harmful compromise. In other periods the Church can best serve the will of God for the salvation of men by close co-operation with the best elements in secular civilization. But it can never do so without preserving an inner detachment from everything that bears the marks of 'the world' in the Johannine sense (which does not mean an ascetic rejection of the material world). **'Love not the world, nor yet what is in the world'** is in this sense a precept always binding on the conscience of its members, and the more reasonably binding because we know that everything that **belongs not to the Father but to the world** is under sentence of dissolution. Only the will of God, and the life that is lived under that will, abides.

[1] Since the above was written, events have emphasized ominously the inherent self-destructiveness of our present civilization.

THE TRUTH AND THE LIE (ii. 18–28)

Children, it is the last hour. You have learned that 'Antichrist 18
is coming.' Well, but many antichrists have appeared—
which makes us sure it is the last hour. They withdrew 19
from us, but they did not belong to us; had they belonged to
us, they would have remained with us, but they withdrew—
to make it plain that they are none of us. Now, you have 20
been anointed by the holy One, and you possess all knowledge. I am not writing to you because you do not know 21
the truth, but because you do know it, and know that no
lie belongs to the truth.

Who is the real liar? 22
who but he who denies that Jesus is the Christ?
This is 'antichrist,'
he who disowns the Father and the Son.
No one who disowns the Son can possess the Father: 23
he who confesses the Son possesses the Father as well.
Let that remain in you which you learned from the very 24
beginning; if what you learned from the very beginning
remains with you, then you will remain in the Son and in
the Father.
Now this is what he has promised you,* eternal life. I am ²⁵₂₆
writing to you in this way about those who would deceive
you, but the unction you received from Him remains 27
within you, and you really need no teaching from anyone;
simply remain in Him, for His unction teaches you
about everything and is true and is no lie—remain in Him,
as it has taught you to do. Remain within Him now, my 28
dear children, so that when He appears we may have
confidence, instead of shrinking from Him in shame at
His arrival.

The writer now proceeds to a direct attack upon the false
teachers whom he has had in mind in the discussion of religious
experience in i. 5 – ii. 6. These teachers denied the real incarnation of the Son of God (as we learn from iv. 3). For our author

* Reading ὑμῖν instead of ἡμῖν.

this is the last apostasy, signified by the mystery of 'Anti-christ.' To meet their claims to superior enlightment, he recalls his readers to the sufficient revelation which every Christian has received in his initiation into the truth of the Gospel.

18   The connection of thought with the preceding section is by way of the eschatological ideas to which the writer has given expression. Christians, he has said, live within the new order revealed in Christ. The old order is passing away: the end of the world approaches; indeed, he now adds, it cannot longer be delayed: it is the last hour. There is proof of this.

To understand his 'proof' we must review certain elements in the eschatology which Christianity carried over from Judaism. Jewish apocalypse taught, as we have seen, that the world was under the (limited and temporary) sway of evil powers, and that in the end God would reveal His Kingdom and make an end of the 'kingdom of the adversary.' But it was a very ancient belief (going back perhaps to primitive mythology) that before that glorious consummation evil would make one last desperate stand. There would arise one supreme adversary of the cause of God, either a man of diabolical power and wickedness or a demonic being from the other world. This adversary appears as a kind of diabolical parody of God's Messiah. Hence he is called 'Antichrist.' (The term appears here for the first time in extant literature, but the idea is present long before.) In the eschatological discourse of Mark xiii. (which is probably an early Christian apocalypse based upon Jewish models, incorporating genuine sayings of Jesus), Antichrist appears in the guise of the 'Abomination of Desola-tion' (Mark xiii. 14, **the appalling Horror**, Moffatt), a term originally applied in the Book of Daniel (xii. 11, **the appalling abomination**, Moffatt) to the idolatrous image set up in the Temple by Antiochus Epiphanes, but here clearly applied to a person (see the Moffatt Commentary on *Mark, l.c.*). The Abomination of Desolation is to defile the Temple ('standing where he ought not'), and this will be the sign that the End is near. Similarly in 2 Thess. ii. 3-4 Paul foretells the appear-ance of the **Lawless One**. He too will profane the Temple by enthroning himself there and claiming divine honours. Until he appears, the second advent of Christ is delayed. His coming will be the immediate prelude to the End. In the Book of the Revelation the myth of Antichrist is elaborated in profuse and not altogether perspicuous imagery. The rôle of the great adversary is played chiefly by the Beast, which is either identified, or closely associated, with the Roman Empire, especially in respect of the claim of the Emperor to divine honours; and here too Antichrist is destroyed by Christ at His second advent. The belief, then, was widespread in early Christianity that before Christ's second advent Antichrist would appear, and that his appearance would be the signal for the End. When therefore Antichrist is recognized, men will know that it is the last hour.

The author of the epistle believes that he has evidence that Antichrist has already appeared, 'which (he adds) makes us 18 sure it is the last hour.' He has rationalized the myth. Antichrist is no monster from the abyss, no potentate wickedly claiming divine honours. There is in fact no single Antichrist. There are many antichrists. For wherever doctrines are taught that subvert the essential truths of the Gospel, there is Antichrist, and the false teachers are themselves in this sense antichrists (see also iv. 3).

This might seem a somewhat far-fetched interpretation of the myth. But the steps that lie behind this interpretation can be recognized. In the Marcan apocalypse it is predicted that false Christs and false prophets will arise and perform signs and wonders to mislead the elect (Mark xiii. 22). They are not indeed identified with the 'Abomination of Desolation,' but they play a similar rôle as antecedents of the End. Similarly, in Rev. xvi. 13, xix. 20, xx. 10 the Beast is accompanied by a false prophet, who shares his fate at Christ's coming. One aspect, therefore, or one concomitant, of the appearance of Antichrist is false prophecy. Prophecy was regarded as the result of inspiration: true prophecy was dictated by the Holy Spirit; false prophecy no less by a 'lying spirit' (cf. 1 Kings xxii. 15–23). If the emergence of prophecy in the Church was evidence of the presence of the Spirit of God (cf. 1 Cor. xii. 8–10; Acts ii.

16–17), then if false prophecy emerged, was it not evidence that a diabolical spirit was at work (iv. 3; cf. 1 Cor. xii. 3)? And might not this be the revelation of Antichrist, as the Holy Spirit was a revelation of Christ's own presence with His Church (cf. 2 Cor. iii. 17–18)?

This would appear to have been our author's line of argument. He had observed with horror persons who were, or had been, members of the Church uttering 'prophecies' which contradicted the fundamental truths of the faith. (What they actually taught we shall see presently.) That they spoke under 'inspiration' he could not deny (cf. iv. 1, 3). But so shocking were their teachings that the inspiration could not be other than diabolical. This must be Antichrist! The world is coming to an end!

It is a curious argument. On the whole, the development of early Christian thought left the Antichrist myth behind. Paul has nothing further to say of it after 2 Thessalonians. It has no place in the Epistle to the Hebrews, or (as such) in the Fourth Gospel. The author of the epistle stands nearer to popular beliefs. But he too has left behind the crude mythology which bulks so largely in the Book of Revelation. The real Antichrist is for him not a person, whether human or supernatural. It is an idea—an idea no doubt embodied in persons who promulgate it, but essentially an idea, with power to poison the minds of men and pervert them from the truth. The final adversary of the truth is the lie, whoever utters it. The supreme enemy of Christ's redeeming work is radically false belief. (The quaint old notion that 'it does not matter what a man believes, so long as he leads a decent life' needs no confutation in a world buzzing with 'ideologies.') The conflict between Christ and Antichrist is fought out upon the field of the mind. 'We do not war,' says Paul, 'according to the flesh. The weapons of our warfare are not fleshly, but they are powerful with the power of God to demolish strongholds. We demolish *arguments*, and every proud thing that lifts itself up against the knowledge of God. We take captive every *thought* into the obedience of Christ' (2 Cor. x. 3–5).

What are we to say of this doctrine that because Antichrist has appeared, in the form of deadly heresy, **it is the last hour?** Clearly enough, in any literal sense (and we have no reason to suppose that the writer intended any but a literal sense), it was not true. The **last hour** of the world did not strike, either then, or for many centuries to follow. But let us consider what Antichrist meant. The idea stood for a concentration of the powers of evil to such a degree that man must stand helpless before it, saved from despair only by the faith that now at last, at the moment of utmost need, the Lord would come. That is to say, to see Antichrist means to have a vision, it may be momentary, of a power of evil in the world (in ourselves) beyond all the resources of human wisdom and virtue, and to be thrown back without reserve upon God.

The supreme example of such a situation is the crucifixion of Jesus Christ, which is, in the 'realized eschatology' of the Gospels, the true 'last hour' of a doomed world. 'This is your hour, and the power of darkness,' says Jesus in Luke (xxii. 53). But also, as the Fourth Gospel has it, 'Now is the judgment of this world; now shall the prince of this world be cast out' (John xii. 31). For the resurrection supervenes, and Jesus is 'at the right hand of God.'

This situation recurs in the experience of the Church, when, confronted by the resurgence of deep-seated evil, it sees the day lost, but for the certainty that Christ is at the right hand of God, principalities and powers being subject to Him. If the evil is disclosed within the Church itself, if its fellowship is shaken by disloyalty to Christ (as the disciples forsook Him and fled in the hour of darkness), then the case is indeed hopeless— but for God. That was how our author saw the situation. He thought it meant, quite literally, that the world was coming to an end. That was an illusion. But it was no illusion that the Church was entering into the meaning of that **last hour** when the cross and resurrection of Christ revealed both the 'mystery of iniquity' (cf. 2 Thess. ii. 7), and the 'working of the strength of His might which He wrought in Christ when He raised Him from the dead' (Eph. i. 19).

19   The false teachers, we learn, had been members of the Church, and had withdrawn from it. This very fact shows, says the writer, that they never had really belonged to the Church, although they were formally members of it. **Had they belonged to us, they would have remained with us.** The words which follow, **but they withdrew—to make it plain that they are none of us,** are a paraphrase of an expression in the Greek which, after the author's manner, is elliptical or compressed, and somewhat obscure. They might be understood to convey the meaning that the heretics withdrew from the Church as a formal demonstration of their fundamental divergence from its principles. But this is probably not what the writer meant. Literally, the words are to be translated, 'but in order that they might be made manifest that not all are of us.' The concluding words, taken *au pied de la lettre*, would mean, 'not all men are genuine Christians,' which is a truism. But in the context the word 'all' can readily be understood as meaning 'all members of the Church,' and the statement that not all those who are in formal communion with the visible Church belong in the true sense to the Church of Christ is an important one (cf. Rom. ix. 6). To make this fact plain was the purpose of their withdrawal. But whose purpose? Not necessarily the conscious purpose of the seceders. Let us recall the expression, frequent in the Fourth Gospel, as elsewhere in the New Testament, 'that the scripture might be fulfilled.' Where this or similar expressions are used, the final conjunction may indicate the purpose, not of the human agent, but of the overruling divine Providence. (When, for example, Matthew says, ii. 15, that the flight into Egypt took place 'in order that the word of the Lord through the prophet might be fulfilled, "Out of Egypt have I called my Son," ' he does not mean that the motive of Joseph in taking the Child and His mother into safety was a desire to fulfil prophecy. He means that he was led to do so in the providential designs of God.) So here, the probable meaning of the writer is that in God's providential care for His Church a situation was brought about in which the heretics overtly declared their disloyalty to the truth of the Gospel, instead of confusing the issue by retaining their

position as prophets and teachers within the Church. They thereby illustrated the truth that a man may be admitted to Church membership, may receive the sacraments, and may even exercise a ministry of the Word, and yet never really belong to the Church, since he has never had the root of the matter in him. In the light of long experience this lamentable fact has become a commonplace. When this epistle was written, we may suppose that an actual secession on doctrinal grounds was still a new and unfamiliar phenomenon. It was a shock to Christian feeling. But, the writer believes, it served the divine purpose, in bringing home to the conscience of the Church the solemn truth that formal membership is no guarantee that a man belongs to Christ and not to Antichrist.

He now turns to these who remain loyal. They **have been 20 anointed by the holy One**, and know the truth of the Gospel. What is meant by this 'anointing' we shall enquire presently. It stands in any case for something given by God, and it brings with it a knowledge which is, by the same token, a gift of God, and no human attainment. **You possess all knowledge.** So some MSS. read; but the older and better texts have the reading, 'You all possess knowledge.' It is a safe assumption that these early heretics, like their successors, the 'Gnostics' of the second century, laid claim to a superior *gnosis*, or knowledge of divine things, of which they deemed the ordinary Christian incapable. The writer denies this. *Every* Christian, in virtue of what God has given him, has saving knowledge of the truth. We may compare the similar emphasis in Col. i. 28 (a letter in which Paul is also dealing with incipient 'Gnosticism'): **We train** *everyone* **and teach** *everyone* **the full scope of this knowledge, in order to set** *everyone* **before God mature in Christ.** Indeed, the New Testament writers normally assume that the ordinary lay Christians whom they address have an effective grasp of the fundamentals of the Gospel, because they are divinely enabled to apprehend them. Thus Paul writes to the Thessalonians, **You need no one to write to you upon brotherly love, for you are yourselves taught by God to love one another** (I Thess. iv. 9); and to the Romans, **You are filled with knowledge of every kind, and you are well able to give advice** to one another. Still, by way of refreshing your memory, I have written you with a certain freedom (Rom. xv. 14–15). ²¹ᵃ Similarly, our present author proceeds, **I am not writing to you because you do not know the truth, but because you do know it.** There is a note of authority in his writing, but it is not an authority which will override the judgment or conscience of his readers. On the contrary he writes with authority just because he is confident that he expresses the corporate convictions of the Church, which will be recognized as such by all humble and sincere believers.

There is light here upon the way in which the Christian tradition was both conserved and developed. Paul said that one purpose for which Christ gave a ministry to His Church was that we should **not be blown from our course and swayed by every passing wind of doctrine** (Eph. iv. 14). The ministry bore this responsibility through the difficult period when Christian thought was fluid, and all sorts of aberrations were possible. What bold experimentation went on, we can judge from the bewildering variety of 'heresies' described by Irenaeus and Hippolytus. It was quite possible, humanly speaking, that the main line of Christian thought should have led through a Valentinus, or a Basilides, whose intricate systems of theosophy had an attraction for many minds. If it had done so, the distinctive character of Christianity would have been largely, if not entirely, lost. The writer of this epistle is one of those who guided the thought of the Church during the obscure period of stress, admitting reinterpretations of the faith, but keeping all such reinterpretations controlled by the central convictions of the Gospel. It is to him and to others like him that we owe it that the faith emerged from the stage of fluidity with new forms of thought and expression adapted to its wider environment, but with its Gospel intact. They succeeded in their task only because they could count upon a solid body of lay Christian conviction, by no means obstinately conservative, but intelligently and experimentally grounded in the Gospel. They could count upon addressing people who, when they met with some unfamiliar form of teaching, could say, from a certain spiritual instinct, 'That is not the Gospel we received,' or, on the other hand, 'Yes: that is the Gospel which we received and by which we were saved.'

He assumes, then, that his readers know the truth, and, he 21b adds, know that no lie belongs to the truth. That is to say, the false and the true are generically different: you cannot say that a lie is an 'aspect' of the truth. To suppose that it is may be a false kind of tolerance, or just muddled or lazy thinking. The situation here in view is too serious for muddled or lazy thinking. As for tolerance, at least it is clear that no one has any business to tolerate falsehood along with the truth in his own mind.

We are now to learn what the lie is. It is the denial that Jesus 22 is the Christ. The form of expression might imply that the false teachers refused to admit the Church's claim that Jesus was the Messiah predicted in biblical prophecy. This of course was the position taken by Jewish opponents of Christianity. But it is unlikely that any person who took this view should ever have been (as these heretics had been) a member of the Church. We must look elsewhere.

We know that in certain schools of 'Gnostic' thought a sharp distinction was drawn between the divine Christ, conceived as an 'emanation' from the eternal Deity, or as an 'aeon,' or member of the hierarchy of supra-mundane essences, on the one hand, and the man Jesus, on the other, and taught that the two were only temporarily, externally, and as it were accidentally connected; that the Christ descended upon Jesus at some point in His life, as, for example, at His baptism, and left Him again before His passion. It is probable that the doctrine here attacked was similar. Thinkers who took this view did not conceive themselves to be denying the doctrine of the Messiahship of Jesus. They were attempting to solve the problem set to Christian thought by the fact that the Gospel told the story of a man who lived and died in Palestine, and at the same time declared Him to be the eternal Son of God. The problem is one with which the thinkers of the Church had to grapple long in seeking an acceptable solution. The kind of doctrine, however, which made a distinction between 'Jesus' and 'Christ' (somewhat as some moderns attach religious value to the 'Christ-idea,' as distinct from the 'Jesus of History') was rather an evasion than a solution of the problem.

He who in this sense **denies that Jesus is the Christ,** says our author, **disowns** in effect **the Father and the Son.** For Christian theism acknowledges God as revealed in Jesus Christ; and this is not the same thing as belief in absolute Being, or eternal Reason, or the Unfathomable Depth, or any other of the abstractions which in various Gnostic systems stood for God, even though such an abstraction might be called by the name of 'the First Father' or the like, and might be held to be mediated to the world by an 'emanation' or 'aeon' described as His 'Son,' or even as 'Christ.' The Gospel speaks of 'the God and Father of our Lord Jesus Christ.' If Jesus is not the Christ, the content of the Christian revelation of God is disin-
23 tegrated, and in this sense **no one who disowns the Son can possess the Father,** while **he who confesses the Son possesses the Father as well.**

The doctrine that our access to God depends upon the acknowledgment of His Son runs through the Fourth Gospel (John xii. 44–5, xiv. 6–9, etc.). It has sanction in a traditional saying of Jesus given by Matthew and Luke from their common tradition: 'No one knows the Son except the Father, nor does anyone know the Father except the Son, and he to whom the Son chooses to reveal Him' (Matt. xi. 27; cf. Luke x. 22).

Further, the antithesis drawn between 'confessing' Christ and 'disowning' Him recalls another saying of the Lord in the Synoptic Gospels, where the same two verbs are used in antithesis (though the fact is disguised in the Moffatt translation):

'Everybody who shall confess me before men
    I will confess him before my Father in heaven;
And whoever shall disown me before men,
    I will disown him before my Father in heaven'

(Matt. x. 32-3: similarly in Luke xii. 8; cf. also Mark viii. 38). The saying is clearly alluded to in Rev. iii. 5, and probably also in Rom. x. 9-10: **Confess with your mouth that 'Jesus is Lord,' believe in your heart that God raised Him from the dead, and you will be saved; for with his heart man believes and is justified; with his mouth he confesses and is saved.**

The currency of this saying in fact probably goes far to account for the special weight and solemnity attaching to the words 'confess' and 'confession' in all early Christian thought (cf. also Heb. iv. 14, x. 23, and xiii. 13-15, where the allusion is probably to the confession of the name of Christ, for which Christians suffered persecution; 1 Pet. iv. 14-16). But our present passage is more closely moulded upon the saying of Jesus than any of the others. It has the same antithetical form, and (if we allow for a certain theological development) its purport is substantially the same. According to Matt. x. 32-3, the confession of Christ establishes solidarity with Him, by which our standing before God is guaranteed. So here to confess Christ is to **possess the Father**—or as it is expressed in iv. 16, to **remain in God** (quasi-mystical categories being substituted for the quasi-forensic categories of Matt. x. 32-3). As for the content of the confession itself, it is here given in terms identical with the confession of Peter in Mark viii. 29. In iv. 15 it takes the form **Jesus is the Son of God,** which recalls the Matthaean addition to Peter's confession, **Son of the living God** (Matt. xvi. 16). Both these may be compared with the Pauline confession, 'Jesus is Lord.'

The interest of these comparisons is to show how closely the author is basing himself upon the common tradition of early Christianity, incorporating the teaching of Jesus Himself. It is only in iv. 2, where it is necessary to put the Church's confession beyond all possibility of misunderstanding, against the aberrations of heretical teachers, that specifically 'Johannine' language is used: **every spirit which confesses Jesus as the Christ incarnate.**

The writer does not here make any attempt to discuss the theological problem which is involved in the confession of Jesus as the Christ, the eternal Son of God. He no doubt

assumes that his readers are acquainted with the Fourth
Gospel, in which this problem is dealt with in masterly fashion
—or, if not with the written Gospel, at least with the Johannine
24 teaching which it embodies. What he is here concerned to urge
is that his readers shall hold fast to that which is the presupposition of all Christian doctrine—namely, the fundamental
content of the Gospel, that which you learned from the very
beginning. If this remains in you, he says, then you will
remain in the Son and in the Father.

As we have seen (note on ii. 5–6), this type of expression is
analogous with language used to describe the experience of
'mystical union.' It is adopted in the Fourth Gospel for that
intimate union with God in Christ which is the result of the
love of God manifested in the life and death of Jesus, to which
the love of man responds in obedience and trust. (See, especially, John xv. 1–10, xvii. 21–3.) In the discourse on the Bread
of Life we read, He who feeds on my flesh and drinks my blood
remains in me, as I remain in him. Just as the living Father sent
me, and I live by the Father, so he who feeds on me will also
live by me. . . . He who feeds on this bread will live for ever
25 (John vi. 56–8). This promise of eternal life the writer now
recalls, assuring his readers that the blessed hope of everlasting
life is not based upon any theosophical speculations, but upon
the Gospel of the God and Father of our Lord Jesus Christ.

26–
27 The writer now returns to the point with which he is immediately concerned—the warning against false teaching—and he
develops what he has already said briefly about Christians
being anointed by the holy One. We must now raise the question: What is meant by the anointing, or unction? The actual
word used is *chrisma*, which is Englished as 'chrism.' It does
not occur elsewhere in the New Testament. It is derived from
a verb which means to 'rub over' or 'smear.' The noun should
by its grammatical form signify, concretely, that which is
smeared or rubbed on, such as paint, or whitewash, or (in
particular) oil. It can however also be used, abstractly, of the
act of smearing, and in the Greek Old Testament it is commonly used of the act of anointing with oil. In verse 27 the
concrete significance seems to be called for, since the chrism is

something which **remains within you and teaches you,** though
it is not at once clear what this 'something' is. That it is
literally the oil used for anointing is altogether unlikely.
We may take it that whatever metaphorical sense of the
word may be intended, it is based upon the use of the verb and
the noun with reference to anointing with oil, especially as a
ritual act.

Anointing was among the Hebrews a rite of consecration.
Priests, prophets, and kings were anointed in token of their
consecration to Jehovah. In common parlance, 'the anointed
priest,' or simply, 'the Anointed,' meant the High Priest,
whose office was a specially solemn one of mediation between
God and the people. More specifically, 'God's Anointed,' or
simply, 'the Anointed,' meant the ideal figure of the future,
variously conceived, in and through whom God's purpose for
His people should be finally fulfilled. In this sense the expression was taken over into Christianity. We are accustomed
either to adapt the Hebrew or Aramaic word, following the
example of the Fourth Gospel, and to speak of 'the Messiah,'
or else to follow the other writers of the New Testament, and
to use the Greek equivalent, *Christos*, Englished as 'Christ.'
The original and fundamental confession of Christianity is in
Peter's words, 'Thou art the Messiah' (Mark viii. 29). The
question could not but arise: How and when was Jesus
'anointed'? There was no record of His having received
the anointing of king or priest. But the tradition affirmed
that He had received consecration to the Messianic office
at His baptism, when the Holy Spirit descended upon
Him. This, then, in accordance with the prophecy of Isa.
lxi. 1 (cited in Luke iv. 18), was the 'anointing' by virtue
of which Jesus was the 'Anointed,' the Messiah or Christ.
So the apostolic Preaching as given in Acts x. 38 declared
how God 'anointed Jesus of Nazareth with Holy Spirit
and power.' There is no other place in the New Testament
where the expression 'to anoint with Holy Spirit' occurs,
though there is a passage cited from the apocryphal Gospel
according to the Hebrews where the prophets are said to have
been 'anointed with holy Spirit.' In 2 Cor. i. 21 we read, 'It is

God who guarantees us together with you in Christ, and who anointed us; He who also sealed us, and gave us the earnest of the Spirit in our hearts.' The collocation of the words 'Christ' and 'anointed' (*Christos* and *chrisas*) shows that Paul has in mind the Messianic consecration as shared by those who are of 'the Body of Christ.' (Christ is the inclusive representative of the People of God as a corporate personality; see Moffatt Commentary, *Romans*, pp. 78–80). It is not, however, said that Christians are 'anointed with the Holy Spirit'; they are 'anointed'—that is, consecrated—in solidarity with Christ, and the 'seal' or guarantee of this fact is the presence of the Holy Spirit in the heart. Such appears to be the Apostle's meaning.

This is (apart from our present passage) the only place in the New Testament where Christians are said to be 'anointed' (in any sense). It is hardly sufficient to account for the use of 'chrism' here as a technical term, which the readers are expected to recognize; for such it seems to be. We must look elsewhere for a clue. We could understand the writer's choice of the term if it were taken from the vocabulary of the heretics whom he is attacking. That it was used by them is made probable by the following considerations.

In each place where the term 'chrism' is introduced, the word 'you' is extremely emphatic in the Greek; indeed, in the second place (verse 27) emphasis is obtained by a construction which is strictly ungrammatical, though not illegitimate in usage. We must suppose that 'you' are contrasted with some other group. In view of the considerations adduced in pp. 9–16, it is improbable that the contrast to 'you' is 'we.' Probably a contrast is intended between 'you,' i.e. true believers, and heretics. Let us then try to bring out this emphasis in translation: 'They withdrew in order that it might be made clear that not all (formal members of the Church) belong to us. *You too* have an unction, an unction from the holy One, and you all possess knowledge. . . . I am writing to you in this way about those who would lead you astray; and *as for you*, the unction you received from Him remains in you.' This way of speaking would have a sharp point if the heretics claimed to have been 'anointed' in some special way which ensured to them a superior *gnosis* or knowledge of divine things. Have we any reason to suppose that such a claim was made?

In a document cited by Hippolytus as representing a 'Gnostic' sect known as Naassenes, we read, 'We alone of all men are Christians, who complete the mystery at the third portal, and are anointed there with speechless chrism' (*Philosophumena*, V. 9. 121-2). The anointing here (probably an actual anointing with oil) is clearly some form of initiation into a mystery. The background of the thought is not the Hebrew and primitive Christian idea of the Messianic consecration, but rituals of anointing such as we know to have been employed in some pagan mysteries. The writer appears to claim that only those who have undergone this special initiation are worthy to be called Christians. Language of this kind could be taken over by orthodox writers. Thus Ignatius (who often uses quasi-Gnostic language) writes: 'Be not anointed with the ill-odour of the doctrine of the Prince of this world, lest he take you captive from the life that is set before you. Why do we not all become wise, receiving the knowledge of God, which is Jesus Christ' (Eph. xvii. 1-2). Ignatius contrasts the true *gnosis* with the false. Initiation into false doctrine he describes (metaphorically) as anointing with ill-odour. (A different verb is used, but its sense is the same.) It is implied that initiation into true *gnosis* could also be described as anointing, only with a different chrism. This true initiation, he emphasizes, is open to *all* Christians. Our author similarly speaks of the true chrism, by virtue of which *all* Christians know the truth—all Christians, and not only those who have received some special initiation; and this chrism is by implication contrasted with the false doctrine that is infecting the Church.

It seems probable therefore that, though the concept of anointing as consecration belonged to the earliest Christian thought as an inheritance from the Messianic ideas of Judaism, yet the immediate background of the present passage is rather that of Hellenistic religion; and 'anointing' suggests initiation into *gnosis*, or supernatural knowledge. But we have still to ask: What is the chrism, which is at once the medium of initiation and the abiding source of a growing knowledge of God?

If rites of initiation are in question, the one such rite which *all* Christians undergo is Baptism. It is reasonable to suppose that the chrism is something connected with Baptism. One view is that it stands for the divine grace conferred in the Sacrament. Indeed, one manuscript actually reads *charisma* ('gift of grace') for *chrisma*; but this is certainly an erroneous reading. That 'chrism' however stands for grace is not impossible; but something more particular than the general notion of grace seems to be called for here, where it is a matter specifically of communication of *knowledge*. Most commentators suppose that the reference is to the Holy Spirit. If we substitute the term 'Spirit' for 'chrism' we get a good sense: **The Spirit you received from Him (in Baptism) remains in you and you really need no teaching from anyone; simply remain in Him, for His Spirit teaches you about everything, and is true and is no lie.** This is in harmony with what is said about the Spirit as Paraclete in John xiv. 16-17, 26. On the other hand, the author of the Epistle, when he comes to give his own doctrine of the Spirit, does not bring it into connection with the chrism. His teaching in iv. 1-6 is not that doctrine must be tested by inspiration, but that inspiration must be tested by the Gospel (see notes on that passage). Further, if the parallel from Ignatius be admitted, the false unction is 'the teaching of the Prince of this world'; and we must suppose that the true unction is also in some way a kind of teaching. We now observe that ii. 24 prescribes a prophylactic against the poison of false teaching as follows: **Let that remain in you which you learned from the very beginning; if what you learned from the very beginning remains in you, then you will remain in the Son and in the Father.** The parallel between this passage and ii. 27, which speaks of the unction which **remains within you,** is unmistakable. **That which you learned from the very beginning** is the Gospel itself, the Word of God, which is said to 'remain in' the believer, as the chrism does in verse 27. Similarly, in John xv. 7, Christ says, **If you remain in me and *my words* remain in you, then ask whatever you like and**

you shall have it, while, on the other hand, in John v. 38 he says to the unbelieving Jews, 'You have not His word remaining in you' [the Moffatt translation again disguises the similarity of the language]. We have here the conception of the Gospel or Word of God, not as a mere set of propositions which may be 'kept in mind,' but as an indwelling power (in accordance with antique ideas of the almost independent reality of the spoken word, which are especially acute in Hebrew thought, but occur also among the Greeks from Homer onward).

In view of all this, it seems natural to conclude that the 'chrism,' which confers knowledge of God, and is also a prophylactic against the poison of false teaching, is the Word of God, that is, the Gospel, or the revelation of God in Christ, as communicated in the rule of faith to catechumens, and confessed in Baptism. This is the Christian's initiation, by water and the Word. So long as the Word (which **is true and is no lie) remains within** him—that is to say, so long as that which he **learned from the beginning** is not merely kept in mind, but continues to be a living power in him, controlling his thoughts, affections and will, he **really needs no teaching from anyone** (though such teaching may be useful for developing the implications of the Gospel), since by virtue of it he **remains in the Son and in the Father,** possesses knowledge of God, and receives further teaching as the occasion demands.

Whether we understand the chrism to be the Holy Spirit, or the Word of God, may perhaps make little ultimate difference to the essential purport of the passage. But there is a difference in the point of view. The appeal to the indwelling Spirit easily declines into an appeal to the individual experience of 'inspiration.' If such experience is made the criterion, persons with little grasp of the central truths of the Gospel may mistake their own 'inspirations' (or bright ideas) for the truth of God, and so the corporate, historical tradition of Christianity is imperilled. Our writer found that this was actually happening within his sphere of influence (see iv. 1–6). If, on the other hand, we are referred to the Gospel itself, which is a recital of what God did for us in the life, teaching, death and resurrection of Jesus Christ—to the Gospel not as merely heard, believed and remembered, but as livingly apprehended and retained as a power in our lives—then there is an objective standard by which the faith of the Church is kept true to what is distinctive in the Christian revelation. The interior testimony of the Holy Spirit is confirmation of the *datum* in the Gospel (see iv. 13).

28   The whole section dealing with the danger of false teaching is now rounded off with an appeal to the loyal members of the Church, echoing a thought that has run all through it: **Remain within Him.** A special motive is now added. If this is **the last hour,** then the Lord may be expected shortly to come again. Just as Paul had written, 'We are ambitious to be well-pleasing to Him; for.we must all appear before the judgment-seat of Christ' (2 Cor. v. 9–10), so our author appeals to this 'ambition' of every loyal Christian, **that when He appears we may have confidence instead of shrinking from Him in shame at His arrival.** We can hardly miss a reminiscence of sayings attributed to Jesus in the Gospels: **Whoever is ashamed of me and my words in this disloyal and sinful generation, the Son of Man will be ashamed of him when He comes in the glory of His Father with the holy angels** (Mark viii. 38). **Everyone who will confess me before men, I will confess him before my Father in heaven; and whoever will disown me before men, I will disown him before my Father in heaven** (Matt. x. 32–3; cf. Luke xii. 8–9). On the authority of these words (to which we have already noted an allusion in ii. 22), he who confesses the Son will remain in union with Him, and can look forward with serene confidence to meeting Him.

The Lord did not return, in the way He was expected to come, shortly after the writing of this epistle. When Christian thought adapted itself to the fact of this delay, the urgency of the appeal to an immediately impending second advent was lost. Attempts to revive it, under the illusion that at particular periods the signs of the times pointed to the end of the world in the near future, have always been artificial and disappointing. With a deeper penetration, the Fourth Evangelist taught that by His resurrection and the gift of the Spirit Christ came to His people, never to leave them again (John xiv. 15–18, 23, xvi. 16–22). At any moment the shame of denial may cause us to shrink from Him; at any moment, remaining in Him, we may have confidence in His presence. The Last Judgment, in all its solemnity and decisiveness, waits upon us in the midst of time.

Nevertheless, our experience in time has an end. The whole unknown future, beginning from the incompleteness of the present moment, is telescoped for us, in our sheer ignorance of what a day may bring forth, into a mere transition from time to eternity. For the world, time to come may prove to be measured in years or in millenniums; for each individual it cannot in any case be long. Death places us in the immediate presence of the Lord, for it sets us beyond time. It would be a pity if we should then **shrink from Him in shame.**

II. LIFE IN THE FAMILY OF GOD
(ii. 29 – iv. 12)

The second main section of the epistle is built about the central theme that Christians are children of God. They are 'born of God' (regenerate), and together make up a family in which all are brothers with God as their Father. The bond of union in the family is that divine love which is, at once and indistinguishably, the love which God showed to us in Christ, the love which we accord Him in return, and the charity we are bound to exercise towards one another. Indeed, 'God is love,' and all that can be said about life in the Christian family depends directly upon that far-reaching theological affirmation.

This main theme is treated in various aspects, without strict continuity of argument, and there are several divagations or excursuses, notably one (iv. 1–6) which, while it is a parenthesis in the present argument, reverts to one of the principal interests of the epistle, the danger of false teaching which denies the Incarnation.

I. THE CHILDREN OF GOD, THEIR PREROGATIVES AND OBLIGA-
TIONS; WITH AN EXCURSUS UPON THE NATURE AND GRAVITY
OF SIN (ii. 29 – iii. 10)

29 As you know He is just, be sure that everyone who practises
iii. righteousness is born of Him. 'Born of Him!' Think what
1 a love the Father has for us, in letting us be called 'children
of God!' And such we are. The world does not recognize
2 us? That is simply because it did not recognize Him. We
are children of God now, beloved; what we are to be is not
apparent yet, but we do know that when He appears we
3 are to be like Him—for we are to see Him as He is. And
everyone who rests this hope on Him, purifies himself as
4 He is pure. Everyone who commits sin commits lawless-
5 ness: sin is lawlessness, and you know He appeared to take
6 our sins away. In Him there is no sin; anyone who remains
in Him does not sin—anyone who sins has neither seen nor
7 known Him. Let no one deceive you, dear children: he who
practises righteousness is just, as He is just; he who com-
8 mits sin belongs to the devil, for the devil is a sinner from
the very beginning. (This is why the Son of God appeared,
9 to destroy the deeds of the devil.) Anyone who is born of
God does not commit sin, for the offspring of God remain
in Him, and they cannot sin, because they are born of God.
10 Here is how the children of God and the children of the
devil are recognized; anyone who does not practise righteousness does not belong to God,[1] and neither does he who
has no love for his brother.

[1] The expression 'to belong to God' represents the Greek ἐκ τοῦ θεοῦ
εἶναι. The preposition ἐκ properly means 'out of,' and is used to indicate the point of origin or departure. It has, however, various extended
uses, and one of these is to express a more or less vague relation of dependence or attachment. This vague sense is represented here, and in
other passages of the Moffatt translation of the epistle, by the English
verb 'to belong.' The actual meaning intended by the writer is not quite
clear. In this place it looks as if ἐκ τοῦ θεοῦ, with its literal meaning
'originating out of God,' were intended as a briefer synonym for 'born
of God,' or 'children of God,' and if so, then ἐκ τοῦ διαβόλου in verse 8
would mean 'born of the devil' and would be the equivalent of 'children
of the devil' in verse 10. But the author may deliberately have used the vaguer
expression here and in some other places. It is however well for the
reader to bear in mind that the Moffatt translation habitually uses the
verb 'to belong' to render a Greek expression which in any particular
case may well bear a more definite meaning.

Verse 29 forms a transition, in the author's manner, from the foregoing section to the following, and might be attached to either. The connection with the foregoing is perhaps through the thought of 'the Lord the righteous Judge'; though it is clear that attention is passing from the Son to the Father. While the 'He' of the first clause might refer to either, the 'Him' of the last clause is clearly the Father. The purpose of the verse is to introduce the idea of divine generation, which is to be elaborated in what follows. God is righteous. [There is no need to vary the translation: all through this part of the epistle 'just' and 'righteous' represent the same Greek word, and 'righteousness' represents the derived substantive.] The Christian who practises righteousness (or in the language of the earlier part of the epistle lives and moves within the light, walks as Christ walked, or obeys the command of love) is born of God.

That God is our Father and we His children is a thought several times expressed in the Synoptic sayings of Jesus. In Paul this thought is set forth in the doctrine of 'adoption.' As Christ is the Son of God, we who are 'in Christ,' members of His Body, are adopted by God as His sons, in token whereof the Spirit within us cries 'Abba, Father' (see Rom. viii. 14–17, 1 Cor. i. 9, Gal. iii. 26–7, iv. 6–7, etc.). The Pauline doctrine makes clear what is always implied in the biblical idea of the Fatherhood of God—namely, that we are sons of God by His grace and not in our own right (see Moffatt Commentary, *Romans*, pp. 130–1). In the Old Testament Israel is the 'son' of Jehovah because Jehovah chose the children of Israel as objects of His love, called them into a covenant with Himself, and so set up a relation between God and man which is, morally and spiritually, that of father and child. In paganism, tribes, or their chiefs and kings, were believed to be actual descendants of a deity. This belief, in a more refined and elevated form, becomes the doctrine that man as such (or the spiritual part of man) is the offspring of God (as we have it in the pagan poet quoted in Acts xvii. 28); or, in other words, a kind of emanation of the Divine (cf. notes on iii. 9, pp. 74–6). This is not the biblical, or Christian, doctrine. God created man in His image, out of the dust of the earth, and the 'natural' relation of men to God is one of creaturely dependence. It is of His grace that they enter into the spiritual relation of children. In 1 Pet. i. 23 this thought is expressed in the words, **You are born anew of immortal, not of mortal seed, by the living, lasting word of God.**

The antecedents of the idea of regeneration lie not within Judaism, but in Hellenistic thought. It is found in some mystery religions; and in the higher paganism, or 'Hellenistic mysticism,' the initiation into *gnosis* is sometimes represented as a process of regeneration (as, for example, in *Corpus Hermeticum*, XIII—a late dialogue, probably of the third century). The Fourth Evangelist adopts the idea, both in the Prologue (i. 12) and in the dialogue with Nicodemus (iii. 3–8), placing it in the essentially Christian context of the Kingdom of God and the Holy Spirit, and connecting it with the sacrament of Baptism, by which a man becomes a member of the Church. The phrase used in our present passage, here translated **'born of God'**, occurs in John i. 13 (where it is differently translated). The idea which it expresses is one of the cardinal ideas of the Epistle. In view of its connection in Hellenistic thought with initiation into knowledge of the divine, we may suspect that **'born of God,'** like 'knowing God,' and 'in the light' (see notes on ii. 4, 9), was an expression used, and in our author's view misused, by the false teachers. At its first introduction, therefore, he emphasizes the point that its true connotation is an ethical one. It is he who **practises righteousness** who can rightly be said to be **born of God,** just as in Matt. v. 45 it is those who love their enemies who are sons of the Father in heaven. In enforcing the ethical criterion our author is simply following the fundamental tradition of the teaching of Jesus.

iii.

1 Having thus safeguarded the ethical purport of the doctrine of divine generation, the writer now takes up the phrase **children of God,** which was already current in Christian circles, and was used, in particular, in the work which was for him most authoritative, the Gospel according to John (i. 12, xi. 52). Behind this lie such sayings of the Lord as Matt. v. 9, 45. In

these sayings the term used is 'sons of God.' In Johannine circles it appears that the term 'Son of God' was reserved exclusively for the 'only-begotten Son,' and the term 'children' substituted when believers were spoken of. It appears, however, that our author had in mind the word of Jesus recorded in Matt. v. 9, 'they will be *called* sons of God.' [The Moffatt rendering obscures the identity of the verb.] He would have his readers consider how deep is the meaning of such an appellation. In harmony with the whole biblical tradition he regards this filial relation to God not as something inherent in human nature, but as due wholly to the love of God. It is a pure act of grace that allows us to be called 'children of God.' Nor are we merely *called* God's children: such we are; born of Him, 'partakers of the divine nature' (2 Pet. i. 4). As the Fourth Gospel has it, we have passed by regeneration out of the sphere of 'flesh' into the sphere of 'spirit' (John iii. 5-6); or, as Paul put it, there is a new creation whenever a man comes to be in Christ (2 Cor. v. 17). That is to say, in the children of God a new kind of humanity has emerged. Similarly, in the Hermetic tractate *On Regeneration* we read, 'He who is born (again) will be another person'; and the initiate says, 'I am now not what I was before' (*Corpus Hermeticum*, XIII. 2, 3). So far our author will go with 'Hellenistic mysticism.' The Christian is (by grace of God) in some real sense a supernatural being.

It is true that he is not ostensibly different from other men. The world does not recognize us as children of God. What of that? Did it recognize Jesus Christ as other than an ordinary man? (For 'Him' here probably refers, not to the Father, but to the Son.) Yet He, we know, was the Son of God. In us, as in Him during His incarnate life, the divine sonship is veiled. But it will not always be so. Paul deals with the same theme 2 in the Epistle to the Colossians. He too taught that Christians possess, by grace of God, a supernatural life. His favourite way of expressing this is, not in terms of regeneration (an idea of which he shows no knowledge), but through the concept of the Christian as dead and risen with Christ. So in Col. iii. 1-4 he says, You have been raised with Christ, but he hastens to add,

Your life is hidden with Christ in God; not, however, hidden for ever: **when Christ, who is our life, appears, then you will appear with Him in glory.** This is the 'revelation of the children of God,' for which the whole creation waits (Rom. viii. 19). Similarly, our author, affirming that in spite of appearances Christians are here and now children of God, looks forward to a fresh stage of existence in which they will be something more glorious still. What that 'something' is, is a question upon which we must be content to remain in ignorance at present: **what we are to be is not apparent yet.** But so much we can say with assurance: **when He appears, we are to be like Him.** Similarly Paul had said, **God decreed of old that those whom He predestined should share the likeness of His Son** (Rom. viii. 29).

But our author gives a fresh turn to the thought. In the clause, **we are to see Him as He is,** he is alluding to that 'vision of God' to which all mystics aspire. Whether the pronouns 'He' and 'Him' refer to the Father or the Son is, here as elsewhere, not quite clear, though the latter is in the context more natural. But it makes little difference, for in Johannine thought to see the Son is to see the Father (cf. John xii. 45, xiv. 9). Our mysterious but glorious destiny, therefore, includes the vision of God, or of Christ, in His true being. In most of the New Testament not much is said about the hope of the vision of God (Matt. v. 8 and Heb. xii. 14, the latter referring primarily to Christ, are the only clear cases; and note that in Matt. v. 8–9 the ideas of seeing God and being His children are in close contiguity, as here). But in the Fourth Gospel it is a frequent theme. Starting from the proposition, **Nobody has ever seen God, but God has been unfolded by the divine One, the only Son** (i. 18), it expounds the whole ministry of Jesus Christ as the realization of the hope of the vision of God and His glory, under the conditions of time and space. In the farewell discourses, when the incarnate life is drawing to a close, Christ promises a further vision of Himself (xiv. 19, etc.), a promise conceived as being fulfilled, in the first place, by the resurrection and the coming of the Spirit. Finally, He prays that His followers **may be beside me where I am, to behold my glory** in the eternal world (xvii. 24). It is here, doubtless, that our author finds direct authority for his teaching in this place.

Grammatically, the clause 'for **we are to see Him as He is**' might be connected (in the Greek as in the English) either (*a*) with the words **we know**, or (*b*) with the words **we are to be like Him**. (*a*) If we adopt the former construction, the meaning is, 'We are to be like Him: this we know because we are to see Him as He is.' The latter is the premise (itself guaranteed by John xvii. 24) from which the conclusion is drawn that we are to be like Christ. But the argument demands another premise which is unexpressed; those who are to see God must be like God. The maxim 'Like is known by like' is frequently enunciated by Hellenistic religious writers in this sense. (*b*) If we adopt the latter construction, the meaning is 'because we shall see God, we shall (as we know) become like Him.' The presupposition of this is the doctrine that the vision, or knowledge, of God makes a man like God. There is no direct authority for this doctrine in the New Testament, but it was widely accepted in 'Hellenistic mysticism,' in the sense that through *gnosis*, direct knowledge of God, a man might become immortal and even divine. It makes no important difference which of these two interpretations we adopt, but it is interesting to observe that in either case our author is assuming principles which he held in common, not only with the 'Gnostic' teachers whom he is combating, but with the higher thought of the Hellenistic world in general. He is naturalizing within Christian theology a widely diffused mystical tradition. But a recognition of this fact enables us to see more clearly where his Christian interpretation of this tradition is distinctive, as the following verses will show.

The profound thought to which he has given such simple and moving expression has entered deeply into the Christian consciousness. The reserve which he exercises about our future destiny, discouraging all fruitless speculation, combined with the serene certainty that we shall see our Lord and be like Him, is the model for all our thinking about the life to come.

We now come to an all-important corollary of the Christian 3 hope. If we are to be like Christ hereafter, we must practise that

likeness by imitating Him here and now, imitating Him (in particular) in purity of living. It is the pure in heart who will see God (Matt. v. 8). It is idle to speak of seeing or knowing God, if we are content to live in sin. The argument returns to the theme which was in view in i. 5 – ii. 11. In Him there is no darkness,
6 we were there told; and that means, in Him there is no sin. God is all light, all goodness; and the Son who reveals the Father reveals His sinless perfection. Consequently, anyone who remains in Him does not sin—anyone who sins has neither seen nor known Him.

4   In speaking of sin, the author wishes to make clear, he is speaking of actual infraction of the moral law; and similarly, when he speaks of being righteous, he means practising righteousness (verse 7)—that is, doing what is right. It appears that it was necessary to say this because there was a tendency to use the term 'righteousness' with an artificial connotation, as though a man might be righteous in a religious sense even though his actual conduct showed no marked conformity with recognized moral standards. There are pretty clear hints in the epistles of Paul that his teaching was misconstrued in this way. He taught that the Christian was 'justified' (declared righteous) by grace. Some said, remain on in sin, so that there may be all the more grace (Rom. vi. 1), implying that the status of 'righteousness' might be maintained without (in our author's words) practising righteousness. But we need not look for any particular heretical doctrine here. Religion and morality are not inherently identical spheres of experience. There is always the possiblity that religious categories may not coincide with the corresponding ethical categories. In the Old Testament the prophets have to protest against a view which identifies sin with breach of taboo instead of with injustice, cruelty, impurity and the like; and righteousness with the punctual observance of feasts and fasts, instead of with justice and humanity. And within the Christian community it is not always clear that a deep 'sense of sin' goes with a sensitiveness to social obligations unfulfilled. Any strongly ethical religion (like Judaism or Christianity) has constantly to be on its guard lest 'religious experience,' whether mystical or

sacramental, should lose its ethical content, or 'cold morality' forget its religious sanctions. This is our author's concern.

His maxim **Sin is lawlessness,** if considered as a general definition of sin, must be considered somewhat superficial, in contrast, for example, with Paul's treatment of the theme (see the Moffatt Commentary, *Romans*, pp. 50–51, 79–83). But his intention is to insist that in the whole discussion the terms 'sin' and 'righteousness' shall be taken in their plain, crude sense: sin is doing wrong; righteousness is doing right. Or this, **let no one deceive you** with any subtle sophistry which blurs the plain meaning of such terms.

If we thus keep crude actuality in view, we shall appreciate 5 the teaching of the Gospel that Christ **appeared to take our sins away.** The immediate authority for this teaching is, once again, to be found in the Fourth Gospel, which speaks of Christ **as the lamb of God, who is to remove** (take away: the same word in the Greek) **the sin of the world** (i. 29). (The Evangelist thinks of *'sin'* as a principle or quality of life, expressing itself variously in thought, word and deed; the author of the epistle thinks of *'sins,'* the multiform outward expression of the sinful principle). In other words, Christ came **to destroy** 8 **the deeds of the devil** (cf. Matt. xii. 25–29, Luke x. 18, Col. ii. 15, I Pet. iii. 22, etc.; and especially John xii. 31). **The devil is a sinner from the very beginning;** but he has no hold on Christ (John xiv. 30), in whom **there is no sin** (verse 5). Hence, **to sin** (meaning to break the moral law, to do wrong) is to **belong to the devil**: to remain in Christ is to be righteous as He is righteous (meaning to **practise righteousness,** to do right, verse 7).

It is all very plain black-and-white. It had to be made so, if the readers were to be sufficiently warned against the dangers of sophistication. Sophistry can as easily prove that evil is an aspect of good as that error is an aspect of truth. But truth and falsehood, good and evil, right and wrong, God and the devil, are irreconcilable opposites. True religion means belonging to God, and therefore it means standing on the side of truth and goodness, to the exclusion of their opposites.

This is now applied to the doctrine of divine generation. If ⁹⁻¹⁰

by being **born of God** you mean 'enlightment', or initiation into a superior grade of 'knowledge,' then this is mere delusion unless the ethical test is satisfied: **anyone who is born of God does not commit sin** (i.e. do wrong); **anyone who does not practise righteousness** (i.e. do right) **does not belong to God,** but is among **the children of the devil.**

9   The argument is supported in verse 9 by a somewhat obscure clause. Literally translated, it runs as follows: 'Everyone who is born of God does not commit sin, because his seed remains in him.' Dr. Moffatt has taken the word 'seed' (*sperma*) as a collective noun, meaning 'offspring,' as 'seed of Abraham' (Luke i. 55, Gal. iii. 29, John viii. 33, 37) means 'offspring' or 'posterity of Abraham,' and he has substituted 'of God' for 'his' to make the meaning clear. The expression 'seed of God' in this sense is not found in the New Testament, but it could find support in parallels elsewhere. **The offspring of God,** then, is taken as a collective equivalent for **anyone who is born of God,** and is the subject of the verb **remain** (Moffatt gives the verb in the plural, since 'offspring' is plural in sense). The same expression is the subject of the verbs in the following clause: **the offspring of God cannot sin because they are** (it is) **born of God.** This gives excellent sense, being closely parallel to verse 6: **anyone who remains in Him does not sin.**

Other interpreters take the word 'seed' as carrying on the metaphor of generation. This may be aptly illustrated from the Hermetic tractate, *On Regeneration*: 'I know not,' says the would-be initiate, 'from what womb a man is born (again), and of what seed.' 'My child,' replies Hermes, '(the womb is) intellectual wisdom (conceiving) in silence, and the seed is the true Good' (*Corp. Herm.*, XIII. 1–2). The divine act of generation is thought of (on analogy with the physical act) as implanting a divine principle from which the new nature of the children of God is produced. This divine principle, once implanted, remains in the child of God (for the word 'him' then refers, not to God, but to the man who is born of God), and it is this divine principle, now immanent in the man, which keeps him from sinning. The subject of the verbs in the last clause of verse 9 (which are both singular, not plural, in the Greek) is then the same as that of the first clause, and the sense is: anyone who is born of God not only does not, but cannot sin, because he is born of God, and a divine seed remains in him.

So far as the grammatical form of expression is concerned, the former way of interpreting the passage has the advantage that it gives to the expression 'remains in him' the usual sense, in which the subject of the verb is the Christian man, and 'Him' refers to God. On the other hand, it has two (not very decisive) drawbacks: (*a*) The clause 'his seed' lacks in Greek the definite article, which is properly required if the expression is to be the equivalent of **anyone who is born of God**, and is in fact inserted in the translation, **the offspring of God**. Some writers, it is true, are loose in their use of the article, in particular such New Testament writers as are under Semitic influence. This writer, however, does not semitize, and is usually precise in his use of the article. If the meaning of the phrase is 'a divine seed,' i.e. a divine principle implanted, then the definite article is not required. (*b*) If 'the seed of God' is a synonym for **anyone who is born of God,** then there is an unnecessary tautology. The meaning could in that case have been equally well given by writing, 'Anyone who is born of God does not commit sin, for he remains in Him and cannot sin.' If, on the other hand, we take the view that 'the seed of God' is a divine principle implanted in man, we have a perfect parallelism of clauses:

'Everyone born of God does not commit sin,
    because His seed remains in him:
and he cannot sin,
    because he is born of God.'

As parallelism is a notable feature of this writer's style, there is a certain presumption in favour of this line of interpretation.

In order to decide the question, we must have regard to the wider context of thought. In 'Hellenistic mysticism' and in the Christian or near-Christian 'Gnosticism' affiliated to it, the doctrine of a divine principle implanted in human nature is one of the most constant elements. To give some examples:

In the Hermetic tractate *Poimandres* we learn that there is resident in men an 'essential Man,' the offspring of the supreme God ('the Father of all, who is life and light'), and it is possible for this essential humanity in us to be liberated, by enlightenment or *gnosis*, from the bonds of matter, and to ascend again to the Father (*Corp. Herm.*, I. 12–15, 24–26). Philo (who is strongly under the influence of Hellenistic speculation) similarly speaks of a 'real Man,' dwelling in the soul of each of us (*Quod Det.*, 22). This indwelling Man he identifies with the heavenly Man, made in the image of God, whom he took to be referred to in Gen. i. 26–7; and this heavenly Man, he says, is not the creature of God (like the man referred to in Gen. ii. 7), but His offspring (*Leg. All.*, I. 31–2). Writing in a more popular strain, he says of the Hebrew nation (God's chosen race) that 'their bodies were moulded of human seeds (*spermata*), but their souls of divine; wherefore they have become kinsfolk of God' (*Vit. Mos.*, I. 279). In the *Book of Baruch* attributed to the Gnostic Justin, man is the progeny of Elohim (God) and Edem (or Earth). His 'soul' comes from Edem, his 'spirit' from Elohim; and it is the spirit, the divine principle in man, that is ultimately to be redeemed (Hippolytus, *Philosophumena*, V. 26–8). In a document attributed to the Gnostic sect of Naassenes God is said to have sown seeds (*spermata*) into the world, through which the whole world is being brought to perfection. The 'perfect Gnostics' are those who receive these seeds (Hipp., *op. cit.*, V. 8. 112–13). The Christian Gnostic Valentinus produced an elaborate myth of the beginning of things. In the course of it he relates how the material universe, including the human body with its animal 'soul,' was made by the Demiurge, or heavenly Craftsman, out of the lower elements; but divine Wisdom, unknown to him, inserted into some men the 'spiritual seed' (*sperma*), also called the 'seed of Achamoth' (Wisdom). Thus there are among men good souls and evil souls. The former are those which are 'receptive of the seed.' The function of Jesus as Saviour is to open a way for the 'seeds' (i.e. the divine element in man) into the Pleroma or celestial society; and final salvation comes 'when the seeds of God have been gathered together' (Irenaeus,

Adv. Haer. [ed. Harvey], I. 1. 10, 12-13; Clement, *Excerpta ex Theodoto*, 38, 40, 49, 53).

It is difficult not to suppose that there is some relation between Valentinus's doctrine of the divine 'seed' which resides in good souls, and our author's doctrine of the 'seed.' It is no wild hypothesis that the heretical teachers here in view, like Philo before them and Valentinus after them, referred to the divine principle immanent in man, as the divine 'seed'; and our author may well have taken over the word from their vocabulary (as he may have taken over the term 'chrism'; see ii. 27, note). It seems therefore best to read, 'Anyone who is born of God does not commit sin, for a divine seed remains in him; and he cannot sin, because he is born of God'; which gives a (formal) parallel to the doctrine of Valentinus, that 'some souls are by nature good, and others by nature bad, and the good are those which are receptive of the Seed, but the bad by nature could never even receive that Seed' (Irenaeus, *op. cit.*, I. 1. 15).

It does not, of course, follow that our author shared the 'Gnostic' metaphysics; for his thought, however influenced by Hellenistic ideas, is rooted in the authentic Christian tradition. In that tradition, regeneration is closely associated with the Word of God. In Jas. i. 18 divine generation is **'by the word of the truth.'** In 1 Pet. i. 23-25 we are said to be **born anew of immortal, not of mortal, seed by the living, lasting word of God,** which is further identified with **the word of the Gospel.** In the Fourth Gospel it is by receiving the (now personified) Word that men become children of God (John i. 12). It is noteworthy that the Naassene writer cited above finds scriptural sanction for his doctrine of the divine 'seeds' in the Parable of the Sower. In the Gospels themselves the seed in that parable is said to stand for the preached Word (Luke viii. 11). There is therefore a fairly well established association of the ideas 'seed' and 'word,' which in Hellenistic Christian circles might well be helped by the Stoic doctrine of the 'spermatic' or seminal *logos*, even though the Stoic *logos* is not a 'word.' In the light of all this, it would seem natural to suppose that when our author speaks of divine 'seed' he is thinking of the Word of God, or the Gospel. And this is confirmed by the observation that, just as he speaks here of the 'seed' remaining in believers, so in ii. 24 he speaks of the original Gospel (**that which you heard from the very beginning**) as remaining in them. As therefore, from one point of view, the Gospel is the 'chrism'—that is to say, it is that which when received and retained initiates the believer into the knowledge of God (ii. 27, note)—so from another point of view the Gospel, as the Word of God, is the immanent divine principle producing in men the regenerate nature which does not sin. It was by receiving the Gospel that we became children of God; it is by loyalty to the Gospel that we continue to live as His children, and conduct ourselves in a manner worthy of our divine parentage.

The teaching of this passage raises a difficulty when it is compared with other parts of the epistle. In i. 8–10 the writer has repudiated in the strongest terms the suggestion that anyone may claim to be sinless. Yet here he says, **Anyone who is born of God does not commit sin.** In ii. 1–2 he contemplates the case of a Christian who commits sin, and assures him that there is a remedy. Yet here he declares that the child of God **cannot sin.**

The difficulty may be relieved by observing a distinction of tenses in the Greek. The so-called present (more properly imperfect) and aorist tenses in Greek do not (except in the indicative mood) express a difference in the *time* of action, but in the *'mode* of action.' The imperfect forms of the oblique moods (including infinitive and participle) express continuous or habitual action; the aorist forms express momentary or occasional action. Now, in ii. 1 the verbs translated **'may not sin'** and **'does sin'** are in the aorist, and indicate single or occasional acts of sin. In iii. 4–10 the relevant verbs are uniformly in the present or imperfect tense: in particular, the expression **anyone who sins** in verse 6 represents an imperfect participle, and the infinite in the expression **cannot sin** is an imperfect infinitive. These expressions therefore should properly refer, not to single or occasional acts of sin, but to habitual sin, or a continuous sinful state. The meaning might be brought out by exaggerating the force of the tenses in translation: 'Anyone who keeps on sinning has never seen Him and does not know Him'; 'He cannot keep on sinning, because he has been born of God.' (The aorist participle and infinitive respectively would have meant, 'anyone who commits a sin' and 'he cannot commit a sin'.) If therefore we interpret the tenses strictly, we may understand the author not to affirm that the Christian cannot possibly commit a sin, but to say that it is impossible to conceive of a child of God being habitually sinful, while it remains possible (ii. 1) for him to fall, once and again, into a single act of sin (though he ought not to do so). In other words, the renewal of our nature consequent upon accepting the Gospel is such that our whole bent is away from sin, and our normal condition one of sinlessness. It may happen that, under stress of temptation, we commit a sinful act; in that case we make our peace with God by virtue of the sacrifice and intercession of Christ, and revert to our normal condition of sinlessness. For, whatever happens, we are children of God, and sin is abnormal and unnatural to us. It cannot be that, while God's word remains in us, we should so belie our heavenly parentage as to be set in sinful courses.

All this is true. Yet it is legitimate to doubt whether the reader could be expected to grasp so subtle a doctrine simply upon the basis of a precise distinction of tenses without further guidance. Moreover, it is not clear that this distinction of tenses is carried right through with the precision which would be necessary if the whole weight of the argument rested upon it. If we are to insist pedantically upon grammatical points, it is difficult to draw a sharp distinction between the statement **Anyone who remains in Him does not sin** (iii. 6, continuous present), and the statement in i. 8, which is literally, 'We do not possess sin' (also continuous present). Logically, it is not clear why a person of whom the former statement is true should not make the latter statement about himself. Yet the former is affirmed, the latter denied.

Moreover, while the statement (roundly made) that a Christian does not and cannot sin is strange to us, there did exist in early days a quite serious expectation that Christians should be actually sinless. This was due, not only to the 'perfectionism' which has often been observed to accompany revival fervour, but also to dogmatic prepossessions. In the eschatology which Christianity inherited from Judaism it was taught that in the Age to Come the people of God should be sinless. Thus in *Enoch* v. 8 *sq.* we read: 'Then too will wisdom be bestowed on the elect, and they will all live and never again sin, either through heedlessness or through pride' (Charles's translation; similarly *Jubilees* v. 12). As it was the general assumption of primitive Christianity that the Age to Come had actually been inaugurated (see pp. 34–7, above), the belief was natural that this, like other prophecies, was fulfilled in the Church. We may suppose that in the fervour of the early days the actual moral renewal that took place in many lives seemed almost to justify the belief: relatively and by comparison at least, converts *were* free from sin. Since this belief was widely held, the readers of the epistle would be likely to understand the writer to be affirming it, without observing too narrowly his use of tenses. Nor is it unlikely that he himself, deeply influenced by popular eschatology as he shows himself to be, shared the belief, when he was thinking theoretically or ideally, rather than looking at the facts.

The apparent contradiction is probably not to be eliminated (though it may be qualified) by grammatical subtlety. In i. 8–ii. 2 on the one hand, and in iii. 4–10 on the other, the author is writing from different points of view, and concerning himself with different problems. The heretical teaching might have different effects upon its adherents. Some of them were led to assume that, being 'enlightened,' they were already perfect in virtue. Others thought it did not matter whether they were virtuous or not, provided they were 'enlightened.' The complacency of the former was castigated in i. 8–10. The moral indifference of the latter is in view in our present passage. In combatting it, the author uses all the resources of antithesis to set forth the essential polarity of ethical religion. God and the devil, children of God and children of the devil, doing right and doing wrong—these represent absolute contraries. To be born of God, to belong to God, to remain in God, to have His word in us, and to do right—these all stand on the one side of a dividing line: there is no alternative but to do wrong, and so to belong to the devil and to show oneself his child. To claim to be a child of God, and yet to be indifferent to moral obligations, is to confuse the whole issue. Of the personal problem raised for one who acknowledges all this, and yet is conscious of sin, he is not at this moment thinking. He is concerned to establish the one fundamental point. When he is facing the facts of personal experience, he is well aware that the pattern of life is not such a perfect chess-board, with its black and white separated by rigid lines. The actual and the ideal do not coincide. Nevertheless, it may be by contemplating the ideal that we best understand the final truth of things which underlies the actual.

The last clause of verse 10 forms a transition to a fresh aspect of the theme. In the author's manner it both carries on the thought of the preceding verses and introduces the idea which is to be the main theme of the verses which follow. He has been speaking of 'righteousness' and 'sin.' He now makes it clear that the specifically Christian form of righteousness is love, or charity, and the lack or denial of charity is, more than anything else, what Christianity means by sin.

2. LOVE AND HATRED; LIFE AND DEATH (iii. 11–18)

For this is the message you have learned from the very begin- 11
ning, that we are to love one another: we are not to be like 12
Cain, who belonged to the evil One and slew his brother.
And why did he slay him? Because his own deeds were evil
and his brother's just. Do not wonder, brothers, that the 13
world hates you. We know we have crossed from death to 14
life, because we love the brotherhood; he who has no love
for his brother remains in death. Anyone who hates his 15
brother is a murderer, and you know that no murderer
has eternal life remaining within him. We know what love 16
is by this, that He laid down His life for us; so we ought to
lay down our lives for the brotherhood. But whoever 17

18   possesses this world's goods, and notices his brother in
need, and shuts his heart against him, how can love to God
remain in him? Dear children, let us put our love not into
words or into talk but into deeds, and make it real.

We have already been told that Christ's new command of
11 love, or charity, is an essential part of the original Gospel—an
old command which you had from the very beginning (ii. 7). The
writer now reiterates this, with the intention of enforcing and
illustrating his thesis that right conduct is the only sure and
sufficient mark of the child of God. For in a Christian valua-
tion love and hatred are the typical forms of righteousness and
12 sin respectively. There is an example of unnatural and horrible
hatred between brothers in the biblical story of Cain and Abel
(our author's one and only explicit reference to the Old Testament). The precise pertinence of this illustration is indicated
in 14b–15. But meanwhile, by a swift transition of thought,
the two primeval brothers become representatives of the evil
world over against the family of God. As Cain hated Abel to
the point of killing him, because his own deeds were evil and
13 his brother's righteous, so the pagan world hates Christians,
and for the same reason; because of the inherent opposition of
wickedness to goodness. Thus the pagan world-order reveals
14 itself as a realm of hatred and of death. Christians on the contrary dwell in a realm of life, whose distinguishing mark is the
love that exists among God's children in His family. Thus the
ethical criterion for 'religious experience,' upon which the
writer has insisted again and again, is made quite precise, and
grounded firmly in fundamental principles. Charity is the
touchstone. The decisive test for all such claims as those which
are reviewed in i. 5 – ii. 7 lies in our attitude to our fellow men,
and this test is one that we can all apply with less risk of self-
deception than any other. The decisiveness of the test is
further emphasized negatively: he who has no love for his
15 brother remains in death; for hatred is murder; murder is the
denial of life: no murderer has eternal life remaining in him.
The thought of these verses is highly compressed, with
abrupt transitions. The connection of ideas may profitably be

studied with reference to a passage in the Fourth Gospel, which was probably in the author's mind. In John viii. 37–47 we have a scene described in which the Jews of Jerusalem (prototypes of the world which hates the righteous in our present passage) exhibit furious hostility to Jesus, culminating (viii. 59) in an attempt to kill Him by stoning. They claim to be **Abraham's children**, and as such to have one father, even **God**. Jesus retorts, **If you are Abraham's children, then do as Abraham did ; but now you want to kill me. . . . Abraham did not do that. . . . If God were your father, you would love me. . . . You belong to your father the devil, and you want to do what your father desires; he was a** *murderer* (the same word as in 1 John iii. 15, though Moffatt translates it differently) **from the very beginning.** Here we can recognize parallels to several of the leading ideas of our present passage: the Son of God over against the children of the devil; love for God's Son as a mark of the child of God; murderous hatred as a mark of the child of the devil; but here the reference to murder is natural and unforced, for the Jews are in the act of attempting to murder Jesus, thus giving overt proof of their descent from that primeval murderer, the devil. With this passage as background it is easier to understand the somewhat abrupt introduction of the idea of murder in 1 John iii. 12–15. For although we have the authority of Matt. v. 21–2 for treating hatred as constructive murder, yet there is nothing in the context itself to prepare for this particular turn of thought.

It is, however, a fruitful turn of thought, for it enables the writer to bring out very effectively a fresh aspect of the contrast of the two orders—the pagan world and the Christian dispensation—which he has already drawn in ii. 7–11. There the contrast was drawn mainly in terms of light and darkness, and light and darkness were correlated with love and hatred. Here the contrast is drawn in terms of life and death; and hatred is shown to belong to the realm of death just because hatred is murder, the denial of life. By contrast, love is the mark of the realm of life. The transition from the one realm to the other (it is implied) is that birth, or rebirth, by which we become children of God, and love between brothers is at once the mark of the child of God and the proof of eternal life.

Hatred, then, is sufficiently characterized as murder, or the negation of life. But how are we to characterize love positively? 16 For the Christian there is one inevitable answer. **We know what love is by this, that He laid down His life for us.** The language is that of the Fourth Gospel (cf. John x. 11–18, xv. 13), but the fact is affirmed in every part of the New Testament (see Mark x. 45, Gal. i. 4, Titus ii. 14, Heb. x. 8–10, 1 Pet. iii. 18, etc.), belonging indeed to the central core of the original *kerygma* or apostolic proclamation. Indeed, among the solid facts of the Gospel history, attested by direct evidence of the senses (**what we heard, what we saw with our eyes, what we witnessed and touched with our own hands**) one of the most securely attested is the fact that Jesus went willingly to death at the hands of His enemies, having a few hours earlier plainly declared by solemn acts and words that He dedicated Himself to death as a sacrifice on behalf of men whom it was His mission to save (1 Cor. xi. 23–5, Mark xiv. 22–4). The interpretation of the saving efficacy of the death of Christ is a task which Christian theology has never yet brought to a completely satisfactory conclusion. Already within the New Testament there are pointers to various lines of interpretation. But that in thus dying He showed, not only a martyr's devotion to a cause, but also a divine charity towards men who had sinned deeply against Him and against God, is a point upon which there is substantial agreement among New Testament writers who otherwise differ considerably in outlook (see Rom. v. 8, Gal. ii. 20, Rev. i. 5; and, by implication, Luke xxiii. 34, Heb. ii. 10–18, 1 Pet. ii. 21–5). It is one of the dominant ideas of the Fourth Evangelist, and he more than any of the others insists upon the point which is essential to any acceptable *theologia crucis*, that the love of Jesus—that is, the loyalty and devotion to His friends, the magnanimity towards His enemies, and the goodwill towards all men, in which He died—is indistinguishably one with the love of the eternal God towards His creatures, which is their only hope and assurance of eternal life (John xiii. 1–4, xv. 13-14, xvii. 19,

x. 11-18, 27-30, iii. 16, etc.). This is the position assumed by our author here and elsewhere. At this point he refers to it for the sake of the consequences that follow for Christian ethics.

It was an immense strength to early Christianity as a system of ethical teaching that its regulative principle was expressed in a term—*agapé*, love or charity—which it was free to define afresh for itself (see pp. 110-12); and that the content of *agapé* was supplied, from the outset, by reference to the concrete action of Jesus Christ upon the field of history, conceived as an expression of the eternal will of God. Thus in explaining what sort of action is intended by the commandment, 'Love one another,' the Christian teacher has neither to fall back upon some speculative, *a priori*, conception of the love of God, nor to become involved in the discrimination of various kinds of 'love' among the chaotic manifestations of human affections and impulses. It is strictly true, in the history of thought and language, that we know what *agapé* means from the fact that Christ laid down His life for us.

The practice of love, or charity, therefore, can be broadly described in terms of the imitation of Christ. It is clear that from the outset the 'law of Christ' (Gal. vi. 2), by which Christians are bound to direct their conduct, was defined in the Church's teaching, not only by the traditional precepts of Jesus, but also by His example. The appeal to His example is explicit in 1 Cor. xi. 1, 1 Thess. i. 6, 2 Cor. viii. 9, x. 1, Rom. xv. 2-3, Phil. ii. 2-8, 1 Tim. vi. 13, 1 Pet. ii. 21, Heb. xii. 3-4; and it is probable that the idea of the *imitatio Christi* had more to say than is commonly recognized by critics, in the selection of incidents from the life of Jesus for record in the Gospels. In the Fourth Gospel there is one incident—the washing of the disciples' feet—which is expressly held up as an example to be followed by Christians in their dealings with one another (John xiii. 12-15); and this is shortly followed by the 'new commandment' which is so emphasized in this epistle: **as I have loved you, you are to love one another** (John xiii. 34). That means, says our author, that **we ought to lay down our 16 lives for** our brothers (it seems a pity to substitute, as the

85

Moffatt translation does, the less simple and concrete expression, the brotherhood). There were occasions in the life of the early Church, as there are certainly tragic occasions at the present day, for a quite literal obedience to this precept. But not all life is tragic; and yet the same principle of conduct must 17 apply all through. Thus it may call for the simple expenditure of money we might have spent upon ourselves, to relieve the need of someone poorer. It is after all the same principle of action, though at a lower level of intensity: it is the willingness to surrender that which has value for our own life, to enrich the life of another. If such a minimal response to the law of charity, called for by such an everyday situation, is absent, then it is idle to pretend that we are within the family of God, the realm in which love is operative as the principle and the token of eternal life.

The reader may be conscious of a certain descent from the sublimity of verse 16 to the apparent banality of verse 17. But this is characteristic of our author. As he was concerned to show (in iii. 4–7) that the terms 'righteousness' and 'sin' are to be understood realistically, as the plain man understands them—'righteousness' as doing right, 'sin' as doing wrong—so he is now concerned to say that Christian charity or love is not to be defined in any artificial or arbitrary sense. It means practical benevolence and beneficence. It may rise to a height of self-sacrifice comparable with the sacrifice of Christ, or it may mean that where another man is in want of necessities of life which you possess, you will give him what he needs. How easy, if the occasion for heroic self-sacrifice has not arisen, to pretend to ourselves that there is no call to 'lay down our lives'! But in any case there is the chance of helping someone at some slight cost to ourselves. No doubt charity means a good deal more than this; but in emphasizing that fact, the moralist is in danger of forgetting that it means at least this kind of thing. It is in any case concrete and realistic. This downright concreteness, almost crudity, in stating the moral requirements of religion, belongs to the genius of New Testament Christianity in general. It is noteworthy that in the Synoptic Gospels the abstract term 'love' scarcely occurs (only in Matt.

xxiv. 12 and Luke xi. 42), and the command to love (except in citations from the Old Testament) rarely in set terms, and hardly ever without concrete exemplification. More often love, or charity, is commended by examples of loving or charitable action, as in Matt. xxv. 35–45, Luke x. 30–5, where the kind of action protrayed corresponds closely with the terms of verse 17. The fact is that Christianity derived this advantage from its origin among a people for whom religion was ethical, and morality was expressed in baldly concrete precepts. In rejecting a false legalism, and insisting upon the inwardness of true morality and religion, Christianity still demanded that the spirit of charity should embody itself in definite outward action. To over-spiritualize religion is to weaken it ethically. And so, our author concludes, whether the situation is tragic 18 or commonplace, let us put our love not into words or into talk, but into deeds, and make it real.

3. FELLOWSHIP WITH GOD (iii. 19–24)

Thus it is that we may be sure we belong to the truth and 19 reassure ourselves before Him whenever our heart may 20 condemn us; for God is greater than our heart, and He knows all. If our heart does not condemn us, beloved, then 21 we have confidence in approaching God, and we get from 22 Him whatever we ask, because we obey His commands and do what is pleasing in his sight. Now this is what He com- 23 mands, that we believe in the name of His Son Jesus Christ, and love one another as He has commanded us to do; he 24 who obeys His commands remains within Him—and He remains within him. And this is how we may be sure He remains within us, by means of the spirit He has given us.

This short section consists of a series of loosely connected statements, set forth briefly and baldly, almost as if the author had made notes which he found no time to work up. Six distinct points are made (some of which reiterate what he had said already): (i) the exercise of charity is the sole and sufficient assurance of our Christian standing; (ii) if through scruples of conscience we lack this assurance, we may rest in God's complete knowledge of us; (iii) if the conscience is clear, then we may live a life of frank fellowship with God, in prayer and obedience to His commands; (iv) faith and charity are the sum of God's commands; (v) obedience to God is the self-authenticating form of mystical union; (iv) the gift of the Holy Spirit is the token of such union.

The closing sentence of this section would suggest (in view of his method elsewhere, e.g. ii. 29, iii. 10) that the author was proceeding to a direct treatment of the theme of the Holy Spirit; but he is led off into a digression in iv. 1-6, and then drops that theme in favour of a very important development of the theme of iii. 11-18. In iv. 13 he recurs for a moment to the theme of the Holy Spirit, but again drops it without further discussion. We never get the full treatment of the theme which iii. 24 would lead us to expect, for when it comes up again in v. 6-8 the treatment is allusive rather than explicit.

So far as the present section has a general theme it is that of the Christian's communion with God as his Father—an intercourse of prayer and obedience with One who knows him altogether, in whom he dwells, and who dwells in him through the gift of the Spirit.

Verses 19-20 are obscure and constitute a notorious *crux interpretum*. The varieties of reading offered by some later manuscripts seem to show that the difficulties which we feel were felt also in ancient times, and led to attempts to improve the text. The best manuscripts are to be followed, but they leave us in doubt about the punctuation and connection of clauses, about the construction of certain Greek particles,[1]

---

[1] The particle ὅτι occurs twice. At its second occurrence it is clearly the conjunction meaning 'that' or 'because.' At its first occurrence it might be taken in the same way, with the following ἐάν as the hypothetical conjunction 'if.' In this case the second ὅτι is redundant, resuming the first, a slight irregularity which is not without parallel. But it is also possible that the first ὅτι is intended for the indefinite relative, 'whatever,' and ἐάν for the untranslatable particle ἄν. This latter alternative is assumed in the Moffatt translation (whenever being a legitimate and necessary paraphrase for a construction which cannot be translated directly). It has the advantage of avoiding any grammatical irregularity, though there is an undoubted clumsiness. The former alternative is perhaps simpler, and more in accord with the writer's general usage of these particles. It is impossible to decide between the alternatives on their merits. Either may be adopted as the general run of the passage seems to demand.

and about the sense in which the word here translated **reassure** is to be understood.

To start with the last of these, the Greek verb *peithein* has three main uses: (i) to persuade someone to do something; (ii) to convince someone that such and such a thing is true; (iii) absolutely, to win a person over by persuasion, to 'talk him over,' as we say. The first sense is clearly not in place here. The second is possible, and we should look for a 'that' clause to follow. The third is also possible if we give to the verb the meaning, **reassure** (as Moffatt does); a quite possible extension of meaning, though one for which it is difficult to find an exact parallel.

Then there is the question of the connection of clauses; and first we must ask how the opening clause of verse 19 is to be related to the context. It runs, literally, 'By this we shall know that we are of the truth.' The form of expression is characteristic of this writer; cf. ii. 3, 5–6, iii. 10, 16, 24, iv. 2, 9, 10. Of these the closest in form to our present passage are ii. 3, ii. 5–6, and iii. 24. In each case the writer takes a proposition which might be regarded as disputable, or at least as lying beyond our certain knowledge, and then asserts that it is known to be true upon the ground of some fact attested by experience or observation. Thus (to give a literal rendering): 'By this we know that we know Him—if we keep His commandments'; 'By this we know that we are in Him—he who says he is in Him must walk as He walked'; 'By this we know that He remains in us—from the Spirit He has given us.' The keeping of the commandments, the imitation of Christ, and the possession of the Spirit are matters of experience, and they are the grounds of our knowledge of further truths. In each case the words **by this** refer to what follows.

If we are to be guided by this clue, the passage might be construed as follows: (A) 'By this we shall know that we are of the truth, and shall convince ourselves (of it) in His presence —namely, by the fact that, (even) if our heart condemns us, God is greater than our heart, and knows all.' The clause 'we shall convince ourselves' is an expansion of the idea 'we shall know,' and the (second) 'that' clause refers back to the words 'by this.' The argument would then be something like this: The Christian believes himself to be living within the sphere of 'the truth.' This belief may be challenged, either from without or, more seriously, by doubts within the heart, since conscience may make us uneasy. How shall we deal with such doubts? We can only fall back upon the undoubted fact that God knows us far better than we know ourselves, and leave it to Him. A man's own heart (or 'consciousness') is not after all the final judge: God knows all. We might compare what Paul says in 1 Cor. iv. 4-5: **Although I am not conscious of having anything against me, that does not clear me . . . The hour of reckoning has still to come, when the Lord will come to bring dark secrets to the light**; or, again, we might recall his repeated insistence that whether or not we know God, He knows us (1 Cor. viii. 2-3, xiii. 12, Gal. iv. 9). If we adopt this exegesis, we must suppose that the writer, having set out to show that it is possible to **be sure that we belong to the truth**, draws back, lest he should seem to attribute infallibility to any human judgment. We can be sure of it only in the sense that we can be sure of God. But if this be his meaning, he has expressed himself obscurely, and the transition of thought is extremely abrupt.

It seems better therefore to suppose that in this case, contrary to his usual practice, the writer intends the words 'by this' to refer back to the foregoing verses. There is a parallel in iv. 6. He has there been considering how to distinguish true inspiration from false, and he sums up in conclusion, 'From this we know the spirit of truth and the spirit of error' (namely, by the tests just applied). Upon this analogy we might in the present passage understand the first clause of verse 19 to mean, 'By this (namely, by loving in deed and in truth) we shall know that we belong to the truth'; that is to say, an attitude of genuine charity towards our brothers, such as has just been described, is something concrete and recognizable in experience, and from it we may conclude that **we belong to the truth**. This gives a clear sense, and it is one which is in harmony with judgments expressed in other places of the epistle. We know that we know God, if we keep His commandments (ii. 3); we know that we are in Christ, if we imitate His conduct (ii. 5–6); the children of God are recognized by love to the brethren (iii. 10); we know that we have crossed from death to life because we love our brothers (iii. 14). And so here: we know that we belong to the truth because our love is in deed and not in word alone. There can be little doubt that this is the meaning intended, and it is represented by the Moffatt translation.

The following clauses therefore do not merely carry on the thought of 19*a*, but add something fresh to it. But in what sense? A respectable exegetical tradition, going back to the Greek Fathers, interprets these clauses as a warning: if our own consciences condemn us, much more will the Omniscient, to whom all our faults lie open, condemn us. The conjunction 'and' must then be understood in a virtually adversative sense, almost as if it were 'but' (parallels for this are not wanting). We should then understand the passage as follows: (B) 'By what I have said we may be sure that we belong to the truth. Nevertheless, we shall do well to convince ourselves[1] in His presence; that, if our own heart condemns us, God is greater than our heart, and knows all.' It is a warning against the complacency that may attend upon 'Christian assurance' (as the history of various movements in the Church can attest). The writer has been urging the necessity of absolute sincerity: he now backs up his plea by reminding his readers that they live in the sight of God, the Searcher of hearts. Such a warning would be in harmony with the severity of tone which makes itself heard in verses 3–8, 12, 15, 17. The demands here made for absolute purity and absolute sincerity in love might well arouse searchings of heart, and these searchings would gain penetration from the recollection that they can never exhaust the possibilities of evil in the human heart, evil which may elude our scrutiny, but cannot elude God's. The readers must not be allowed to come too readily to the conclusion that they love in deed and in truth, or that in other respects they are qualified to enjoy the assurance of 'belonging to the truth.'

[1] If the passage is so construed, it would be easier to read, with some inferior manuscripts, the subjunctive, 'let us convince,' rather than the future indicative of the best manuscripts.

But in spite of the recurrent note of severity, it does not seem to be the intention of the passage as a whole to awaken a sense of sin which would amount almost to self-despair. Its main purport is that which is expressed in the words **We are children of God; we know that we have crossed from death to life because we love the brotherhood.** That is to say, the writer seems to assume that his readers are entitled to be sure that they belong to the truth, because (unlike the false teachers) they have a sincere love for the brotherhood. They are not indeed perfect. **If we say, 'We are not guilty'** (he reminded them in i. 8–9), **we are deceiving ourselves.** But in the same breath he reassured them, **if we confess our sins, He is faithful and just, He forgives our sins.** And so here, having contemplated the possibility that our heart may condemn us, he adds the reassurance that God, who is faithful and just, whose children we are, 'knoweth our frame; He remembereth that we are dust' (Ps. ciii. 14).

The passage therefore may be understood as follows: (C1) 'By what I have said we may be sure that we belong to the truth, and reassure our heart in His presence, whenever our heart condemns us; because God is greater than our heart, and knows all'; or, alternatively (C2), 'By what I have said we may be sure that we belong to the truth; and we may convince ourselves in His presence that, (even) if our heart condemns us, God is greater than our heart, and knows all.' There is little to choose between these two renderings. The former is substantially that of Moffatt. In either case the general sense is much the same.

21–22   The writer now brings his readers back to what he must consider, in spite of all our imperfections, the normal state of the Christian life; the state in which we are not under the condemnation of conscience, and have no sense of sinful alienation from God. In this state we live in the free and happy intercourse of children with their Father: we ask Him for what we need, and do as He bids. The sequence of thought (or rather of experience) from verses 19–20 to verses 21–2 may be aptly illustrated from the *Conversations* of Brother Lawrence, who said 'that when he had failed in his duty, he only confessed his fault, saying to God, "I shall never do otherwise, if You leave me to myself; 'tis You must hinder my falling, and mend what is amiss." That after that he gave himself no further uneasiness about it. That we ought to act with God in the greatest simplicity, speaking to Him frankly and plainly, and imploring His assistance in our affairs, just as they happen. That God never failed to grant it, as he had often experienced' (*The Practice of the Presence of God*: Second Conversation). Brother Lawrence's expression, 'to act with God in the greatest simplicity, speaking to Him frankly and plainly,' comes very near to our author's meaning in the words, **We have confidence in approaching God**; for the word rendered **confidence** stood in ancient Greece for the most valued right of a citizen in a free state, the right to 'speak his mind'; and although the meaning of the word became wider and vaguer in course of time, yet there always hangs about it this special association with the thought of freedom of speech, unhampered by fear or shame. In our relation to God such freedom of speech is not an inherent right, but is strictly dependent upon an equally frank and straightforward obedience to the divine will (verse 22).

The assurance that our requests to God will be granted upon this condition finds its justification (as is usual in this epistle) in statements of the Fourth Gospel. In John viii. 28-9 the unbroken communion with God which marked the earthly life of Jesus is grounded in His complete dependence upon, and unswerving obedience to, the Father. **I do nothing of my own accord, but speak as the Father has taught me. He who sent me is at my side; He has not left me alone; for I always do what pleases Him.** Living in this intimate communion, Jesus knows that His prayers are always heard (John xi. 22, 41-2). But, further, His own relation to the Father is archetypal of the relation into which He brings His followers. United with Him in faith, love and obedience, they too may be sure of having their prayers answered. **If you remain in me and my words remain in you, then ask whatever you like, and you shall have it. . . . As the Father has loved Me, so I have loved you; remain within My love. If you keep My commands you will remain** within my love, just as I have kept my Father's commands and remain within His love (John xv. 7, 9–10). The same thought is put in other words in xiv. 14–15: I will do whatever you ask me in my name. If you love me you will keep my commands; and in xvi. 26–7: On that day you will ask in my name, and I do not say to you that I will ask the Father on your behalf; for the Father loves you Himself, because you have loved me and believed that I came forth from God. To pray 'in the name' of Christ is to pray in virtue of our union with Him, and that union is one of love and obedience, in which Christ's love and obedience to the Father are reproduced in us through faith. This whole complex of ideas reappears in a slightly different form in the verses before us. Our requests to God are heard, because we **obey His commands** and (like Christ Himself, John

23 viii. 29), **do what is pleasing in His sight.** And what are those commands? First, that we should have faith in Christ (cf. John xvi. 27), and, secondly, as the proper manifestation of such faith, that we **love one another as He has commanded us to do** (cf. John xv. 12, following upon the assurance of answer to prayer in 7–10). That faith in Christ is a part of the service of God is taught in John vi. 29, while for the close association of faith and charity we may refer to Gal. v. 6: **'faith active in love'** is a Pauline definition of the Christian

24a life which our author would readily have accepted. Finally, in simple obedience to the commands of God (of Christ) we recognize the reality of that intimate union between God and His children which is described as a mutual indwelling (cf., again, John xv. 7–10).

Verse 24*b* forms (once again after our author's manner) a transition from the theme of iii. 19–24*a* to that of iv. 1–6, which is an almost parenthetical section.

With the words **remains within Him,** we have been brought back to an idea which played a prominent part in earlier sections of the epistle. It was first introduced at ii. 6, where we saw reason to suspect an allusion to the misuse of 'mystical' language by the heretical teachers. Their claim to 'remain in' Christ—that is, to be in mystical union with Him—can be allowed only if they imitate His example. In the verses which follow, another expression is substituted: 'to remain in the light,' and the writer insists that to be in the light necessarily means to obey the command of love. The subject is then dropped for a time; but in ii. 24-9 we are brought back to it. Here we learn that the condition of 'remaining in the Son and the Father' is that the Word of God, or the 'chrism,' should remain in us. In other words, there is no union with God in Christ which is not conditioned by loyal adhesion to the Gospel, in which is included the 'new command' of love. Then the idea of 'indwelling' gives place to that of divine generation, and this in turn is brought into connection with the command of love. The thought is developed that the only sure proof by which we may know that we have been born into the life of God is to be found in our love for our brothers. And then, finally, the thought thus developed is linked with the earlier line of thought by recalling the language of 'indwelling': **He who obeys His commands remains within Him—and He remains within him** (iii. 24*a*). This is a virtual reassertion of what has already been said; but it is designed to lead up to the very profound and significant conclusion in iv. 7-12, where the doctrines of divine generation and divine indwelling are shown to be rooted in the conception of the divine nature as love, and consequently to involve by logical necessity the obligation of mutual love among those who are the objects of the love of God.

Meanwhile, however, the author is reminded that there is another aspect in which the new life in Christ can be represented (beside regeneration and the mutual indwelling of Christ and the believer)—namely, the possession of the Holy Spirit. This is a part of the primitive Gospel (**that which you learned from the very beginning**). In the speech of Peter at Pentecost, which is a kind of programme of the apostolic Preaching, the gift of the Spirit is an integral part of the **triumphs of God** (Acts ii. 11), by which the redemption of man has been effected: **This Jesus God raised, as we can all bear witness. Uplifted then by God's right hand, and receiving from the Father the long-promised Holy Spirit, He has poured on us what you now see and hear** (Acts ii. 32-3). In Paul the Spirit is represented as the mode of Christ's indwelling in the Church. In the Fourth Gospel the Spirit, conceived in fully personal terms as the Paraclete, is the abiding representative of Christ, in whom He Himself returns to His flock, to help, guide and enlighten them, and through them to reveal to the world the true nature of sin and righteousness and the reality of the divine judgment (John xvi. 7–15). It is remarkable that in this epistle there is little trace of the 'high' Pauline and Johannine doctrines of the Spirit. The thought is closer to the level of primitive Christianity, as it is represented in the Acts of the Apostles and inferred from allusions in the Pauline epistles. The Spirit is there primarily the spirit of prophecy —that is to say, an afflatus, or 'inspiration,' granted to certain individuals, 'prophets,' by which the truth of the Gospel is confirmed to those who hear (Acts v. 32; cf. 1 John v. 6). So here, the fact of the mutual indwelling of Christ and His people is confirmed by the gift of the Spirit, which is (as in Gal. iii. 2) a *datum* of experience from which an inference can be drawn. But since it is fatally easy to mistake a false 'inspiration' for the true, it is necessary to consider how the two are to be distinguished, and this leads to a digression in the verses which follow.

EXCURSUS ON INSPIRATION, TRUE AND FALSE (iv. 1–6)

iv.

1 Do not believe every spirit, beloved, but test the spirits to see if they come from God; for many false prophets have emerged
2 in the world. You can recognize the Spirit of God by this: every spirit which confesses Jesus as the Christ incarnate comes
3 from God, and every spirit which does not confess Jesus incarnate does not come from God. This latter is the spirit of antichrist; you were told it was coming, and here it is
4 already in the world. Dear children, you belong to God, and you have conquered all such, for He who is within you is greater than he who is in the world.
5 They belong to the world,
therefore they speak as inspired by the world,
and the world listens to them:

we belong to God—   6
   he who knows God listens to us,
   he who does not belong to God does not listen to us.
This is how we recognize the spirit of truth and the spirit of
error.

This section presupposes that the Church still has experience, as in the time of Paul, of inspired prophetic utterance by
its members. A study of 1 Cor. xiv. is a valuable preparation
for understanding the situation here contemplated. That
chapter has much to say of the extreme form of 'inspired'
utterance known as 'speaking with tongues.' That phenomenon no longer plays a part here. But over against this
irrational and unintelligible type of 'inspiration' Paul sets the
rational and intelligible 'inspiration' of prophecy, by which the
Church is instructed and 'built up' (1 Cor. xiv. 1–5). The
actual effect of prophecy is vividly described in 1 Cor. xiv.
24–5: If everybody prophesies, and some unbeliever or outsider
comes in, he is exposed by all, brought to book by all; the
secrets of his heart are brought to light, and so, falling on his
face, he will worship God, declaring, 'God is really among you.'
Observe here the two functions of the Spirit of prophecy: to
mediate divine judgment (as in John xvi. 8–11); and to
demonstrate the reality of the divine presence in the Church
(as iii. 24, above). Even prophecy, however, is not necessarily
to be taken at its face value. It is subject to criticism. Let only
two or three prophets speak, while the rest exercise their judgment upon what is said (1 Cor. xiv. 29). To what extraordinary
lengths uncontrolled 'inspiration' might go is indicated by
1 Cor. xii. 3, where Paul contemplates the possibility of an
'inspired' person crying out, 'Cursed be Jesus!' Such an utterance he would no doubt class with the irrational 'speaking with
tongues.' A prophet would hardly be guilty of such an aberra-
tion, since prophets can control their own prophetic spirits
(1 Cor. xiv. 32). But even prophecy is not always on the same
level of truth or 'edification.'
   We now turn to the situation contemplated in our epistle.
The danger, always present, of a false inspiration has been

realized. Many false prophets have emerged in the world (iv. 1),
or, to translate more literally, have gone out into the world;
have gone out, that is to say, from the Church and in its name
(cf. 2 John 7 and note). They are the heretical teachers already
referred to in ii. 18–19. They had been, nominally, members of
the Church, but, says our author, they can never have been
true members of the Church, else they would never have
separated themselves from it (ii. 19). No; their spiritual home
is the pagan world; the sources of their teaching are pagan;
and for that reason they find ready acceptance in the pagan
world (iv. 5). The description would fit the 'Gnostics' whose
teachings we know, for we must conclude that in most of them
the pagan element is their real basis, and the Christian element
a comparatively ineffective appendage. Some of them (not all)
no doubt intended, by 'reinterpreting' Christianity in 'Gnostic'
terms, to commend the Gospel to the pagan world. Our
evidence suggests that for a time their missionary activities
made a wide appeal, and seriously rivalled those of orthodox
Christianity, with its conservatism and intransigence in the
face of the religious tendencies of the time. When our information becomes copious, towards the end of the second century,
the Church is almost 'out of the wood,' but behind this
appears to lie a period in which central or traditional Christianity had its back to the wall, and saw the increasing success
of these compromising systems. That period is but faintly
illuminated for us. We may take our present passage as
representing an early stage in it.

The forerunners of second-century 'Gnosticism' have only
just declared themselves, and left the Church. They appeared
as prophets, speaking under inspiration. It may be suggested
that much of the fantastic material of 'Gnostic' literature could
well be understood as originating in the unbridled enthusiasm
of 'inspired' men, who claimed special 'revelations' of the unseen world, such revelations having been later organized by a
misplaced ingenuity into the elaborate systems known to us
from Irenaeus and Hippolytus. Our author is confronted by
this phenomenon: men speaking apparently under an inspiration as real as that of any Christian prophet, and yet proclaim-

ing doctrines which he knew to be radically un-Christian. Whatever their claims to inspiration, he could not regard their teaching as other than 'of the world'—that is, pagan in essence; and their success with the pagan public he could only regard as proof of a fundamental affinity with paganism. And yet these men were prophets; they were 'inspired.' He could not deny it. Their utterances had all the familiar marks of 'inspiration.' No wonder simple-minded believers were impressed by them, and wavered in their convictions. How was the situation to be met?

For an answer to the problem, he goes back to the principle, long recognized, that prophecy is subject to criteria lying outside the mere fact of its 'inspired' character. 'Inspiration' as such is not a criterion of truth. **Do not believe every spirit, but** 1 **test the spirits to see if they come from God,** for there is diabolical as well as divine inspiration. What then is the test? Paul had laid down the principle: **No one is speaking in the Spirit of God when he cries, 'Cursed be Jesus'; and no one can say, 'Jesus is Lord,' except in the holy Spirit** (1 Cor. xii. 3). But this criterion now needs to be made more precise, in the light of the developed theology of the Church (especially in its Johannine form). The heretics also might say, '**Jesus is Lord,'** but they would not mean by it what the Church meant. To 2 confess Jesus as Lord, in the sense of the Church's faith, is to confess Him as the Son of God incarnate. Whatever else the heretics might affirm of Christ, they would not confess the reality of the Incarnation. By that test their teaching, however powerfully 'inspired,' was condemned. The spirit by which 3 they spoke was not the Spirit of God. It was the spirit of Antichrist (see ii. 18-19, and notes). As such, it represented the most deadly assault of the powers of evil against the Church of Christ—and an assault, let us remember, which at the time looked like succeeding, for **the world listens to them** (5). The readers therefore must be reminded of that assurance of victory over 'the world' (over the forces of paganism, and consequently over the insidious propaganda of paganism under Christian colours) which is, as they have already been told, an essential part of the Gospel (see ii. 12-14, and notes). All that

4 they need to know is, **You belong to God,** and it follows, **You have conquered all such, for He who is within you is greater than he who is in the world** (i.e. the Evil One, v. 19). (All that is implied in the expressions **You belong to God** and **He is within you,** has already been set forth, and the readers are 5 expected to have it in mind). As for the success of the heretical propaganda, if **the world listens to them,** it is true on the other 6 hand that **he who knows God listens to us.** (The first personal pronoun plural here stands for the Church as a whole, speaking through its responsible teachers, who embody the authentic apostolical tradition.)

5–6   The line is drawn, in the spirit of ii. 15–17, with the utmost sharpness. On the one side is the pagan world, including, as we now know, the heretical teachers with their semi-pagan doctrines. On the other side is the Church affirming the true faith. The antithesis is absolute: **they belong to the world, therefore they speak as inspired by the world, and the world listens to them: we belong to God—he who knows God listens to us; he who does not belong to God does not listen to us.**

If these words are taken in their strict literal sense, they would seem to imply that missions to the pagan world have no chance of success, since the 'world' lies wholly in **the power of the Evil one** (v. 19), and therefore does not belong to God, and cannot hear the word of God. The writer obviously does not mean that. He is speaking out of the experience of Christian missionaries and teachers. The Gospel is proclaimed broadcast. Some respond to it, as though they had a natural affinity with it. Others remain untouched, as though there was nothing in them to respond; or, worse still, they make an apparent response, and enter the Church, only to lend a ready ear to semi-pagan teaching, thereby proving that their affinity is with the 'world.' Before the message was heard, there was nothing to distinguish these two classes of persons. When they had heard it, the difference between them became manifest. If the question were asked, Why did A receive and B reject the same message, proclaimed to both in the same terms and under the same conditions? there seemed to be no answer except that they were that kind of people: A was already a potential Christian (*'anima naturaliter Christiana'*); B was not.

There is a similar implication in those passages of the Fourth Gospel which speak of Christ's **other sheep** who have yet to be brought into His fold (x. 16), and of the **scattered children of God** whom Christ must gather in (xi. 52). The emphasis is different. The Evangelist has his eye upon people in the Gentile world, who, although outside the Jewish 'fold,' were within the scope of Christ's saving work just as much as those among whom He lived. That is to say, the statements are meant positively and inclusively, without attention to their negative and exclusive implications. Yet they do suggest that there are in the world people who are, so to speak, predestined Christians. But the very use of the term 'predestined' is a warning that we are approaching one of the irresolvable antinomies of human existence, the problem of 'fate, foreknowledge and freewill,' which the devils discussed in Pandemonium 'and found no end, in wandering mazes lost.' If the antithesis is stated absolutely, and understood as a metaphysical principle, then we fall into the Gnostic dualism, which held that certain souls were created from the first 'receptive of the Seed,' and others not (see notes on iii. 9. Upon our author's attitude to this dualism, see notes on ii. 15–18).

It must be admitted that he has expressed himself somewhat incautiously; but he is not intending precise philosophical statement, and should not be held committed to the apparently logical implications of what he says. He has his eye upon the actual situation. Empirically, it is true that there is a diversity in the response of different people to the Word of God, which cannot be explained beyond saying that they are that kind of people. Many centuries of experience have taught us that a negative response may often be due to a defect in the preacher's presentation of the message, or to his failure to understand sympathetically the people to whom he appeals. Not all heresy and unbelief are exhibitions of a radical affinity with 'the world,' or hostility to God. Yet, when all allowance is made, there is here a mystery beyond our understanding. Even as proclaimed by our Lord Himself, the Gospel was 'hidden from the wise and prudent and revealed to babes' (Matt. xi. 25), and in spite of all complications and obfuscations, men do come face to face with the truth, and, for ultimate reasons which we cannot penetrate, range themselves by their response to it.

Our author's immediate intention, however, is not to deal with this mystery. It is to reassure those who are perturbed by the success of semi-pagan teaching. That success was only to be expected in a world like this. But it is limited by the fact that God has those who belong to Him, and *they* cannot be misled. And since He is greater than he who is in the world, the final victory must lie with Him. To this we may surely add that this victory must involve the salvation of the world itself (ii. 2, iv. 14), and so, in some way beyond our understanding, the salvation of those who belong to the world, and appear at present as irredeemable enemies of the truth.

6b   Verse 6b sums up the purport of the section. The word this clearly refers (contrary to the author's usual practice) to what precedes. The reference is not to the immediately preceding sentence taken alone, but to the section as a whole. It deals with the problem of 'inspired' utterances which convey false doctrine. Such inspiration, it is assumed, is diabolical and not divine, and the test by which true inspiration may be distinguished from false is the conformity of its deliverances with the fundamental faith of the Church, set forth by its responsible teachers. It is interesting to recall a somewhat similar treatment of the problem of false prophecy in the Old Testament. Several of the greater prophets are troubled by the appearance of men whose inspiration is superficially similar to their own, while their influence upon the people is disastrous. In Deut. xiii. 1–5 the case is contemplated of a prophet who attempts to lead the people into idolatry, and it is laid down that even though his word should be confirmed by signs and wonders, he is to be rejected. (We may fairly conjecture that such cases had occurred.) This affords a real parallel to the treatment of the matter in the passage before us. The fundamental doctrine of Judaism is monotheism; no utterance, however inspired, which contradicts the principle of monotheism can be accepted as true prophecy. The fundamental doctrine of Christianity is the Incarnation; no utterance, however inspired, which denies the reality of the Incarnation, can be accepted by Christians as true prophecy. Both religions recognize the freedom of the Spirit, and both owe something of their essential character to its exercise. But both of necessity draw a line beyond which such freedom is restrained by the demands of some fundamental truth.

In order to appreciate the significance of the passage before us, it will be well to consider further the history of prophecy in the Christian Church. In the early Church, as we know it from the Pauline epistles and the Acts of the Apostles, great store was set upon what are called 'spiritual gifts,' among which Paul includes both moral and spiritual qualities like knowledge, wisdom and faith, and what we may describe by contrast as abnormal phenomena, like spiritual healing, prophecy and speaking with tongues. Among the abnormal gifts he recognizes prophecy as having the greatest value for the building up of the life of the Church. (1 Cor. xii. 8-11, xiv. 1-5). He also places prophets along with apostles and teachers as persons specially endowed for the ministry of the Church (1 Cor. xii. 28, Eph. iv. 11). All this careful distinction and grading of spiritual gifts is, so far as we know, part of Paul's personal contribution to the doctrine of the Spirit and the Church. At the beginning, to judge from the report in Acts, the outpouring of the Spirit was regarded as the normal accompaniment of baptism into the Christian Church, and the various 'spiritual gifts' might manifest themselves indiscriminately in the same or in different persons. The apostles in particular possessed not only that peculiar 'grace' of apostleship which Paul distinguishes from other gifts (Rom. i. 5), but also the gifts of healing and of speaking with tongues, and (we may assume though it is not directly stated) of prophetic utterance. That which distinguished the Twelve from other persons to whom inspiration is attributed (such as Stephen and his colleagues, Acts vi. 3, 5, vii. 55) was not so much any peculiarity in spiritual endowment as their qualification to witness to the Gospel facts (Acts i. 21–2).

During the whole of the apostolic age inspired utterance, having the direct and enthusiastic quality associated with Old Testament prophecy, played an important part in forming and guiding the life and thought of the Church, and its importance outlasted that of the other 'abnormal' gifts. But in the course of the second century we find prophecy taking more and more a subordinate position. The attempt at a prophetic revival known as Montanism failed to win the support of the Church at large, and its failure served further to depreciate that type of inspiration. It is thus certain that prophecy declined (whether for good or ill) between the apostolic age and the close of the second century. The stages in that decline are not all clear. The passage with which we are dealing may throw some light upon it. It implies that spiritual gifts, and in particular prophecy, are still a part of the living experience of the Church, but its effect is to establish a somewhat drastic control of the freedom of prophetic utterance, by the standard of a rule of faith, and by the authority of an acknowledged ministry.

It is to be remembered that from the beginning Christianity was not to be defined exclusively as a 'religion of the Spirit.' Prophets had an important rôle, but they were subordinate to apostles: 'First apostles, then prophets' is the order (1 Cor. xii. 28, and so in all relevant passages). Though the clarification of the position may be due to Paul, it is clear that, from the first, prophets who were not also apostles were in some sense subordinate to the Twelve. This was not because their spiritual endowment was inferior, but because the apostles possessed a peculiar qualification which could not be shared by others. They were the primary witnesses to the evangelical facts by which the Church was constituted. Thus prophecy was never fully autonomous, nor were prophets ever exempt from criticism by virtue of their inspiration. In the earliest extant Christian writing, Paul both affirms the value of prophecy and prescribes criticism of its deliverances: **Never quench the fire of the Spirit; never disdain prophetic revelations, but test them all,**

retaining **what is good, and abstaining from whatever kind is
evil** (1 Thess. v. 19–21). The criterion which he recommended,
as we have seen, is conformity with the fundamental Christian
affirmation 'Jesus is Lord.' Behind that affirmation lies the
total content of the Gospel, which in the last resort rests upon
the apostolic testimony. In a Pauline formula, the Church
is built upon the twofold foundation of apostles and prophets
(Eph. ii. 20), the apostles representing the authority of
primary witness to the Gospel facts, while prophets represent
the living guidance of the Spirit by which the facts were apprehended in ever fuller meaning and scope.

There was, however, always the possibility of tension between the spontaneity of prophecy and the principle of
authority embodied in the apostolic witness to the Gospel.
That tension revealed itself when persons who had secured
recognition as prophets put forth teaching which was opposed
to fundamental elements in the evangelical tradition. Such is
the situation contemplated in this epistle. It was one of extreme danger to the Church. The freedom of the Spirit was the
life-blood of Christianity, and yet that freedom was being used
to disintegrate the life of the Church. In fact, one side of the
twofold foundation upon which the Church was built was
crumbling. In face of this danger the writer falls back upon the
other side, the apostolic witness to the evangelical facts—
**what we heard, what we saw with our eyes, what we wit-
nessed and touched with our own hands** (i. 1), **the word which
you heard** (ii. 7), **that which you learned from the very beginning** (ii. 24). From the first the apostolic Gospel, which brought
the life of the Church into being, was prior to prophecy, in
which that life found expression. That priority now becomes
of direct practical importance. The writer has no wish to
see prophecy suppressed or discredited. On the contrary, he
would secure the value of prophecy in the Church by distinguishing true inspiration from false. In a situation of almost
desperate gravity it was a matter of life and death to establish
the principle that 'inspiration' does not in itself provide a
guarantee of truth. A man may possess an exalted sense of
direct guidance and enlightenment by the Spirit of God, and

the freedom and enthusiasm with which he speaks may persuade his hearers that he is indeed one of those whom 'God
whispers in the ear'; and yet it may all have nothing to do with
genuine Christianity. That alone is Christian which coheres,
intellectually and morally, with the fundamental facts of the
Gospel; and those facts we know, in the last resort, only
through the witness of the apostles, transmitted to us by such
channels as are available.

Here we have the basis of that appeal to apostolic testimony
which was powerfully developed by Christian teachers of the
second century in the conflict with 'Gnostic' heresy, and led to
the safeguarding of the tradition by the threefold defence of
the Creed, the succession of the Ministry and the Canon of the
New Testament. The history of the Church shows that this
appeal to tradition could work in the direction of a sterile
institutionalism, robbing the Church of the freedom of the
Spirit which is its birthright: it shows also that enthusiasm,
mystical experience, assurance of special guidance, and all the
marks of inspiration, may be associated with doctrines sub-
versive of the Gospel. The tension between authority and
freedom, between tradition and inspiration, cannot safely be
resolved either by the repudiation of authority or by the
repression of inspiration. The Church fares best when apostle
and prophet stand together as the firm foundation of its life.

4. THE LOVE OF GOD (iv. 7–12)

7 **Beloved, let us love one another, for love belongs to God, and**
8 **everyone who loves is born of God and knows God; he who**
9 **does not love, does not know God, for God is love. This is**
how the love of God has appeared for us, by God sending
His only Son into the world, so that by Him we might
10 **live. Love lies in this, not in our love for Him, but in His**
love for us—in the sending of His Son to be the propitiation
11 **for our sins. Beloved, if God had such love for us, we**
12 **ought to love one another. God no one has ever seen; but**
if we love one another, then God remains within us,
and love for Him is complete in us.

Verses 1–6 have been in the nature of a parenthesis, dictated by the necessity of removing any possible misunderstanding of the appeal to the witness of the Spirit in iv. 24. We now return to the main theme.

The position has already been established that any real relation to God—whether we express it as 'knowing God,' or as 'remaining in Him,' or as being 'born of God'—involves obedience to His commands; and that His supreme and all-inclusive command is **that we love one another.** All this is now succinctly expressed in the words, **Let us love one another, for love belongs to God, and everyone who loves is born of God, and knows God; he who does not love, does not know God.** Then the writer adds a theological statement of the utmost importance, which provides the final justification for the teaching he has given: **for God is love.**

In its form, this statement might appear to identify God with an abstract principle, and so to imply an impersonal conception of Deity (the same might be said of his other statement, **God is light** (i. 5)). But it is clear that this is not the writer's intention; for in the context he speaks of **the love of God,** and says that love **belongs to God,** and that **God had love for us.** God therefore is presented as the personal Subject of the act of loving. Yet the proposition, **God is love,** is clearly intended to go further than the proposition 'God loves us.' What is its meaning?

Christianity always presupposes the Hebrew conception of Deity as the 'living God.' In the Old Testament there is little or no speculation about the nature of God as He is in Himself. He is known to men in His actions as the Creator of the world, Ruler of mankind, and the King and Saviour of His people. History is the field of His self-revelation, and communion with Him is conditioned by obedience to His commands. Accordingly, the Word of God is not primarily the communication of knowledge about the divine nature; it is active energy by which the world was made and is sustained, and by which men are called into active fellowship with God in carrying out His purpose. If therefore we ask what God is, the answer must be given in terms of what He does. He creates and sustains the universe; He judges the world in righteousness; He succours men in distress; He guides those who submit to His will; He forgives the repentant; and the like. Now Christianity takes over this Hebrew conception of the 'living God.' It is implied in the Gospel teaching about the Kingdom of God; for the idea of the Kingdom of God is essentially dynamic, not static. The Kingdom is something that *comes*, as an event in history. Its coming means that God has acted, for the fulfilment of His purpose. The Kingdom of God came with Christ. Consequently the character of His action is to be discovered from the life, teaching, sufferings, death and resurrection of Jesus Christ. If this is to be put in terms of the 'Word of God' (as defined in the Old Testament), it may be expressed in the proposition that 'the Word was made flesh' in Jesus Christ.

What, then, is God's 'word' to men? Or, to put the same question in another form, What is the character of that divine action which is the coming of His Kingdom? The answer given in the Fourth Gospel is: **God loved the world so dearly that He gave up His only Son, so that everyone who believes in Him may have eternal life, instead of perishing** (John iii. 16; a passage obviously alluded to in our present passage, verse 9). The Word of God to men is love; the coming of His Kingdom is an act of love. Hence, if we ask, What is God's nature? the answer must be given in terms of love.

Over against the Hebrew conception of the 'living God' we may set the highly abstract conception of Deity which is characteristic of much Greek thought. Here the term 'God' stands for absolute Being, timeless, changeless, unmoved, and best described by negation of all that belongs to our sensible experience of the world. But in the period to which the Johannine writings belong some Hellenistic thinkers were feeling after a less abstract conception. Thus a writer in the Hermetic Corpus uses the argument that the universe implies the existence of a Creator, whose 'essence' is just the fact that He creates. 'And if you compel me to speak more boldly, it is His essence to produce and create all things. And just as it is impossible for anything to exist without a maker, so it is impossible for the Creator to exist without perpetually making everything' (*Corp. Herm.*, V. 9). Another says, 'As man cannot live without life, so God cannot live without making what is good. For it is this that is God's life, as it were; His movement, as it were; to cause all things to move and live' (*Corp. Herm.*, XI. 17). The tendency of such thought is towards the position that if you can describe God's characteristic activity, as, for instance, that of creating the world, or of giving life, or of originating goodness, you may at once transfer this to the definition of His Being, since 'being self-operating He always exists in His work' (*Corp. Herm.*, XI. 14). Thus, you can say, 'This is life; this is the beautiful; this is the Good; this is God' (*Corp. Herm.*, XI. 13).

Such attempts to define the divine nature no longer confine the idea of God to that of abstract Being. Whether or not this movement in Hellenistic thought was stimulated by contact with Judaism, it clearly comes nearer to the Hebraic strain in both Judaism and Christianity; but it stops short of ascribing personality to God, and makes God and the world mutually dependent in a way strange to Hebrew and Christian thought.

As we have seen, the writer of this epistle shows several signs of contact with Hellenistic religious thought. It is therefore permissible to understand his doctrine that **God is love** from the kind of teaching just referred to. If we say that God must be defined in terms of His characteristic activity—as life, because His activity is manifested in the life of created beings, or as the Good, because all good is His work—then the Christian, who believes that God loved the world, may define God as love; not meaning thereby to identify God with an abstraction, but meaning (to adapt the Hermetic formula) that His 'essence' is to love.

But there is something further to be noted. All Hellenistic thought shrinks from ascribing personality to God. Though its exponents may use the language appropriate to personality, they almost always betray in the end an unwillingness to take such language with full seriousness. And in the activities which they attribute to the Divine there is nothing that logically compels us to conceive it as personal. A 'life-force' or an 'Idea of the Good' would be enough. But if the characteristic divine activity is that of loving, then God must be personal, for we cannot be loved by an abstraction, or by anything less than a person. Thus even in using an abstract term the writer is not reducing God to an abstraction, since he is to be understood (on the analogy suggested) as attributing to God an activity which is radically personal.

We are now in a position to say what is implied in the statement 'God is love,' over and above what is implied in the statement 'God loves.' The latter statement might stand alongside other statements, such as 'God creates,' 'God rules,' 'God judges'; that is to say, it means that love is *one* of His activities. But to say 'God is love' implies that *all* His activity is loving activity. If He creates, He creates in love; if He rules, He rules in love; if He judges, He judges in love. All that He does is the expression of His nature, which is—to love. The theological consequences of this principle are far-reaching.

9- 10 Verse 9 is a restatement of the great Johannine declaration of the love of God (John iii. 16) in terms differing only slightly from the form given in the Fourth Gospel. It reminds us once again that in speaking of the love of God we are thinking of loving *action*, definite, concrete and recognizable on the historical plane (see iii. 16 and notes). Verse 10 underlines one point in this declaration which is of fundamental importance: the Christian religion starts not with man's love for God, but with God's love for man, and with God's love expressed in specific action in history.

This differentiates the specifically Christian experience from all kinds of erotic mysticism, the classical expression of which is to be found in Plato's *Symposium*. Plato takes as the primitive type of love, sexual desire, which is a passionate craving for beauty. But beyond physical beauty, beyond the beauty of the mind and soul, lies Beauty itself, 'that beauty which always is, never coming into being or passing away, neither growing nor diminishing. . . . It will not be present to the imagination as a face, or hands, or anything else which is bodily; nor again as thought, or knowledge of any kind; nor does it exist in something other than itself, as in an animal, or in earth or heaven, or anything else; but it always **is**, itself in itself and by itself, sole and unique' (*Symp.*, 210e–211b). 'What then do we think,' he continues, 'if it should fall to the lot of a man to behold Beauty itself, absolute, pure and unalloyed . . . if he could contemplate divine Beauty itself in its uniqueness?' The answer is that 'he if any man is dear to God and immortal' (*ib.*, 211d–212a).

This aesthetic and passionate mysticism is turned by Aristotle into a metaphysical doctrine of the relation of God to the world. God is absolute Reality, and therefore changeless and unmoved. Yet He is the cause of all change and movement in the universe. But how? 'He moves the world as being the Object of its love (or desire)' (*Metaphysics*, XII. 7). Love therefore becomes a cosmic principle, and the mystical craving for union with the eternal is given a metaphysical basis. The type of religion to which this language belongs is not only Greek. It is an an extremely widespread type. In such religion love is essentially the love of man for God—that is to say, the insatiable craving of limited, conditioned, and temporal beings for the Infinite, the Absolute, the Eternal. Love for man cannot be attributed to God, for the Absolute must be passionless and unmoved.

This way of thinking was certainly dominant in the religious world of Hellenism, though actual religious experience kept breaking away from it in various ways. Over against it stands 10 the Christian affirmation: **Love lies in this, not in our love for Him, but in His love for us.** Appropriately, a different word is used for 'love.' In Plato and Aristotle, as in Greek religious writers usually, the word is *érōs*, a term connoting primarily sexual desire. Here, as all through the New Testament, the word is *agapé*. The noun is scarcely found in non-biblical Greek. The verb generally has such meanings as 'to be content with,' 'to like,' 'to esteem,' 'to prefer.' It is a comparatively cool and colourless word. It is this word, with its noun, that the translators of the Old Testament used by preference for the love of God to man and man's response, and by doing so they began to fill it with a distinctive content for which pagansim, even in its highest forms, had no proper expression. In the New Testament this fresh content is enlarged and intensified through meditation upon the meaning of the death of Christ. As Paul puts it, **God proves his love for us by this, that Christ died for us when we were still sinners** (Rom. v. 8); and our present author similarly, **We know what love is by this, that He laid down His life for us** (iii. 16: see note, pp. 84–5). The meaning of the word must in fact be understood from the Gospel itself; and the pith and marrow of the Gospel is this: **God's sending of His Son to be the propitiation for our sins.** The meaning of the word traditionally (but infelicitously) translated **propitiation** is explained in the note on ii. 2. It means that the coming of Christ, and in particular His death 'for our sins, according to the scriptures' (1 Cor. xv. 3), constitutes the means by which we are cleansed from the taint of sin, and enter into the sphere of divine forgiveness, with the newness of life that it brings. That God provided such means for us, at such a cost, indicates what is meant by the love of God.

11 After what has just been said, the command of love comes with greater cogency than ever. Already in iii. 16 it has been enforced by the example of Christ's sacrifice. That sacrifice has now been shown to express the 'essence' of God Himself as love. It can now be very plainly seen that the **new command** is no arbitrary or optional addition to the original Gospel (ii. 7). For the Gospel is the proclamation of the love of God—of God Himself as love—and consequently to accept the Gospel is to place ourselves under the obligation of love to our fellow men. Indeed, such love is the appointed way of communion with

12 God. The mystics talk of the 'vision of God,' but in fact **God no one has ever seen** (as the Fourth Gospel also declares, i. 18). We may recall that for Plato the love of divine Beauty culminates in 'beholding' it, 'absolute, pure and unalloyed.' The New Testament, however, is notably reticent about the vision of God. Here again it carries forward the thought of the Old Testament. In Hebrew religion hearing, not seeing, is the key to religious experience. Communion with God is a matter of 'hearing the word of the Lord'—that is, receiving from Him the knowledge of His will, and ordering one's life according to it. This is true blessedness: 'Blessed are they that hear the word

of God and keep it' (Luke xi. 28). This saying of our Lord sanctions the Hebrew outlook in religion, which is also the Christian. The promise 'They shall see God' in Matt. v. 8 refers to the blessed 'life of the age to come.' In so far as the age to come has already dawned upon the world in the coming of Christ, the Fourth Gospel finds a place for the vision of God, not in the sense of mystical rapture, but in the sense that in the incarnate Christ we behold the glory of the Lord: **He who has seen me has seen the Father** (John xiv. 9). There is indeed a hint of fuller vision in the life after death (John xvii. 24), and this hint is taken up in our epistle (iii. 2; see note). But in Gospel and Epistle alike the direct mystical vision of God as a goal of religious aspiration in this life is set aside. It is the 'Word' of God that comes to us in Christ. That word is a word of love. Communion with God, therefore, is established in the act of loving. **If we love one another, then God remains in us, and love for Him is complete in us.** The last clause is virtually repeated from ii. 5. There the completion of love resides in keeping the word of God. We now know that the word of God to us is both the expression of His love for us and at the same time the command to love one another. Hence love to God, which has no meaning apart from obedience, is completed in loving our fellows.

III. THE CERTAINTY OF THE FAITH (iv. 13 – v. 13)

We now begin the third and last main division of the Epistle, which has its character from the great affirmations in which it culminates in v. 4–12. The division is not (here or anywhere else in the Epistle) clear-cut. It appears, however, that it was the author's intention to lead up to a conclusion affirming the certainty of the faith, at a moment when many minds were made doubtful or hesitant by the doctrinal disputes which had broken out; and we may mark at this point the transition to this final theme. Already in iii. 19–24 the writer had begun to speak of 'assurance' and 'confidence,' and apparently his intention was to turn at iii. 24*b* to the theme of the witness of the Spirit, which in the Epistle as we have it forms part of the concluding passage (v. 7). Thus the last main division might have been made to begin at iii. 19. But after iii. 24*b* the author was diverted to the distinction between the true witness of the Spirit and its counterfeit (iv. 1–6), after which, feeling that his treatment of the theme of divine love (iii. 1–18) was not yet complete, he added a passage (iv. 7–12) which provides its indispensable culmination. This passage, therefore, cannot be separated from the second main division of the Epistle. At iv. 13 wè are back at the same point as iii. 24*b*, and the theme of divine love now passes (though with many backward references) into that of the certainty of the faith.

I. THE NATURE AND GROUNDS OF CHRISTIAN ASSURANCE
(iv. 13–18)

13 This is how we may be sure we remain in Him and He in us,
14   because He has given us a share in His own Spirit; and we have seen, we do testify, that the Father has sent the Son
15   as the Saviour of the world. Whoever confesses that 'Jesus is the Son of God,' in him God remains, and he remains in
16   God; well, we do know, we have believed, the love God has for us. God is love, and he who remains in love remains in
17   God, and God remains in him. Love is complete with us when we have absolute confidence about the day of judg-
18   ment, since in this world we are living as He lives. Love has no dread in it; no, love in its fulness drives all dread away, for dread has to do with punishment—anyone who has dread, has not reached the fulness of love.

We are now to have a full and final treatment of the subject which is one of the main themes of the epistles: that of union with God, expressed in terms of mutual indwelling; and, more particularly, in terms of the question (already posed and answered in various ways in ii. 5, iii. 24), how we may be sure that we remain in Him. After the disclosure of the supreme truth that God is love, it is possible at last to give an entirely satisfying answer to that question. This is how we may be sure we remain in Him and He in us—the word 'this' refers to what follows, and in the first place to the next clause—because He

has given us a share in His Spirit—which is only a slightly expanded repetition of the statement in iii. 24. But we shall do well to regard the whole passage down to verse 16 as giving, in effect, the grounds of assurance.

The first ground, then, is the gift of the Spirit. When this **13** aspect of the Christian life was mentioned before (at iii. 24), the writer was diverted from his immediate purpose by the necessity for distinguishing sharply between genuine divine inspiration and its counterfeit. Now he restates his point positively. He does not, however, develop it, and it remains somewhat obscure. The first mention of the Spirit, in iii. 24, at once suggested to him the Spirit of prophecy, and he pursued that subject in the following verses. But it is not clear that this was his first intention. Prophecy, indeed, was for early Christians a powerful proof of the presence of God in the Church (cf. 1 Cor. xiv. 24–5). But in iii. 24 it is the individual Christian (within the fellowship of the Church) who is the subject of that union with God described as mutual indwelling; and it is of this that the gift of the Spirit is a proof. Although in the present passage the verb is plural, the reference would seem to be the same. Prophecy is after all only one of the manifestations of the Spirit, and behind all such manifestations lies the fundamental experience which is described by Paul in Rom. viii. 15–16: **When we cry 'Abba, Father!' it is this Spirit testifying along with our own spirit that we are children of God.** Probably, then, we are intended here to think of the 'interior witness of the Holy Spirit,' the immediate, spontaneous, unanalysable awareness of a divine presence in our life. The author is well aware of the danger of any appeal to such types of experience, and that is why in iv. 1–6 he guarded against the danger (in the special case of prophecy) by reference to the central article of the Christian creed. Similarly here, he passes rapidly from the 'interior witness' to the observable facts of the Incarnation.

Secondly, then, the 'interior witness' finds its complement **14** in the external testimony to Christ as Saviour: **We** (that is, the Church and its ministry continuing the apostolic witness to the Gospel (see pp. 9–16)) **have seen, we do testify, that the**

Father has sent the Son as Saviour of the world. The verb 'to see' which is used here is the same as in verse 12 above, where the 'vision of God,' in the sense of 'Hellenistic mysticism,' is denied. While God in His eternal being is invisible, the Incarnate is visible, and that is sufficient to meet our 15 need for knowledge of God (cf. John xiv. 8–9). In the light, therefore, of observed facts (cf. i. 1, where again the same verb of seeing occurs) we confess the Church's faith, **Jesus is the Son of God;** and we now know (in the light of iv. 7–10) that the ultimate content of that confession is nothing less than the love of God, manifested in the incarnate life, and 16 the death, of Jesus: **we do know, we have believed** (for the same combination of verbs, though differently translated, cf. John vi. 69) **the love God has for us.** And so, finally, the truth of the divine indwelling becomes luminously self-evident: **God is love, and he who remains in love remains in God, and God remains in him.**

By thus drawing together several strands of thought which have run through the epistle, the author has produced a balanced, comprehensive and singularly impressive account of the grounds of Christian assurance. The Christian life is, to use the language of mysticism, a life of union with God, where God dwells in us and we in Him. Empirically, it is a life whose ruling motive is love to God and man. But simply to say that, is to fall short of the truth; for such love might be the expression of a natural disposition, or of an effort made from a sense of duty. A man might be said to love God because he had, what is very common, a craving for the infinite; and he might love his fellow men because he had a naturally kindly disposition, or because he acknowledged the duty of benevolence. All that is good and desirable, though the craving for the infinite sometimes takes odd ways, a philanthropy based on a sense of duty is seldom welcome to its objects, and natural kindliness may break down under stress. But Christianity is more than this. It holds the belief that the love with which we love God and our neighbour really is the love of God (**Love lies in this, not in our love for God, but in His love for us,** iv. 10); it is a divine power indwelling, for God Himself is love. In speaking of the love of God Christianity means something quite concrete; for we confess that **Jesus is the Son of God,** and, having before us the way in which He actually lived and died, we recognize in that **the love God has for us.** That confession has behind it the authority of the primary witnesses, whose testimony resides in the continuous tradition of the Church from the beginning. At the same time, we do not ground our assurance solely upon external testimony, for this testimony is confirmed in experience by an inward conviction, wrought, we must needs believe, not by our own minds, but by the Spirit of God. And, yet again, our assurance does not depend solely upon such interior witness (for we might mistake the spirit of error for the Spirit of truth); it is corroborated by the objective facts of the Gospel (14–16*a*). The aphorism which follows (16*b*) resumes in compendious form the conclusions of verses 7–12: **God is love; and he who remains in love remains in God, and God remains in him.** The restatement is no mere repetition, for it is now related directly to the theme of Christian assurance which has occupied verses 13–16. We know we are in union with God, because His Spirit testifies within us. But not only so; we have external, objective evidence, in the life and death of Christ, that God loves us; that indeed the very nature and property of God is to love. Hence follows a very direct ground of assurance. To live in love is to live in union with God: and that points to the final test for the validity of all religious experience.

The expression 'to remain in love' is suggestive rather than exact. It is not clear whether the meaning is 'to continue to live as the objects of God's love,' or 'to continue to love God,' or 'to continue to love our brothers,' It is in fact impossible, according to the teaching both of this epistle and of the Fourth Gospel, to make a clear separation between these three modes or manifestations of love. The energy of love discharges itself along lines which form a triangle, whose points are God, self and neighbour; but the source of all love is God, of whom alone it can be said that He *is* love. Whether we love God or our neighbour, it is God's love that is at work in us—assuming, that is, that our love is that authentic *agapé* which is exemplified in God's gift of His Son, and in Christ's sacrifice for us all.

The last point is not unimportant. The famous aphorism of 16*b*, in its English dress, readily lends itself to falsely sentimental interpretations if it is detached from its total context. It does not mean that anyone who feels for another person any sort of liking, affection or passion, which we loosely include under the term 'love,' is *ipso facto* in union with God. The true nature of divine charity is sufficiently defined by reference to the Gospels, and it is this love, or charity, that is meant.

This closely knit statement therefore places the reality of the Christian experience of God beyond question, guarding against the dangers of subjectivism on the one hand, and of mere traditionalism on the other; placing equal and co-ordinate stress on love to God, which is the heart of religion, and love to man, which is the foundation of morality, without allowing religion to sink to the level of mere moralism, or morality to be dissolved in mysticism. The passage is the high-water mark of the thought of the epistle.

17   We are now led to a further development of the doctrine of Christian assurance with which the foregoing verses have dealt. We have been told that in a region where there is no direct vision (for no one has ever seen God) we can nevertheless have complete assurance that we are in union with God. We have the interior witness of the Spirit, confirming the evidence of the facts of Christ's incarnate life and death; and the essential purport of this evidence is that God loves us. That conviction, however, is ineffectual unless we 'remain in' God's love (in the complex sense already indicated). Assuming, however, that by this test **love is complete in us,** and we are thus **assured** that we remain in God, and He in us, then we proceed **to a** further consequence of this fulness of love. A literal trans-

lation will perhaps better bring out the connection of thought. 'In this fact love is made complete with us—namely that we have confidence on the Day of Judgment.' (It may be that Moffatt is right in giving the sense 'about the day of judgment'; but the preposition properly means 'in,' and it is probable that it is intended, quite simply, to indicate a point of time— namely, the now visibly impending Judgment Day.) In other words, when Doomsday comes the Christian will possess confidence before God, as the final outcome of a life lived in the love of God on earth. (For the background and meaning of the word translated 'confidence,' see note on iii. 21.) This recalls ii. 28: **Remain within Him now . . . so that when He appears we may have confidence, instead of shrinking from Him in shame at His arrival.** In both contexts the writer is speaking of that union with God which is described as mutual indwelling; but in the present passage that idea has been made more precise and perspicuous through the doctrine that God is love, so that to 'remain in God' is to 'remain in love.' Confidence on the Day of Judgment, in fact, is the ripe fruit of a life lived in the love of God—or, to put it otherwise, of a life lived in this world in conformity with the pattern of Christ. (For the suggested contrast between the absolute perfection of unity with God which belongs only to Christ in His glorified existence in the eternal world, and the relative and progressive unity which is possible for His followers in this world, see John xvii. 9–19.)

The conformity of the Christian life with the divine character as revealed in Christ is a thought never far from the writer's mind. Sometimes it is expressed precisely in terms of *imitatio Christi* (ii. 6, iii. 3, 16); sometimes more vaguely (as i. 7, ii. 29— where the sequence of thought may be compared with that in our present passage). Here the context shows that he is appealing to the example of Christ as the One of whom it can be said, without qualification, that He **remains in love** and **love is complete in Him.** In the Fourth Gospel we learn that Christ is in perfect union with the Father, Father and Son dwelling mutually in one another (John xiv. 10–11); and this union with God by mutual indwelling is held up as the archetype, or ideal, of the communion of the Christian with God (John xv. 9–10, xvii. 21–3). All this is in our author's mind when he says, in this world we are living as He lives.

If then we take the picture of Christ in the Fourth Gospel as the pattern of what it means to 'remain in love,' we can give a full and precise meaning to that expression as it is used here. The Father loves the Son and shows Him all that He is doing Himself (v. 20): in fact, it is the Father, who remains ever in the Son, who is performing His own deeds (xiv. 10) (which are deeds of love towards the world, iii. 16); in other words, Christ, as the incarnate Son of God, is the point at which the love of God operates for the welfare of men; and it is with the love of the eternal God that Christ loves His own in this world, to the end (xiii. 1). Again, by virtue of keeping God's commands, Christ remains in the love of the Father (xv. 10); which must mean that He lives with the Father in a relation of mutual love (which can also be described as mutual indwelling). Hence, to remain in love, living in this world as Christ lives, means for us that we keep our place in God's family, as the objects of His love, that we return His love in keeping His commandments, and that by exercising the divine charity towards our fellows we become points of operation for the love of God in the world.

Such is the way of living which reaches its perfection in an absolute confidence on the day of judgment: and naturally so, since it is a way of living which unites us with our Judge (John v. 22, 27; cf. 2 Cor. v. 10). But, further, since it is a life 18 within the love of God, it is exempt from fear. Love has no dread in it; love in its fulness drives all dread away. The love spoken of is mutual love between God and ourselves (with its corollary of charity towards our neighbours); but perhaps with the emphasis, in this case, upon the love we bear to God; for this seems to be implied in the negative clause, anyone who has dread, has not reached the fulness of love. It is self-evident, even in merely human relationships at their best, that the more truly two persons love one another, the less they will be likely to be afraid of one another. It is true that each may have a very real fear of hurting one another (as we should fear to affront the love of God); but not because he is afraid of what

the other may do to him. *A fortiori*, to live within the love of
God is freedom from the ultimate fear.

Our author, as we have seen, carries on from the earliest days
of Christianity a very vivid and forcible sense of the near
approach of Doomsday (see ii. 18, and notes, pp. 48-50). As
a matter of chronology, he was mistaken. History went on,
and is still going on. This, however, does not alter the facts of
the essential transiency of this world, and of its subjection to
the judgment of God. In these times of 'crisis' (as we call
them, using the Greek word for 'judgment'), when the evil
tendencies resident in a whole epoch of history reveal themselves in their disastrous consequences, the awakened conscience acknowledges that the judgments of the Lord are in
all the earth. Such recurrent 'crises' (whether in the history of
nations or on the small stage of the individual life does not
matter) are flash-lights upon the nature of our existence in this
world. Our sense of living at the end of a world epoch, and of
witnessing the reaction of a moral universe against the wickedness and folly of mankind, is no illusion, but one more testimony to the unescapable truth that this world comes to an
end (sooner or later, and for each of us at death), and leaves
us exposed to the final realities. In the end we must face the
truth about ourselves and our doings, as seen through the eyes
of God. If our belief is true, that our Maker is a God of righteousness, and that He has made us with a certain freedom
(however relative and limited) to choose and act responsibly,
then our life can hardly be said to make sense unless each of
us is to be given, at some moment soon or late, an understanding of himself as he really is and of his actions as they
really are; that is, as God sees them, for the interim judgments
of conscience are partial and fallible (cf. 1 Cor. iv. 3-5). This
is the Last Judgment we await. (It is effectively suggested in
the Prayer Book version of Ps. l. 21: 'I will reprove thee, and
set before thee the things that thou hast done.') However we
imagine it to ourselves, it is a terrifying prospect. The dread
which it awakens is described in a classical passage in the
Epistle to the Hebrews: **nothing but an awful outlook of doom,**

of that burning Wrath which will consume the foes of God . . . It is an awful thing to fall into the hands of the living God (Heb. x. 27, 31). But no Christian need, or should, feel dread like that, says our author. Such dread has to do with punishment; or perhaps his meaning is that fear carries punishment with it—is in fact punishment. The Greek would bear that sense, and it is at any rate a fact: there is hardly a worse mental torment than utter terror; and many people have felt it at the thought of judgment to come. But it is not the intention of the Christian religion that we should live in dread. For to be a Christian is to live in love, and love has no dread in it, love in its fulness drives all dread away.

2. LOVE, OBEDIENCE AND FAITH (iv. 19 – v. 5)

19,20 We love, because He loved us first. If anyone declares, 'I love God,' and yet hates his brother, he is a liar; for he who will not love his brother whom he has seen, cannot possibly love

21 the God whom he has never seen. And we get this command from Him, that he who loves God is to love his

v. brother also.

1 Everyone who believes that Jesus is the Christ, is born of God; and everyone who loves the Father, loves the sons born

2 of Him. This is how we are sure that we love God's children,

3 by loving God and obeying His commands (for love to God means keeping His commands). And His commands

4 are not irksome, for whatever is born of God conquers the world. Our faith, that is the conquest which conquers the

5 world. Who is the world's conqueror but he who believes that Jesus is the Son of God?

It might seem that in these verses we are reverting to the themes of the second main division, for they are in part a résumé of what was said in iii. 11–18 and elsewhere about love to God and love to man. But all this is here recalled in the context of the theme of assurance, and with v. 3-4 the emphasis passes from love to faith, and it is this idea of the Christian faith and its irrefragable evidence that prevails down to v. 12.

The grounds of confidence on Judgment Day have been so stated that they might seem to place too great a burden on the conscience of the diffident Christian, who asks himself, 'But do I love God enough to put fear aside?' To correct any such impression, the writer repeats what he said in iv. 10 (see also notes there). The love of which he is speaking is essentially 19 the love of God for us, and our love only derivatively: **we love, because He loved us first.** 'We love,' he says: not, 'we love *God* because He loved us first,' though that is true; but in the widest possible sense, our very capacity to love, whether the object of our love be God or our neighbour, is given to us in the fact of our being loved by God. Thus, in facing the expectation of judgment to come, we find our real ground of assurance **not in our love for God but in His love for us—in the sending of His Son to be the** expiation for our sins (10); though it would be paradoxical if, being so persuaded of His love, we did not return it in a love for Him which excludes fear.

This return of love, however, must find its object also in 20 our fellow men, as our author now insists, reverting to the theme of verse 11 above (as well as of iii. 11–19, where love of our brothers is said to afford a ground of confidence before God). There is here a serious possibility of self-deception. A man may say, 'I love God,' and mean it to the best of his belief. He may experience the emotions of love to God; but love in the sense intended by this writer is not merely, not even primarily, emotion. Feelings may be delusive. The proof that love is real, in the full Christian sense, lies in the overt action to which it leads (cf. iii. 17, and notes). There is no real love to God which does not show itself in obedience to His commands (see v. 3 below); and God's command is quite explicit: **that he who loves 21 God is to love his brother also.** The reference is clearly to the tradition of the teaching of Jesus, as we have it in Mark xii. 28–31 and parallels. Hence the overt proof of love to God— the proof that is to convince not only observers but the man himself—lies in the practical exercise of charity towards his fellow men. Negatively, **if anyone declares, 'I love God,' and yet 20 hates his brother, he is a liar; for he who will not love his brother whom he has seen, cannot possibly love the God whom**

he has not seen. The meaning of this latter clause is not quite clear. The word 'cannot' might bear either of two meanings, which may be illustrated as follows. A schoolmaster might observe to an idle pupil, 'Unless you attend to your lessons, you *cannot* become an educated man'; and, on the other hand, the recipient of an anonymous letter might remark, 'A person who writes like that *cannot* be an educated man.' Similarly, here the meaning might be either that, unless one practises himself in loving his fellows, he is incapable of the more difficult task of loving God; or that the observed absence of practical charity is a proof that a person does not love God. The context seems to demand the latter meaning; for the writer is not here concerned with the stages by which we may learn to love God, but with the tests by which it may be known whether or no we love God; and the most straightforward and convincing test is that of charity towards our neighbours. We have here in effect a fresh interpretation and application of the evangelical commandment of love to God and neighbour. For the 'first and greatest commandment,' and the second which is 'like unto it,' are in the last resort one commandment. Being the objects of God's love, we are to love our neighbour in Him and Him in our neighbour; and that is what it is to remain in His love.

v. The intimate connection between love to God and love to
1-3a neighbour may be illustrated in another way. And here the writer harks back to the doctrine of divine generation from which the argument started in iv. 7. There the point was made that it is the nature and property of the child of God to love, since it is his Father's nature to do so. Here the point is made that the child of God is a person *to be loved*, because of his parentage. **Everyone who believes that Jesus is the Christ** (every true Christian), **is born of God.** But it is a general principle that if you love the parent you will love the child. (It is not necessary to give the word 'father' a capital letter, for the writer is enunciating a general maxim: love me, love my child; although, of course, in the application which he gives it the parent is God and the child the Christian man.) The conclusion we expect is: therefore if you love God you will love

your fellow Christian. But verse 2 is not quite unambiguous. Literally translated, it would run: 'By this we know that we love the children of God when we love God and keep His commands.' The Moffatt rendering assumes that the words 'by this' refer to what follows (as in this epistle they usually do), and are explained by the words 'when we love God and keep His commandments.' This would imply that if we are uncertain whether or not we really love our fellow men, we should ask ourselves whether we love God; or, in other words, whether we keep His commandments (verse 3*a*): the evidence of our love to man is the fact of our love to God in the keeping of His commands. This is not the usual order of thought in the epistle. In iii. 14, 17–19, and negatively in iii. 15, iv. 20, it is suggested rather that the immediate *datum* of experience is our love to man, and from it we derive assurance of our relation to God. No doubt the author holds that love to God and love to man are so inseparable that the presence of either is evidence of the other. Yet it is a little surprising, in view of his general attitude, to find him treating our love to God as the more immediate certainty, from which we are to deduce the reality of our love to man. The words of verse 2, however, are capable of another meaning, which may be represented by a slight alteration of the order of words in English: 'By this we know that, when we love God, we love the children of God.' The words 'by this' now refer to what precedes (cf. iv. 6, iii. 19), and we have a perfectly logical argument, which may be thus stated in syllogistic form:

He who loves the parent loves the child:
Every Christian is a child of God:
　Therefore, when we love God we love our fellow Christians.

This would appear to be the author's meaning. He assumes the solidarity of the family as a fact of ordinary experience, and argues directly from it to the solidarity of the family of God. To be **born of God** is to be born into a family, with obligations, not only towards the Father of the family, but also (as part of our obligation to Him) towards all His children. This needed saying, because for many people to be a 'child of God' meant an exalted spiritual status, accompanied by mystical experiences of union with the Divine, without any necessary recognition of social obligations.

3b   The reader has just been reminded that to love God means to keep His commands. Love which does not include obedience is not worth the name. But is it not a very hard thing to keep God's commands? The Christian standard of conduct is high and exacting. Yet the Lord Himself said, 'My yoke is kindly and my burden light' (Matt. xi. 30). With this saying (we may suppose) in mind, the writer adds, **His commands are not irksome,** He does not mean that God's demands upon us are less exacting than we supposed, but that they are accompanied by the assurance of power to fulfil them. In our attempts to live according to the will of God, we have against us the powers of 'the world'—that is, of paganism, or human society organized without God, bearing the marks of **the desire of the flesh and 4 the desire of the eyes and the proud glory of life** (ii. 16). But **He who is within you is greater than he who is in the world** (iv. 4). When the writer last appealed to that truth, he was concerned with the victory of the Church over the forces of error outside it. Now he is concerned with an even more insidious attack of the powers of 'the world,' the attack which is delivered against the Christian man through the pressure of pagan motives and standards upon his own moral life. In face of that pressure it is still true that we have in us something which is more powerful than 'the world.' For we are children of God, and we have in us something of God Himself. The good in us is after all stronger than the evil, because it is the energy of God: **Whatever is born of God conquers the world.**

Here, then, is the way to victory over paganism, the paganism of the human heart, manifesting itself both in a godless world-order and in the power of evil inclinations, false standards and bad dispositions which we have to overcome in ourselves in obeying God's commands. The way to victory is not a confident assertion of our own better selves, but **faith,** and faith necessarily refers us to something beyond ourselves. The victorious faith of the Christian is trust in God as He is revealed in Jesus Christ His Son. It means committing our-

selves to the love of God as it is expressed in all that Jesus
Christ was and all that He did. Such faith in God has its 5
intellectual basis in belief in the Incarnation of the Son of
God. Without that basis the conception of God as a God of
love remains precarious, in face of the many facts which seem
to contradict it. Granted that basis, we have a faith against
which all the forces of evil in the world and in ourselves are
powerless to prevail.

3. THE WITNESS TO THE FAITH (V. 6-13)

Jesus Christ, He it is who came by water, blood, and Spirit— 6
not by the water alone, but by the water and the blood.
The Spirit is the witness to this, for the Spirit is truth. The 7
witnesses are three, the Spirit and the water and the blood, 8
and the three of them are in accord.[1] If we accept human 9
testimony, God's testimony is greater; for God's testimony
consists in the testimony he has borne to His Son. He who 10
believes in the Son of God possesses that testimony within
himself; he who will not believe God, has made God a liar
by refusing to believe the testimony which God has borne
to His Son. And the testimony is, that God gave us life 11
eternal and this life is in His Son.

He who possesses the Son possesses life: 12
he who does not possess the Son of God does not possess
life.

I have written in this way to you who believe in the name 13
of the Son of God, that you may be sure you have life
eternal.

[1] The Authorized Version reads here: 'There are three that bear
record in heaven, the Father, the Word, and the Holy Ghost; and these
three are one. And there are three that bear witness in earth, the spirit,
and the water, and the blood; and these three agree in one.' This represents the so-called 'Received Text,' which goes back to Stephanus's
edition of the Greek New Testament, 1550. The sentence about the
'Three Heavenly Witnesses' is found in no Greek MS. earlier than the
fourteenth century, in no ancient Greek writer, in no ancient version
other than the Latin, and in no early MS. of the Old Latin version or of
Jerome's Vulgate. It is first quoted as a part of the text of I John by
Priscillian, the Spanish heretic, who died in 385, and it gradually made
its way into MSS. of the Latin Vulgate until it was accepted as part
of the authorized Latin text. In the first printed Greek Testament to be

The writer now wishes to insist upon the whole rich content of belief in the Incarnation, which is the pledge of victory over the world. He does so in terms which are obscure to us, though his first readers no doubt had the clue to his language. 6 Jesus Christ, he says, is He **who came by water, blood and Spirit**.[1] That He came by Spirit we can understand by reference to the evangelical tradition. The Synoptic Gospels trace the beginning of the public Ministry of Jesus to the descent of the Holy Spirit which accompanied His baptism by John (Mark i. 9–11, Matt. iii. 16–17, Luke iii. 21–2). According to Acts x. 38, this constituted the 'anointing' by virtue of which He appeared as the 'Christ' (= 'Anointed'). Again, these Gospels designate Jesus as the One who is to 'baptize with Holy Spirit' (Mark i. 8, Matt. iii. 11, Luke iii. 16; cf. Acts i. 5), and in the Acts it is He who pours out the Spirit upon the Apostles (Acts ii. 33). The Fourth Evangelist has brought these two together in a notable passage: **John (the Baptist) bore this testimony also: 'I saw the Spirit descend like a dove from heaven and rest on him; I myself did not recognize him, but He who sent me to baptize with water told me, "He on whom you see the Spirit**

published, that of Erasmus, 1516, the words do not appear. Erasmus was attacked for the omission, and undertook to introduce them in subsequent editions, if any Greek MS. could be produced which contained them. One of the poor and late MSS. which do contain them was produced, and, true to his word but against his own judgment, Erasmus printed them in his edition of 1522. Meanwhile, the stately Complutensian edition of Cardinal Ximenes, which gives, in parallel columns, the Greek text (printed from the most beautiful Greek fount, perhaps, ever cast) and the Latin Vulgate, had been issued (it had been in print since 1514), and this gives the disputed sentence in a Greek text differing slightly from that of Erasmus. It was retained as part of the text by Stephanus, and so passed into the Received Text. There is no doubt whatever that the words are a spurious interpolation, made first in the Latin version, and that the various forms in which they appear in Greek are all translations from the Latin.

[1] It is to be observed that the words 'and spirit' are not to be found in all our MSS., and they are omitted from the texts upon which our Authorized and Revised Versions are based. They are, however, attested by those two excellent MSS., the Sinaitic and the Alexandrine, as well as by some minor authorities. Some texts, again, seem to have omitted the word 'blood,' since the passage is sometimes cited by ancient writers in the form 'by water and spirit,' recalling the language of John iii. 5. The true text remains uncertain, but the reading adopted above, as well as being strongly attested, gives a good sequence of thought.

descending and resting, that is He who baptizes with the holy Spirit." Now I did see it, and I do testify that He is the Son of God' (John i. 32–4). Here we have a 'witness' to the fact of the Incarnation, the witness of John the Baptist; but that witness rests on a prior witness of God Himself, in the descent of the Spirit (for the Baptist did not recognize Christ until the divine sign was given). It is in accord with this that our author says 7 that **the Spirit is the witness,** and (he adds) a witness to be accepted, because **the Spirit is truth** (cf. John xvi. 13). In history, the descent of the Spirit was evidence of the Messiahship of Jesus. In the present experience of the Church, the activity of the Spirit is evidence of His power to baptize with the Spirit, and therefore of His divine Sonship. The writer is here thinking, it is probable, not so much of the 'interior witness of the Holy Spirit,' but rather of the outward expression of that inner witness in the corporate life of the Church, and particularly in inspired or prophetic utterance (itself dependent on the 'interior witness') by which the Church proclaimed and confirmed the truth of the Gospel.

So far, then, we can follow our author's meaning. The 8 difficulty lies in the statement that Christ **came by water** and **blood** as well as by Spirit, and that the witness of **the water and the blood** is united with that of the Spirit. If we are to turn, as usual, to the Fourth Gospel for a clue, we naturally think of John xix. 34. The evangelist reports that **blood and water** issued from the pierced side of the crucified Jesus; and he underlines the importance of the fact by adding, **He who saw it has borne witness (his witness is true; God knows he is telling the truth), that you may believe.** Once again the idea of 'witness' is introduced; but it is the witness of an observer to the fact, and not the witness of the water and the blood, as here. Clearly the Evangelist attached some mysterious significance to the fact, but what the significance was he has not made clear. In view of the symbolism of the Fourth Gospel as a whole, we should think of the blood of the Son of Man which is **real drink** and confers eternal life (John vi. 54–5); and of the **living water** which Christ bestows (John iv. 14). This **living water** is said, according to a probable construction of John

vii. 38, to issue from the body of Christ, and it is there equated with the Holy Spirit. All this, however, does not seem to throw direct light on our present passage, which states that Christ came by water and blood, and that the water and blood bear witness (consentient with that of the Spirit) to the truth of the Gospel, and in particular to the reality of the incarnation of the Son of God.

6 The author has found it necessary to insert an emphatic parenthesis: **not by water alone, but by the water and the blood.** This implies that someone taught that Christ came by water, but not by blood. If we knew what this meant, we should be well on the way to an understanding of the passage. Unfortunately, we are not sufficiently informed about the special form of false teaching attacked. It is, however, known that there were teachers of Gnostic tendencies who held that Jesus was a mere man until at His baptism the divine Christ descended upon Him; that the Christ remained united with Him during His ministry, but left Him before His crucifixion, since the divine cannot suffer. Thus through His baptism Jesus, by union with the divine Christ, was qualified to reveal divine mysteries to mankind, but since it was as mere man that He suffered, His death had no redemptive efficacy. This view might conceivably have been expressed (though we do not know that it was so expressed) by saying that Christ came by the water (of baptism) but not by the blood (of the Cross). If so, the meaning of the words **he came not by water alone, but by the water and the blood** would be tolerably clear. The Gospel affirms, upon the testimony of those who saw and heard, that Jesus Christ was both baptized and crucified, and both these facts are essential to our faith in Him, because both taken together bear the meaning that Jesus is the Christ or Son of God incarnate (iv.2), and that as such He is the Saviour of the world (iv. 14), and not merely its Enlightener.

8 In what sense, then, do the water and the blood bear witness? The question may perhaps be answered by drawing an analogy with the witness of the Spirit. The Spirit is, as we have seen, both a factor in the historical life of Jesus, and a continuing factor in the experience of the Church. Similarly, the

baptism and the crucifixion are authenticated facts in history, and as such bear witness to the reality of the incarnate life of the Son of God; but further, the Church possesses a counterpart to the baptism of Christ, in the sacrament of Baptism, and a counterpart to His sacrificial death, in the sacrament of the Eucharist. Both sacraments attest and confirm to believers the abiding effect of the life and death of Christ. It seems likely that our author is thinking of these two sacraments as providing a continuing witness to the truth of Christ's incarnation and redemptive death. Their value as evidence lies precisely in their being concrete, overt, 'objective' actions, directly recalling (or 're-presenting') historical facts of the Gospel, while at the same time they are the vehicles of a supra-historical life in the Church. As *verba visibilia*, they confirm the prophetic word inspired by the Spirit. Thus the apostolic faith is authenticated against all false teaching by a threefold testimony: the living voice of prophecy, and the two evangelical sacraments; and **the three of them are in accord.**

In verses 9 and following the theme of 'testimony' is further elaborated. The movement of thought becomes clearer if we refer to an important passage in the Fourth Gospel dealing with the same theme at greater length. The discourse in John v. 19–47 explains and defends the claim of Jesus to be Son of God. Briefly (we learn), it means that His every act is done, His every word spoken, in absolute dependence upon the Father and absolute obedience to His will; so that the words He speaks are God's words, and the acts He performs are 'works of God'; and these are, specifically, judgment upon sin and the bestowal of eternal life. Such a claim needs to be substantiated by independent testimony, since a man's bare assertion about himself is not valid evidence (v. 31). Accordingly, three forms of evidence are offered. First, there is the testimony of John the Baptist (cf. i. 29–34). This however is no more than an *argumentum ad hominem*, directed to those who were predisposed to give credence to the Baptist (33–5). The real testimony is that of God Himself, which is given, primarily, in two ways: in the actual effect of what Jesus did

(36), and in the Scriptures (39). What Jesus did was manifestly the work of God, since His coming brought judgment and eternal life into the world, and God alone is the Judge and the Giver of life; and it is God who speaks in the Scriptures.

In this argument we seem to discern the lines along which Christian apologetic ran in early days. But though to the Christian believer the evidence of the redeeming work of Christ was manifest, and the corroborative evidence of Scripture seemed conclusive, the fact remained that both failed to win credence from the Jews, to whom the Gospel was first offered, both by Jesus Himself and by His first disciples. Why was this? The answer suggested in the Johannine discourse is that the unbelieving Jews have not the word of God dwelling in them ('You have not His word remaining in you,' is the literal translation of John v. 38, the language being similar to that of the Epistle, though the similarity is disguised in the Moffatt translation). They study the Scriptures diligently, but lack an inner clue to their meaning (v. 39). Thus the external testimony, of the works of Christ and of the Scriptures, remains unconvincing, because the internal testimony is lacking. It is lacking (says Jesus to the Jews) because **you do not believe him whom He sent** (v. 38), and because **you refuse to come to me for life** (v. 39). The ultimate testimony is apprehended only by the believing Christian. That is as much as to say that the claim of Christ is in the end self-evidencing. External evidence will bring a man so far, but the truth becomes luminously clear when faith ventures over the line.

Thus far the Fourth Gospel. The echoes of language make it probable that our author had that passage in mind. In any case, it provides a plain key to his meaning. The apostolic faith, he has said, is authenticated by a threefold testimony. In the ordinary affairs of life we are ready to be convinced by the testimony of an honest and competent witness. *A fortiori*, in the highest concerns of all, we must accept the testimony of God Himself; and the consentient testimony of the Spirit, the water and the blood is His testimony. For the historical career of Jesus, from the descent of the Spirit at His baptism to His death on the cross, is a revelation of God; and it is God also who speaks now in the Church, whether through the inspired word of prophecy or through the 'visible words' of the sacraments. But just as the Jews of the time of Christ remained uncon- 10 vinced in face of the evidence, not only of John the Baptist, but of the Scriptures and of the very works of Christ, so now there are those who refuse assent to the strong testimony of God in history and in the experience of the Church. The writer no doubt has especially in mind those false teachers who, having been within the Church, and therefore directly exposed to the testimony of the Spirit, the water and the blood, nevertheless deny the reality of the Incarnation and the redeeming efficacy of the Cross. Such denial is tantamount to making **God a liar**—accusing the Truth of falsehood. The reason for their unbelief he traces to the same source as the incredulity of the Jews of Palestine: they have not the word of God abiding in them, and consequently no external testimony, however strong, will move them. On the contrary **he who believes in the Son of God possesses that testimony within himself.**

Finally, the essential content of the divine testimony can be 11 stated very simply: **God gave us life eternal and this life is in His Son.** And with these words the author brings us back to the thesis from which he started: **The Life has appeared; we saw it, we testify to it, we bring you word of that eternal Life which existed with the Father and was disclosed to us** (i. 2). In the course of the epistle that central concept has been turned this way and that, illuminated from one angle and another, and 12 now we are brought back to it with a clearer and fuller sense of its meaning, and reminded of the stark alternatives: with Christ, we have life; without Him we are dead.

The epistle is thus rounded off, and the author appears to have intended to wind up with the brief summary of his purpose in verse 13, recalling as it does the words with which the 13 Fourth Gospel was apparently at first intended to close: **These signs are recorded so that you may believe that Jesus is the Christ, the Son of God, and believing may have life through His Name** (John xx. 31). As a literary whole, the epistle must be held to be complete here. The rest is postscript.

POSTSCRIPT
(v. 14–21)

I. ON PRAYER AND INTERCESSION (v. 14–17)

14 Now the confidence we have in Him is this, that He listens
to us whenever we ask anything in accordance with His
15 will; and if we know that He listens to whatever we ask, we
16 know that we obtain the requests we have made to Him. If
anyone notices his brother committing a sin which is not
deadly, he will ask and obtain life for him—for anyone
who does not commit a deadly sin. There is such a thing
17 as deadly sin; I do not mean he is to pray for that. All
iniquity is sin, but there are sins which are not deadly.

The first theme treated in the postscript is that of prayer,
which received only brief mention in the body of the epistle,
iii. 21–2. In reading the present passage, it will be well to
keep in mind both this earlier section of the epistle, and the
passages from the Fourth Gospel which were adduced in the
notes on it (pp. 93–4). The writer takes up again the thought of
14 the confidence with which Christians may approach God, being
assured that He hears and answers their prayers. Nothing,
however, leads us to suppose that God will grant just anything
we choose to ask, simply because we want it. There are limiting
conditions. In iii. 22 the condition is that of obedience to God;
in John xv. 7 it is that we should remain in Christ, and have
his words remaining in us; in John xiv. 14 it is that prayer
should be in the name of Christ. These all come to much the
same thing. Similarly here, the condition is that prayer should
be in accordance with the will of God. The same is clearly
implied in the prayer which Jesus taught, the regulative
clauses of which are, 'Thy kingdom come: Thy will be done';
and it is conclusively exemplified in His own prayer in Geth-
semane. For prayer rightly considered is not a device for
employing the resources of omnipotence to fulfil our own
desires, but a means by which our desires may be redirected
according to the mind of God, and made into channels for the
forces of His will. Granted this one condition, our assurance is

2. THE GREAT CHRISTIAN CERTAINTIES (v. 18–21)

18 We know that anyone who is born of God does not sin; He who was born of God preserves him, and the evil One never catches him.

19   We know that we belong to God, and that the whole world lies in the power of the evil One.

20   We know that the Son of God has come, and has given us insight to know Him who is the Real God; and we are in Him who is real, even in His Son Jesus Christ. This is the

21   real God, this is life eternal. My dear children, keep clear of idols.

Turning away now from the gloomy contemplation of an unpardonable apostasy, the writer comes back to the positive certainties of the faith, which he sums up in three aphorisms, each beginning with a confident 'We know.'

18   First, we are (as he has constantly affirmed, see ii. 29, iii. 1–10, iv. 7, v. 1–4, and notes) God's children, born of Him, belonging to Him as members of His family; and God's children, having within them the divine seed which is the word of God (iii. 9), do not live in sin (the tense of the verb here implies this continuance, see notes on iii. 9). They may from time to time be in danger, but the Son of God *par excellence*, the eldest Brother of the family (cf. Rom. viii. 29), is there to preserve them. Hence the Enemy of mankind, who holds sway over un-redeemed human nature (cf. ii. 15–17, and notes), cannot make them his prey.

Put in these general terms, the maxims may pass through our minds almost as Christian commonplaces. But for the writer 'the world' meant precisely that organized pagan society in which he and his readers had to live. In its idolatry, its violence, its corruption he, like other Christians of his time, recognized the actual manifestation of the devil himself, the spirit of evil. To lose vital contact with the means of grace afforded by the fellowship of the Church was to expose oneself to the immediate peril of falling into his power. The line between Christianity and paganism, between the Church and 19 the world, was absolute. This absolute opposition is expressed

absolute. We know that He listens to us whenever we ask; and that means, since the will of God is efficacious in this world, that our requests are there and then taking effect in it: we 15 know that we obtain the requests we have made to Him. The verb is in the present tense: it is not that we *shall* obtain our requests, but that we *obtain* them. The Greek is in fact even more emphatic than this: it says (literally), 'We know that we *possess* the requests we have made.' The saying of Jesus which gives authority to all our assurance is reported in Mark xi. 24 in still more emphatic terms: 'Whatever you pray for and ask, believe you *have got it*, and you shall have it.' Here is the paradox that contains the secret of prayer: that in proportion as it becomes real prayer it carries its answer within it.

The principle thus laid down is now to be illustrated from 16a the prayer of intercession for our fellow Christians. All through the epistle it is assumed that the normal condition for a Christian is one of serene enjoyment of communion with God and of filial obedience to His will. But it is recognized that this condition is liable to be interrupted by our falling from time to time into sin (see pp. 21–3). In such a case the will of God is that the sinner should be restored. He has provided in Christ an expiation for sin; Christ is our Advocate; and the Father Himself is faithful and just to forgive (i. 9–ii. 2, iv. 10). Conse-quently we can pray for a fellow Christian who has fallen into sin, with the knowledge that our prayer is in accordance with the will of God, and so with full assurance that our prayer is answered: we ask and obtain life for him.

No clearer case, it would appear, could be adduced. But the 16b writer hesitates. Is it, after all, certain that in every case it is God's will that the sinner should be restored? All iniquity 17 indeed (all wrong-doing of any kind) is sin, and certainly a Christian may do wrong and recover. But there is such a thing 16b as deadly sin—that is to say, sin which places the sinner beyond the pale of that communion with God which (in the language of this epistle) is 'life.' It seems that the writer is thinking of an overt sinful act or course of action, and not of an inward state of mind, for it is something that can be observed by others and known for what it is. What particular sin or kind of sin he has in mind is not made clear. A precise definition of 'mortal' and 'venial' sins is provided in the developed Moral Theology of the Church, but it would be an anachronism to try to apply it here. Nor do the partial parallels adduced from Judaism give much help. No doubt the category of 'deadly sin' was one well recognized by the community to which the epistle was addressed. In the Epistle to the Hebrews we are told that those who deliberately and defiantly repudiate their Christian faith are incapable of restoration, like Esau, that 'profane person,' who **got no chance to repent though he tried for it with tears** (Heb. vi. 4–6, xii. 16–17). It would seem likely that our present author too is thinking of apostasy or denial of Christ as the sin that places a man beyond the pale. We know that he traced the presence and power of Antichrist in the denial of the Incarnation (iv. 2–5); and if a man had become identified with Antichrist it was perhaps natural to feel that he was past praying for.

Besides, the writer may well have thought that he had warrant in the teaching of Jesus Himself for this stern conclusion. We have seen that his words about the sin of denying Christ in ii. 22–3 probably rest upon a reminiscence of the saying variously reported in Mark viii. 38, Matt. x. 32–3, Luke ix. 26, xii. 8–9. Again, he has said that to deny the truth which is attested by the Spirit is to make God a liar; and tradition reported a saying of Jesus, variously given in Mark iii. 28–9, Matt. xii. 31–2, Luke xii. 10, to the effect that blasphemy against the Holy Spirit was an unpardonable sin. If our author believed that he had before him a case to which these Gospel sayings directly applied, he may well have concluded that it was idle to pray for one who had thus sinned unpardonably, and whom Christ Himself denied before the Father.

It will be observed that the argument here turns upon inferences and probabilities. The writer, addressing readers who would know what he meant, has not made himself explicit to us. On the main point, however, his meaning is hardly doubtful, in spite of the efforts of some commentators to soften it. He does not indeed expressly forbid prayer for one who is in deadly sin, but he emphatically

discourages it. Again, he does not expressly say that suc[h] sin places a man beyond redemption, but only a clear conv[iction] tion that such was the case would justify his exclusion fr[om] the prayers of the Church.

The questions of the forgiveness of post-baptismal sin and [of] the restoration of the lapsed continued to agitate the minds [of] Christians for generations. The decision ultimately went i[n] favour of the milder view, which admitted the lapsed to pen[it]ance. The general sense of the Church has not endorsed the[?] view that we are competent to decide that a given person has sinned himself beyond the pale of the divine mercy, and consequently is past praying for. (The matter is discussed historically in K. E. Kirk, *The Vision of God*: see especially pp. 221–9, and his observations on our present passage, pp. 161–2.) It was not for nothing that the Church which preserved in its tradition the severe saying of the Lord about the sin of denying Him, also preserved the story of Peter's denial, of Christ's prayer for him, and of his ultimate recovery (Mark xiv. 66–72, Luke xxii. 31–4, John xxi. 15–17).

It may be that our author was misled by a too rigorous exegesis of the sayings of Jesus; it may be that he has misapplied them under the tension of a situation of extreme peril to the Church. In any case, it seems clear that it was with reluctance that he felt obliged to admit a qualification which really weakens the force of his affirmation about prayer and its answer. Upon the ground of the general teaching of the Gospels, and of the New Testament as a whole, and in agreement with the general sense of the Church, we may take leave to accept the affirmation and to ignore the qualification. We cannot think that it can ever be contrary to the will of Him who came to call sinners to repentance that we should pray for even the worst of sinners (who may after all be—ourselves). If we have in mind any case where, to our limited view, such a prayer seems unlikely to be answered, we may recall what Jesus said when a man had refused what looked like his only chance of salvation—**For men it is impossible, but not for God; anything is possible for God** (Mark x. 27).

in the second of the three aphorisms: **We know that we belong to God, and that the whole world lies in the power of the Evil One.**

To cross the line in the one direction was to pass from death to life (iii. 14); to cross it in the other direction was to pass from life to death. To yield to pagan standards was to make the passage; to compromise with paganism was a breaking down of the defences. Consequently the Christian's tenure of 'life,' threatened as it was at every point by the forces of death, would have been precarious from moment to moment but for the assurance that the whole power of God was exerted for his defence. The conflict presented itself to the Christian of the first century in desperately concrete terms. If for us the situation is for the present in some measure disguised, in the last analysis it is the same, and the assurance that we need, ánd are given, is the same.

The third aphorism brings us back to the ground of this **20a** assurance: **the Son of God has come and has given us insight to know Him who is the Real God.** It is upon the historical fact of the coming of Christ that our faith is founded; but its significance reaches beyond the merely historical: it gives knowledge of that which transcends history; of that which is 'real' in the full sense of the word; or, rather, of Him who is the final Reality. The full weight that here attaches to the word **real** can best be appreciated if we recall that the religious quest of the ancient world had become more and more, under the influence of Platonic teaching, an attempt to escape from the illusions of this transitory world into communion with the world of eternal reality. Christian teachers in the Gentile world were quick to see that their Gospel was directly relevant to this quest, and could readily be stated in its terms. The revelation of God which they found in Jesus Christ was a revelation of the Real, over against the illusions of idolatry. Accordingly, our author, who is about to warn his readers to **keep clear of idols** (verse 21), lays stress here upon that aspect of the Incarnation in which it is a way to knowledge of the Real. Nor is this mere knowledge in the sense in which we know objects external to us. It is the knowledge which is communion. In so far as we are (in the familiar Pauline phrase) 'in Christ,' we are in Him who is real.

To a Greek reader of the first century this was as much as to say that Christianity possessed that which was the goal of his own religious quest. What would surprise him would be the way by which the Christian teacher declares this goal to be attained. Most religious teachers and prophets of the time agreed in recommending a *via negativa* by which the soul was gradually detached from the world of ordinary experience and concentrated more and more upon the highest abstractions, till it could dwell upon pure Being, eternal, changeless, un-differentiated, and free from all particularity. This was what was implied by knowledge of God, or of the Real, in much of the highest religious thought of the time. The Christian Gospel, on the other hand, affirmed that such knowledge is given by the Son of God who came to earth in the flesh—that is to say, in an actual, historical human life. The world of our ordinary experience is consequently no longer a realm of mere illusion, but is capable of becoming a means of communion with the highest realities. That the Christian faith is thus rooted in the concrete, the actual, the historical, has been a constant theme all through the epistle. Now at the end the author emphasizes the other side: it is at the same time concerned with the supra-historical, the eternal, the ultimately real.

20*b* **This, he adds, is the real God.** In strict grammar, the word **'this'** should refer to the last person named. Some commentators accordingly take the sentence we are considering to mean, 'This Person, namely Jesus Christ, is the real God.' It is more likely that the word **'this'** has a wider and vaguer reference. The writer is gathering together in his mind all that he has been saying about God—how He is light, and love, how He is revealed as the Father through His Son Jesus Christ; how He is faithful and just to forgive our sins; how He remains in us —and **this**, he adds, **is the real God**, the one eternal Reality of which the mystics talk, though they do not know Him as He is known through Christ. And **this**, he also adds (meaning now the *knowledge* of the Real God of which he has just spoken) **is eternal life.** For illustration of this we need only recall

John xvii. 3: This is life eternal, that they know Thee, the only real God, and Him whom Thou hast sent, even Jesus Christ. But it is also worth while to recall that the maxim that eternal life comes by knowledge of God, or of the Real, was a religious commonplace of the time. The new thing distinctive of Christianity is the revelation of God *in a human life*, with all that that involves.

The proper contrast to the Real is idols. The Greek word 21 (*eidōla*) always carries with it the suggestion of unreality. Plato used it for the illusory phenomena or appearances which he contrasted with the eternal and immutable 'ideas' or 'forms.' In the Greek Old Testament the same word was adopted to designate the images worshipped by the heathen, as being counterfeit gods over against the one real God. In this sense it was taken over by Christianity. The warning keep clear of idols no doubt means 'avoid any contact with paganism.' Not perhaps that the readers would be likely deliberately to take part in idolatrous rites; but where pagan practices penetrated every aspect of social life it was easy for Christians to follow ways of accommodation that might insensibly lead them into harmful compromise. Moreover, our author has in view a movement among professing Christians advocating a far-reaching accommodation, if not with actual idolatry, at least with pagan ways of thought incompatible with true Christianity. It is probably this movement that he has in view here as elsewhere in the epistle: and by idols he means not only images of the gods, but all false or counterfeit notions of God such as lead to the perversions of religion against which he has written.

It is in this sense that his warning is apt to our own situation. In our time there have appeared within what was once Christendom movements using the language of religion and offering God-substitutes—that is, idols—in the place of the living God of Christian revelation. Some of these idols of our time have shown themselves, by their fruits, to be no better than the abominations of the heathen which the Hebrew prophets denounced. It is no longer plausible either to hold that a man's theology—that is, his thought about God—does not matter; or to pretend that there is no great difference between the Christian faith and any sort of religiosity that may appeal to this man or that. Christians believe that the God revealed in Christ and attested in the Scriptures is the one real God, and the worship of any God-substitute is idolatry. The issue is defining itself clearly in terms of contemporary history. It behoves the individual Christian to be on his guard against any such God-substitute, whether it be a political idea, or some fashionable cult, or merely the product of his own 'wishful thinking.' The safeguards which this epistle recommends are, to live within the fellowship of the Church, and to adhere loyally and with understanding to the authentic tradition of the apostles; keeping always in view that which the apostles attest, and which creates the fellowship of the Church—the historical revelation of God in the life and words of Jesus Christ. To put it briefly for our own situation: a concentration upon the New Testament, and the Gospels in particular, in the context of a living Church fellowship, is our best safeguard against modern idolatries.

THE SECOND EPISTLE OF JOHN

**The presbyter, to the elect Lady and her children whom I love 1
in the Truth (and not only I but all who know the Truth)
for the sake of the Truth which remains within us and will 2
be with us for ever: grace, mercy, peace will be with us 3
from God the Father and from Jesus Christ the Son of the
Father, in truth and love.**

The manner in which the epistle opens is based upon the
current epistolary style of the time, which is well represented
by the opening of 3 John; but while 3 John is quite obviously
a genuine personal letter, which would not be out of place (in
spite of the difference of subject) in any collection of private
correspondence of the first or second century, these opening
verses have an elaborate solemnity of phrase which, at the outset, suggests that we are dealing with a different type of
composition.

As in the Third Epistle, the writer does not give his name, 1
but calls himself simply 'The Presbyter.' On the meaning of
this, see note on 3 John 1. The recipient is denominated by a
form of words capable of more than one construction. In view
of the fact that general epistolary usage would lead us to
expect a proper name, it has been suggested that the words
should be translated (as they well might be), either 'to the lady
Electa' or 'to the elect Kyria.' The former suggestion, though
it has some ancient support (see p. xiii), is on all grounds
improbable. In favour of the alternative suggestion it may be
urged that Kyria (= 'Lady,' like Martha in Aramaic and
Domna in Latin) is a well-attested proper name, and that the
epithet 'elect' with a proper name is to be found in an epistolary greeting in Rom. xvi. 13 (though the Moffatt translation disguises it). If we are to find a proper name at all,
then Kyria has the preference.

But is it really credible that the epistle is addressed to an
individual? The Lady (we learn) is beloved, not only by the

Presbyter, but by all true Christians everywhere. She has many children; some of them live with her, and are joined with her in the Presbyter's greeting; others he has met elsewhere; *some* of them are good Christians, others, possibly, not. In addition, the Lady has a sister and a family of nephews and nieces residing, it would appear, at the place from which the letter is written. Yet of all this large family, no single name is mentioned; there is no allusion which would serve to bring any of them before us as individuals; and of all the reflections and injunctions contained in the epistle, there are none which seem relevant to the special situation of an individual or a family. All this stands in marked contrast to the Third Epistle. There, in spite of its brevity, Gaius, Diotrephes and Demetrius stand before us as individuals; the relations of the Presbyter to them are intelligible; the reflections and injuctions are such as to apply to these particular individuals in that particular situation, and to no others. In short, it has all the marks of a piece of actual correspondence between two individuals. Precisely these marks are absent from the Second Epistle.

The probability is that the **elect Lady** is a disguise for a community. If this appears to us somewhat far-fetched it must be remembered that the personification of cities, countries and provinces in female form was a well-established convention. In the art of the time the city of Rome appears as a stately woman crowned (the original of the less flattering portrait in Rev. xvii. 4). The 'Britannia' of our pennies is the direct descendant of the personified province of Britain on Roman coins. The coins which celebrate Titus's victory over the Jews show a mourning woman, with the inscription, 'Captive Judaea.' This chimes in with a usage familiar among the Jews themselves, amply illustrated in the Old Testament and elsewhere. Thus, 'the daughter of Zion' frequently personifies the Jewish people. In Isa. liv we have a sustained passage in which the holy nation is figured as wife and mother, and the members of the nation as her children. Similarly, in Baruch iv.–v. Jerusalem is the mother who bewails the calamity of her children, and is comforted with the promise of their restoration. This usage was easily transferred to the Christian

Church. In Gal. iv. 21–31 the present Jerusalem is in servitude with her children, while the free city, Jerusalem on high, is the mother of all Christians. The elect Lady and her children form a similar figure. Some ancient commentators took her to stand for the catholic Church. This however does not seem possible. The catholic Church has no 'sister.' We conclude that the elect Lady with her children is a local church with its members; and her 'sister' is another such local church—that, namely, in which the Presbyter is residing. There is a close parallel in I Pet. v. 13, where Moffatt boldly, and rightly, gives the sense in the words, your sister-church in Babylon, but the literal rendering is: 'she in Babylon who is elect together with you.'

Why was this mystification adopted? The possibility should perhaps not be excluded, that, in the unfavourable situation of Christianity at the time (see I John iii. 13), it was judged safer, in case a document implicating the Church should fall into hostile hands, that it should appear to be a harmless letter to a friend. It is possible that the names of the writer and of the church addressed are omitted for similar prudential reasons—though both may have appeared, for all we know, on the outside of the postal packet, according to custom. On the whole it seems likely that the device is little more than a 'conceit,' conforming to the taste of the period. However that may be, the fiction is kept up all through: the language is such as might be addressed to a pious matron, but it is a thin disguise for a pastoral epistle to a Christian congregation.

The Presbyter first assures the church of his love for its members. The expression 'whom I love in truth' might, in another author, mean no more than 'whom I regard with sincere affection' (see note on 3 John 1). But the emphatic repetition of the word 'truth' in different connections within the same context suggests that it is being used with a more special meaning. In these epistles 'truth' is not merely, as in ordinary speech, that which corresponds with the facts, but also, specifically, the ultimate Reality as revealed in Christ (cf. I John ii. 21, iii. 19, iv. 6, v. 7). And so, in the present passage, all who know the Truth are the whole body of believing Christians. Having responded with faith to the revelation in Christ, and accepted the obligations it imposes, they possess, through that revelation, saving knowledge of God (cf. I John ii. 3–5). Similarly, the Truth, which is the Word of God, **remains within us** (2) as a perpetual source of enlightenment and moral power (cf. I John ii. 14, 24, and notes on ii. 20, 27, iii. 9). The Truth, or the Word of God, comes to us, not only as Gospel, but as Commandment (cf. I John ii. 7–8); and the content of that commandment is love or charity (cf. I John iii. 23, iv. 11–12). Thus the expression, 'whom I love in the Truth,' probably conveys the idea that the love which the Presbyter has for members of the church is not merely the natural affection of ordinary human friendship, but that divine charity which, as it is God's gift to us in Christ, is also the proper relation of Christians one to another. This same divine charity, he adds, unites the congregation to which he writes with all Christian believers, in the fellowship of the 2 catholic Church. Within that fellowship all Christians love one another **for the sake of the Truth**—that is, the Word of God in Christ to which they are all committed.

This reiterated emphasis upon **the Truth,** as directing and controlling the entire system of Christian attitudes and relationships, clearly reflects the writer's concern about the inroads which 'the Lie' is making upon the fellowship of the Church (cf. I John ii. 21–4). There is, for him, no real charity, no Christian fellowship in the proper sense of the term, which does not rest upon a sincere acceptance of the Christian faith in its totality. The false doctrines which are going about are undermining, whether their authors mean it or not, the very foundations of the Christian life. He addresses himself to those who because they are firm in loyalty to the Truth know what Christian charity is.

3   The epistolary address should, according to the practice of the time, lead up to a greeting. The customary, and indeed almost invariable, form of greeting in secular correspondence of the period is not found in the New Testament except in two epistles: Acts xv. 23, James i. 1. Elsewhere we have a Christian adaptation of it; usually 'grace and peace to you,' or (in the two Epistles to Timothy) 'grace, mercy and peace.' The latter

form is adopted here, but with a curious variation. Instead of expressing a *wish* that God should grant grace, mercy and peace to his correspondents, the writer turns it into a *promise* or *assurance* of these divine blessings to all Christians: **Grace, mercy, peace, *will be with us*** from **God the Father and from Jesus Christ the Son of the Father;** and he adds, **in truth and love,** because the grace of God is shown in that revelation of Himself which is the Truth, and in the divine charity expressed in the work of Christ (1 John iv. 9–10); and takes effect in the true belief and mutual charity of Christians.

THE CHRISTIAN LIFE (4–6)

I was overjoyed to find some of your children leading the true 4 Life, as we were commanded to do by the Father. And 5 now I entreat you, Lady—not as though I were writing you any new command, it is the command which we have had from the very beginning—let us love one another. To live 6 by His commands, that is what love means: and the command is, live in love as you have learned to do from the very beginning.

In correspondence of the time it was a familiar (and very 4 natural) custom to begin a letter by expressing the writer's pleasure at hearing good news of his correspondents (for some examples, see note on 3 John 3). Following this custom, the Presbyter expresses his pleasure at finding that some members of the church to which he writes are leading a truly Christian life ('walking in the Truth' is the literal rendering of his words; the meaning of which should be clear in view of the note on 'truth' above), and so fulfilling God's commandment through Christ (cf. 1 John iii. 23). Significantly, it is **some** only of whom this is true: the church is divided.

To this church, already suffering from internal troubles, 5 the Presbyter appeals to renew and maintain the threatened fellowship by the exercise of Christian charity. In doing so, he adds, he is not laying upon them any fresh obligation; for charity is an essential part of the original and unchangeable Christian Gospel (see 1 John ii. 7–8, and notes). To live in

6 charity is to live in obedience to the command of God in Christ, and without such obedience there can be no real Christianity (see 1 John ii. 3-5, iii. 11-18, v. 3, and notes).

FALSE TEACHERS AND HOW TO TREAT THEM (7-11)

7 I say this, because a number of impostors have emerged in the world, men who will not acknowledge the coming of Jesus Christ in the flesh; that marks the real 'impostor' and

8 'antichrist.' Watch yourselves; you must not lose what you

9 have been working for, but gain your full reward. Anyone who is 'advanced' and will not remain by the doctrine of Christ, does not possess God: he who remains by the doc-

10 trine of Christ possesses both the Father and the Son. If anyone comes to you and does not bring this doctrine, do

11 not admit him to the house—do not even greet him, for he who greets him shares in his wicked work.

7 The Presbyter now comes to the immediate purpose of his writing. His correspondents should know that a widespread movement of heretical propaganda is afoot, and may at any time reach their city. The expression **have emerged in the world** is a paraphrase of the Greek, which, literally translated, runs, 'have gone out into the world.' The paraphrase may give the sense which the author intended; but the literal rendering as it stands seems to yield a perfectly straightforward meaning (cf. 1 John iv. 1 and note). The heretics have 'gone out into the world' in the sense in which that expression is often used of the missionary work of the Church, after the model of Mark xvi. 15 (where the language is similar, though a different verb is used). That is to say, they have set on foot a general appeal to the public, and especially to the pagan public (which was for an early Christian 'the world' in a special sense). That they were in fact carrying on a highly successful mission we learn from 1 John iv. 5 (see note there). From their own point of view, they were Christian missionaries. From the standpoint of the Presbyter they were impostors, because the doctrines they taught implied a denial of fundamental articles of the faith. Indeed, anyone who is guilty of such denial is not

only an impostor; he is antichrist (see 1 John ii. 18, iv. 3–6, and notes).

The error of the false teachers is described in words which are not entirely free from ambiguity. In any good Greek writer we could hardly help taking them to mean, 'They do not acknowledge that Jesus Christ *is coming* (i.e. will come) in the flesh' (whereas in 1 John iv. 2 we have the past tense: ' . . . that Jesus Christ *has come* in the flesh'). If this is the meaning, we should have to suppose that the error of the false teachers touched the Church's hope of the second advent of Christ, upon which the First Epistle lays some stress (see 1 John ii. 17–18, 28, iii. 2, iv. 17). It may be that in this period of ferment there was controversy upon the question whether the second advent, like the first, was to be 'in the flesh'; but if so, it has left no clear trace in our sources (*Epistle of Barnabas*, vi. 9, which is sometimes cited as a parallel, is nothing of the kind, as any attentive reader will see). We shall perhaps do best to assume that our writer is not skilled in the niceties of Greek idiom, and to understand the present passage in the light of the First Epistle. The heresy is that of denying the reality of the Incarnation; denying, that is to say, that the eternal Christ, the Son of God, ever really lived a human life in history. This denial was an element in a very widespread and influential 'reinterpretation' of Christianity in early times (see Introduction, p. xix, and notes on 1 John ii. 18–23, iv. 1–6). If it had prevailed, the distinctive character of the Christian religion would have been fatally obscured. To lose hold upon the true 8 humanity of the Saviour, we are reminded, would be to reduce the Christian life to frustration (cf. also 1 John i. 1–3, iv. 14–16).

The heretics no doubt spoke of their doctrine (with some 9 pride) as 'advanced.' The Presbyter retorts that it is possible to 'advance' so far as to be quite outside the boundaries of genuine Christian belief. What signifies is, not to exploit Christian ideas in the spinning of able and brilliant speculations, but to possess God (cf. 1 John ii. 23) or, in other words, to maintain fellowship with the Father and with His Son Jesus Christ (1 John i. 3); and such fellowship cannot be maintained without loyalty to the fundamental truths of the Gospel. Where that loyalty exists, it is possible (as indeed the example of 1 John shows) to embark upon far-reaching re-interpretations of Christian doctrine, and in doing so to enrich its content without obscuring its central purport. It must, however, be admitted that the writer has incautiously expressed himself in terms which might seem to stigmatize any kind of 'advance' as disloyalty to the faith, and so to condemn Christian theology to lasting sterility. This extreme position has not in fact been taken by any of the great Christian communions, however strongly they have emphasized the necessity of maintaining **the faith which has once for all been delivered to the saints** (Jude 3).

10 11- The Presbyter is not sure whether this dangerous propaganda has yet reached his correspondents, but he will instruct them what course to take in case one of its agents should approach them. If they find that any travelling missionary is bringing a doctrine different from that **doctrine of Christ in** which they have been instructed, he is to be treated as excommunicate. No true believer must allow him to 'darken his door.' If he meets him in the street, he must not even speak the conventional word of greeting. The separation between heretic and true believer is complete and final.

These instructions contemplate primarily the arrival of a travelling missionary (like those of 3 John 5–8, only on the wrong side) from some other place. Such missionaries depended upon the support and hospitality of Christian brethren in each place to which their mission took them. To deny them all hospitality was an effective way of frustrating their attempts at propaganda. But there is more in the boycott than this. **He who greets** the heretic **shares in his wicked work**; and, conversely, to send him to Coventry, pointedly and publicly, is to range yourself decisively on the side of orthodox belief. It is the intense seriousness of the crisis in the Church that leads the Presbyter thus to insist that all who accept his authority shall declare themselves unmistakably against the heretical movement, by joining in the boycott.

This 'short way with dissenters' strikes a harsh note in our ears. To ostracize people whose opinions we dislike is natural enough, but to find it recommended as a Christian duty is another matter. In this country we have not yet had (in recent times) experiences tragic enough to give us an understanding of the situation in which the Presbyter writes. But suppose the Church was struggling for its very life in a paganized society; and suppose people calling themselves Christians, and using the language of Christianity, were propagating doctrines which caricatured its creed, parodied its worship, and perverted its moral standards. Many devout Christians in Germany, both Catholic and Evangelical, have seen the contemporary situation in their own country in just that way. If we could imagine ourselves in such a situation, we could better understand this fierce intolerance. We could understand better such a story as that which is told of the amiable and saintly Polycarp. Marcion, now a heretic, met him and asked, 'Do you recognize me?' 'I recognize Satan's firstborn,' was the reply (Irenaeus, *Adv. Haer.*, III. 3. 4). There is a similar story told of 'John, the disciple of the Lord,' who may have been the author of this letter. One day he was at the public baths when the heretic Cerinthus came in. He leapt out of the bath unwashed, crying, 'Let us hurry away lest the building collapse on us, because Cerinthus, the enemy of the truth, is here!' (Irenaeus, *loc. cit.*). We observe that he was not disturbed by the presence of the usual pagan crowd of bathers. It was the traitor in the camp, the 'impostor,' whose mere proximity was dangerous. Such stories belong to a situation of extreme danger to the Church. How near it actually came to being overwhelmed by a plausible and pseudo-Christian theosophy, we do not now know exactly. There are hints that at one time it was touch-and-go. The Presbyter and other responsible leaders had grounds for thinking that neighbourly tolerance might easily pass over into harmful compromise, and compromise end in apostasy. It is possible that the boycott of heretics was the only policy that could have succeeded in preserving the distinctive witness of the Church.

It is possible. Yet we must doubt whether this policy in the end best serves the cause of **truth and love,** upon which our author lays such stress. Does truth prevail the more if we are not on speaking terms with those whose view of the truth differs from ours—however disastrous their error may be? And if the norm of charity, as the First Epistle so eloquently sets forth (I John iv. 7–11), is the love of Christ, who died for our sins—and **not for ours alone but also for the whole world** (I John ii. 2)—is it possible to exclude from its operation even the most obdurate heretic?

We have observed that the Church has not, in the long run, maintained the teaching of the First Epistle that certain sinners are past praying for (see I John v. 16–17, and notes). We may similarly decline to accept the Presbyter's ruling here as a sufficient guide to Christian conduct. In any case, emergency regulations (such as this is) make bad law. And the spirit which in the hour of stress led to the boycott of heretics, declined only too readily into the spirit of persecution when orthodoxy came to command temporal power.

But if we take the responsibility of rejecting the Presbyter's ruling upon this point as being incompatible with the general purport of the teaching of the New Testament, and not really consistent with teaching of these epistles themselves, we must not in doing so evade the sense of urgency in witness to the truth that lies behind it, for that is something that always belongs to the situation of the Christian Church in the world. A good-humoured tolerance which is more than half indifference does not meet the seriousness of that situation, and is in any case not likely to maintain itself under the strain of divergent convictions upon questions which touch our emotions. The problem is to find a way of living with those whose convictions differ from our own upon the most fundamental matters, without either breaking charity or being disloyal to the truth. A genuinely Christian tolerance must rest upon a profound understanding of the meaning of **truth and love** as disclosed to us in Christ. If the Presbyter fails to command our full assent to his practical policy, he has given us the indispensable starting-point for any discussion of the problem, in his insistence upon these two fundamentals, and upon their inseparable unity in the Christian revelation and in the living of the Christian life.

EPISTOLARY CONCLUSION (12–13)

I have a great deal to write to you, but I do not mean to use paper 12 and ink; I hope to visit you and have a talk with you, so that our joy may be complete.

The children of your elect Sister greet you. 13

The Presbyter has much more to say, but prefers to leave it 12 for a personal interview with his friends when he visits them in the near future. But if he had already written 1 John, in which these themes are discussed at length, why did he not enclose a copy, or (if his correspondents had already seen it) at least make a reference to it? Or are we to suppose that 1 John was written to churches which he found himself unable to visit at this time? We have no material for answering these questions, but the raising of them should forestall any too confident dogmatism about the inter-relations of the Johannine writings. It may be that the apology for brevity of the letter is little more than common form. We may, however, take it for granted that the Presbyter really is looking forward to a visit which will give an opportunity of personal discussion of this thorny situation, **so that our joy may be complete**—an expression which, in view of 1 John i. 4 (see note) and John xv. 11, xvi. 24, probably means more than the simple gratification which naturally comes from the reunion of old friends.

The letter ends with greetings from members of the Christian 13 congregation in the place from which the Presbyter is writing.

THE THIRD EPISTLE OF JOHN

**The presbyter, to the beloved Gaius whom I love in the Truth. 1
Beloved, I pray you may prosper in every way and keep 2
well—as indeed your soul is keeping well.**

The letter begins after the conventional manner of the time 1
(see examples quoted below). It is, however, an exceptional
feature that the writer, instead of giving his name, calls himself
here (as in 2 John 1) 'The Presbyter.' This has no parallel in
the New Testament, and it would be difficult to cite a precise
parallel from known Greek correspondence of the period. It
may be that the circle of Gaius and Demetrius had the habit
of calling their revered leader 'The Presbyter' and nothing
else, and that he has adopted their practice in writing to one
of his adherents. But in what sense is the term to be understood? The word 'presbyter' means, in itself, no more than an
'elderly man.' We could imagine Gaius and his friends speaking
among themselves of 'The Old Man,' and, perhaps, the old
man accepting the affectionate nickname; but it would be
difficult to conceive him using it in a formal pastoral letter to a
Church, as we have it in the Second Epistle. We may in all
probability rule out this explanation of the term. Equally
improbable would be the suggestion that it is used in the
technical sense which it bore in the early Church (after Jewish
precedent) as the title of one of the board of Elders who
ministered as rulers and teachers of a local congregation. The
authority with which our author speaks is more than local. It
appears, however, that another quasi-technical use of the term
was current for a short time, mainly or even exclusively in the
Province of Asia—the home, to all appearance, of our Presbyter. Christians of this province seem to have spoken of 'the
Elders' (Presbyters) in referring to a group of teachers who
formed a link between the apostles and the next generation
(Eusebius, *Eccl. Hist.*, III. 39. 3–4). 'The Elders, disciples of
the Apostles' is the formula in Irenaeus (who came from the

Province of Asia: *Adv. Haer.*, V. 36, cf. V. 33. 3). They were apparently a small group; and it was quite possible for one of them to be spoken of, in appropriate circumstances, as '*The* Presbyter.' Irenaeus, for example, several times refers to things which he had learned from 'The Presbyter,' or 'The Presbyter, the disciple of the Apostles,' without naming him (Irenaeus, *op. cit.*, IV. 47. 1, 49. 1, I. 8. 17; Eusebius, *op. cit.*, V. 8. 8). Papias, also a provincial of Asia, refers to 'The Presbyter' (Eusebius, *op. cit.*, III. 39. 15), meaning, apparently, the Presbyter John, whom he distinguishes from John the Apostle. It is probable that the term is here being used in a similar way. As Irenaeus spoke of his early teacher, who had transmitted to him the apostolic traditions, so Gaius and Demetrius spoke of *their* teacher, the man who stood to them for the authority of the Apostles, as 'The Presbyter,' simply. He need not have been, and probably was not, the same person as Irenaeus's 'Presbyter.' He need not have been, though he may have been, the same as Papias's 'Presbyter John.' In any case, we must suppose that he held so outstanding a position among Christians of the province of Asia, as a mediator of the apostolic tradition, that he could write, whether to an individual adherent or to a local congregation, under the title 'The Presbyter,' without feeling the necessity of adding his name.

Of the recipient of the letter, who bears the exceedingly common name of Gaius, we know nothing but what may be inferred from the letter itself. It is indeed stated in the *Apostolical Constitutions* (VII. 46. 9) that he was ordained by John as bishop of Pergamon. There is nothing unlikely about it, but the document is late, and there is no early support for its statement. From the letter itself we deduce that Gaius was a leading member of some unnamed Christian church in the province of Asia. He may or may not have been one of its clergy. In any case, he possessed influence, and some means, since he is expected to give generous support to travelling missionaries (verses 5, 6). He is a faithful adherent of the Presbyter in the unhappy disputes that were troubling the church. The Presbyter claims him as his 'child' in the faith (verse 4), which possibly implies that he had been the means of Gaius's conversion, and in any case that he stood in a special pastoral relation to him.

In place of the customary greeting (for which see note on John 3) the Presbyter sends his love: **To the beloved Gaius whom I love in the Truth.** The turn of phrase might in another author mean no more than 'whom I love sincerely.' In very similar terms an Egyptian farmer writes, in a letter of A.D. 110, 'Greet all who love you truly,' and in another letter, 'Greet Epagathus and all who love us truly' (Grenfell and Hunt, *Fayyum Papyri*, Nos. 118, 119). Even in the present letter, if it stood alone, we should not necessarily read anything more into the expression. But in 2 John 1 the word 'truth' does seem to bear a pregnant meaning (see note there), and since it is throughout these epistles a word of far-reaching significance, we should perhaps understand the Presbyter here also to be reading a deeper meaning into a conventional phrase. In sending his love to Gaius he is not simply expressing the affection of ordinary human friendship; he is giving utterance to that divine charity which, as it is God's gift to us in Christ, is also the proper relation of Christians one to another in the fellowship of the Church.

The courtesy formula, 'I pray that you may keep well,' 2 seems to have come into vogue during the first century, and is extremely common in letters of that period. (For examples, together with some other varieties of the formula, see Moffatt Commentary, *Romans*, p. 6). The Presbyter expands the current form slightly and writes, **I pray you may prosper in every way and keep well.** The word translated **prosper** literally means 'to have a good journey,' but as there is no suggestion in the letter that Gaius is travelling, we may fairly take it metaphorically, especially in view of the turn given to it in the next clause, where the same verb recurs: 'as indeed your soul is prospering' (for so it should be rendered: the Moffatt translation, **as indeed your soul is keeping well**, which would presuppose the repetition of the other of the two verbs, is perhaps due to inadvertence). The Presbyter, who, as we shall see, highly approves of Gaius's line of action in a very trying situation, is satisfied that he is 'having a fair journey' spiritually; he hopes that his temporal affairs may be no less prosperous.

GAIUS AND THE TRAVELLING MISSIONARIES (3-8)

3 For I was overjoyed when some brothers arrived and testified to the truth of your life, as indeed you do lead the true Life;
4 I have no greater joy than to hear of my children living in
5 the Truth. Beloved, you are acting loyally in rendering service to the brothers and especially to any who are strangers; they have testified to your love before the church.
6 Pray speed them on their journey worthily of God;
7 they have started out for His sake and declined to take
8 anything from pagans; hence we are bound to support such men, to prove ourselves allies of the Truth.

3   In correspondence of the time it was a familiar (and very natural) custom to begin the main part of a letter by expressing the pleasure of the writer at hearing good news of his correspondent. Thus, a letter written between A.D. 70 and 80 begins, 'Chaeremon to his dearest Apollonius, greeting. I received your note of the (?) th. inst., in a damp condition. On reading it, I rejoiced that you were well, with all your family, for I make this a matter of prayer' (Bror Olsson, *Papyri aus der frühesten Romerzeit*, No. 43: my translation). Again, we have an expression almost identical with the Presbyter's, in a letter written in the reign of Claudius (A.D. 42-54), which may be quoted in full as a typical example of a private letter of the first century, with several points of similarity to 3 John (Teres is having alterations done to his house, and Capito is supervising the work on his behalf).

'Capito to his dearest Teres, many greetings. Before all things I was overjoyed, upon receipt of your letter, that you are well, and have found your wife and child in good health. About the dining-room, I shall of course do exactly as you wish. I have undertaken to do all, if not more than all; for I am deeply interested and set great store by your friendship. You will find that all the instructions you gave me in your letter have been accomplished. Indeed, I hope that when you come you will find even more accomplished. I am most grateful to Primus and Tycharius, because they attend to your instructions and assist us. The plasterers have done, and are doing, all the work in polychrome. About the veranda, write me what you intend, since you are renovating it. What would you like there—pictures of the Trojan War, or what you will? The place requires something. Farewell. Sertorius and his people greet you. Greet all your family' (*op. cit.*, 34: my translation).

The Presbyter too has been made happy by good news of his ᣟ friend. He has recently been visited by certain Christian 'brothers,' who brought him the assurance of Gaius's complete loyalty, in a situation where many proved disloyal. The Presbyter, conscious of a pastoral responsibility for the churches within his sphere of influence, is above all things anxious that his **children** shall **live in the Truth**—that is to say, shall hold the full Christian faith, follow the teaching and example of Christ, and adhere to the fellowship of the Church. In some quarters he sees the faith perverted, the Christian way of life dishonoured, and the fellowship broken. Consequently, he is **overjoyed** to hear that Gaius at least **leads the true life.** He can still be counted on.

He has given especial proof of his loyalty by the service he 5 has rendered to these **brothers**—**strangers** as they are (for the language of the original makes it perfectly clear that the term 'strangers' is a further description of the same persons as those called 'brothers'—'strangers as they are' would be a fair rendering). They do not belong to the same locality as Gaius, and upon the conventional human level they have no claim upon him. But they are 'brothers,' as being fellow members of the Christian Church. Gaius has fully recognized this claim, and has shown his loyalty to the Church (as well as to his spiritual 'father,' the Presbyter), by offering them hospitality, as they themselves **testified before the church**—that is, the Christian congregation in the place of the Presbyter's resi- ᣟ dence. Here was downright proof that Gaius practised that

charity, or love, which is the mark of the Christian life.
6 The Presbyter has now a request to make. The **brothers, we**
learn, have set out upon a journey in the cause of Christ. They
are, in fact, Christian missionaries. Following the directions
which Christ gave to His apostles (Mark vi. 8–9, and parallels)
7 they have set out without providing money for their journey,
relying upon such support and hospitality as they may receive
on their way. They conscientiously refuse, however, to take
anything from pagans. We should bear in mind that the
wandering preacher was a familiar figure of the times. Devotees
of various religions tramped the roads, extolling the virtues of
the deity of their choice, and collecting subscriptions from the
public. Thus a 'slave' of the Syrian Goddess has put on record
(in an inscription cited by Deissmann, *Light from the Ancient
East*, pp. 108 *sqq.*) how he travelled in the service of his
'Lady,' and 'at each journey brought back seventy bags.'
(His collecting-bag is the same, in Greek, as the **wallet** which
is forbidden to the apostles in Mark vi. 8.) The Christian
missionary must not be confused with these 'begging friars.'
We may perhaps read between the lines that there were
Christian missionaries who had no scruples about accepting
contributions towards their expenses from well-disposed
pagans, but the Presbyter's friends are praised because they
refuse to do so: they will accept nothing but what is given in
Christian fellowship, as an expression of brotherly charity.
Consequently, they are entirely dependent upon the generosity
of their fellow Christians, and Gaius is asked to provide on a
liberal scale for the expenses of their mission. The word which
6 is translated **speed them on their journey** is something like a
technical term of early Christian missions. It occurs also in
Acts xv. 3, xx. 38, xxi. 5, Rom. xv. 24, 1 Cor. xvi. 6,
Tit. iii. 13. A comparison of these passages shows that while
the actual meaning of the verb is no more than 'to speed a
person on his way' (colloquially, 'to give him a send-off'), it
had come to imply the assumption of financial responsibility
8 for the journey. This is what is asked of Gaius. The Presbyter
adds that in thus defraying the expenses of missionaries **we
prove ourselves allies of the Truth,** inasmuch as we collaborate

in the dissemination of the Christian message, which is the truth of God revealed in Christ.

THE RECALCITRANCE OF DIOTREPHES (9–11)

I have written to the church: only, Diotrephes, who likes to take 9 the lead among them, repudiates me. So when I come, I 10 shall bring up what he is doing, babbling against me with wicked words—and, not satisfied with words, he refuses to welcome the brothers, checks those who want to welcome them, and excommunicates them from the church. Beloved, do not imitate evil but good; he who does good 11 belongs to God, he who does evil has never seen God.

The Presbyter now passes to a less agreeable topic—the 9 opposition to his authority which has developed in some un-named church. I have written to the church, he says; Gaius will know at once which church is meant. It might seem natural to suppose that he was one of its members. But if so, it is difficult to see why it should be necessary to give him in-formation about the proceedings of the rebellious party in it. We may perhaps take it that Gaius was not a member of the offending congregation, but possibly a neighbour, and in any case acquainted with its situation, though not with the latest developments of it. At this point the Presbyter takes up his tale. He has written a letter to the church, upon a subject which Gaius will readily divine without being told.

It is tempting to assume (as many commentators do) that this letter is our 2 John; but upon consideration the assumption is not very probable, since there is nothing in the present letter to connect it with the doctrinal controversy with which 2 John is concerned. It would seem more natural to suppose that it dealt, like the letter to Gaius, with the business of the travelling missionaries. We might reasonably conjecture that the Presbyter had appealed to the church to welcome the missionaries and help them on their way, but the appeal had been rejected; or, it may be, he had reason to fear that it would not even be brought before the church; and that is why he now writes to Gaius, upon whose support he can count. The

centre of the opposition is one **Diotrephes, who likes to take the**
10 **lead among them.** Diotrephes **repudiates** the Presbyter,
babbling against him with wicked words. But apparently he is
in a position to do more than make abusive speeches. It may
be that he was able to prevent the Presbyter's letter from
reaching the church. At any rate, he **refuses to welcome the**
brothers, he puts obstacles in the way of those who would
welcome them, and he goes so far as to excommunicate the
party favourable to them. It would indeed be possible to soften
the import of the words by giving to the Greek verb a 'cona-
tive' sense: 'he is for excommunicating them,' 'he moves for
their excommunication.' Or, again, it is possible that the
words, which might be literally rendered, 'he throws them out
of the church,' are not to be understood as implying formal
excommunication, but mean that Diotrephes used physical
violence to exclude his opponents from the church-meeting. It
seems, however, most natural to understand that Diotrephes
either possessed, or arrogated to himself, the authority to
excommunicate, and exercised it effectively. This authority
belonged, so soon as the monarchical episcopate was fully
established, to the bishop. Whether the church to which
Diotrephes belonged already possessed a fully episcopal constitution, we cannot say. The churches of this region are
represented in the Acts of the Apostles and the Pastoral
Epistles as governed by a board of presbyters, who might also
be called bishops (Acts xx. 17, 28, Tit. i. 5–9). In the Ignatian
Epistles (about A.D. 115) they are governed by bishops, assisted
by a board of presbyters. At what stage this church stood at
this moment, we do not know. All we can say is that Diotrephes
acted in the capacity of a bishop, as understood from the
second century onwards. But what was his actual position?
There seem to be three possibilities: either (i) he was the
acknowledged bishop of the church, pursuing a policy hostile
to the Presbyter; or (ii) he was one of the board of presbyters
who, by force of character, or by successful demagogy, over-
rode his colleagues; or (iii) he was a layman, who had usurped
quasi-episcopal functions. The Presbyter regards him as
nothing but an ambitious demagogue. From his point of view

at least, Diotrephes was no bishop. In any case, however, he must have secured the support of a majority of the congregation; else we should have been told, not that he excommunicated persons from the church, but that he separated from the church with his followers (like the false teachers of 1 John).

The exact conditions governing the appointment of ministers in the sub-apostolic period are obscure. Clement of Rome appears to state the general view at the close of the first century when he describes the presbyter-bishops of Corinth as 'established by the apostles, or in the meantime by other competent persons, with the consent of the whole church' (1 Clem. xliv. 3). His letter, however, shows that there was a party at Corinth which took the view that the consent of the church might be withdrawn, and the existing ministry might be superseded by popular choice. It may be that Diotrephes and his party took a similar view. The Presbyter (if we have rightly identified him as one of the group which perpetuated the apostolic tradition at one remove) naturally stood for the element of apostolic authority in the appointment of ministers (the element for which Clement also contends against the refractory Corinthians). The period was one of transition. In the foreign missions of the Church at the present day it is a familiar observation that a time arrives when the control of the foreign missionary, accepted without question in early days, begins to chafe the indigenous church, as it grows in numbers, experience and self-consciousness. A phase of tension sets in, which, if development is healthy, ends in the graceful withdrawal of the foreign missionary in favour of the local indigenous ministry. It is probable that a similar phase of tension arose in the sub-apostolic Church. The Apostles in their lifetime had enjoyed an almost unquestioned authority, based not merely upon their personal prestige, but upon their unique position as personally commissioned by the Lord. Their successors for a time seem to have assumed a similar undefined authority. The Pastoral Epistles assume that Timothy and Titus would exercise a supervision of ministerial appointments and other ecclesiastical concerns, over a whole province, as wide and unquestioned as Paul himself had exercised. When, however, the church emerges from the 'tunnel' (see p. xviii), in the course of the second century, there are no Timothys and Tituses visible. The apostolic authority is now assumed to be transmitted, in some sense, through the succession of local bishops, who are not as yet under any 'metropolitan' control.

There must therefore have been a stage at which the authority of local ministers was growing at the expense of the waning authority of 'apostolic men,' like our Presbyter. It is likely enough that this stage was marked by some tension. Ageing men do not always yield with good grace an authority which under changed conditions they can no longer exercise effectively. Younger men, conscious of the growing needs and opportunities of a fresh generation, are not always considerate in grasping powers which are their due. It may well be that this letter reflects such a stage of transition and perhaps of tension. But if so, there are two different ways in which the situation might be construed.

It may be (i) that Diotrephes is in fact the first 'monarchical bishop' known to history in the province of Asia; one of a board of presbyters who, with large support from the laity, made himself what the bishop was to become, and flouted the obsolescent authority of a substitute-apostle. In that case we should conceive the Presbyter as the last champion of a lost cause, and his opponent as the pioneer of a new order which prevailed.

On the other hand, it may be (ii) that Diotrephes is a symptom of the disease which the quasi-apostolic ministry of monarchical bishops was designed to relieve. When the prestige of apostolic authority at a remove, in the persons of the Timothys and Tituses and their peers, declined, the very vigour and independence of the growing local congregations offered an all too tempting field to the ambition of able individuals. It seems clear that the danger which this state of affairs threatened to the unity and continuity of the Christian Body was one motive in the development of the catholic episcopate during the second century. If this view be taken, we shall conceive the Presbyter as confronting at an early stage the threat of disunion and anarchy in the Church, which was to occupy the energies of its leaders for a long time to come.

It does not appear that there was any question of doctrine involved. Diotrephes is not charged with heresy. He may, of course, have been suspected of a leaning to the false doctrines denounced in 1 and 2 John; but if so, the Presbyter would surely have mentioned the fact; he is not wont to be mealy-mouthed when heresy is concerned. It is, to all appearance, purely a question of order and discipline. The measures he takes are tentative. First he appeals to the personal loyalty of those who still acknowledge his authority. Then he proposes to visit the church, and to expose (presumably in the presence of the congregation) the misdemeanours of Diotrephes. The language which he uses—**When I come, I shall bring up what he is doing, babbling against me with wicked words**—suggests that the Presbyter is not too sure of his ground. He can do no more than stake his personal influence and prestige against those of Diotrephes. Whether his appeal succeeded, we are not told; but the very fact that his letter is preserved tells, so far, in favour of the view that it did. But that was hardly a final solution. The problem, as we have seen, was ultimately solved by the development of the catholic episcopate. It may be that the traditions which make 'John' the principal organizer of the episcopate in the province of Asia refer to our Presbyter and not to the Apostle. It may even be that he himself appointed Gaius as bishop, in accordance with the tradition preserved in the *Apostolic Constitutions*. But there is no suggestion of this in the letter, and conjecture is not profitable .

In verse 11 we have what looks like a purely general maxim; **11** but we are probably safe in understanding that the evil example is that of Diotrephes, who out of personal ambition hinders the work of Christian missions, tyrannizes over his fellow members of the congregation, interrupts communications between the congregation and its apostolic pastor, and flouts and slanders the Presbyter himself. All this constitutes a flagrant example of breach of fellowship and denial of charity. This example Gaius must on no account imitate. To **do good** (that is, before all things, to exercise charity, see notes on 1 John ii. 7–11) is the mark of one who **belongs to God.** Here the language of the First Epistle is echoed. A reference to 1 John ii. 3–5, iii. 4–10,

iv. 7 *sqq.*, and notes, will serve to illustrate what the writer means by 'belonging to God' and 'seeing God.' To put it briefly, there is no 'religious experience' which can rightly be called Christian unless it attests itself in the practice of Christian charity. Diotrephes, for all his ability and powers of leadership, has shown himself no Christian. Gaius must not follow his bad example. (Was he tempted to throw in his lot with the majority?) There are better examples for the Christian to follow.

A TESTIMONIAL FOR DEMETRIUS (12)

12 **Everybody testifies to Demetrius, and so does the Truth itself: I testify to him too, and you know my testimony is true.**

12 A third name is now introduced, that of Demetrius. Who he was we do not know. According to the *Apostolic Constitutions, loc. cit.*, he was appointed by John to be bishop of Philadelphia, but there is no early support for the statement. Conjectural attempts to identify him with Demetrius the silversmith of Ephesus (Acts xix. 24) or with Paul's unsatisfactory assistant Demas (Col. iv. 14, Philem. 24, 2 Tim. iv. 10) are little better than trifling. It may be that he was a member of the disturbed congregation or of that to which Gaius belonged; and at a time when there were cross-currents, and personal loyalties were uncertain, the Presbyter wished to assure Gaius that he was to be trusted. Or it may be (and this seems more probable) that he was one of the travelling missionaries, perhaps their leader. A likely suggestion is that he was the bearer of this letter, which introduces him to Gaius and the loyal minority, and serves as his credentials. Commendatory letters (or **certificates,** as the Moffatt translation has it, 2 Cor. iii. 1) played an important part in the life of the early Church, as we can well understand in the circumstances of the time. We have an example of such a 'certificate' in Rom. xvi. 1–2. In Col. iv. 7–8 Paul introduces Tychicus, the bearer of the letter, as a **faithful minister and fellow-servant in the Lord,** who will be able to give the Colossians accurate news of him. Similarly, it may be, the Presbyter entrusts Demetrius

with the delivery of his letter, and guarantees him as an entirely trustworthy person. **Everybody testifies to Demetrius,** he writes. By way of comparison (and contrast) we may take the language of a letter written in 13 B.C. by a freedman to his patron, who (he complains) has been listening to slanderous tales about him. 'I believe,' he writes indignantly, 'that I do not deserve to be insulted, as your friends will testify to you. I have done you no wrong, and your friends will not think it right for me to be insulted when I am meeting your claims' (Olsson, *Papyri aus der frühesten Römerzeit*, No. 9: my translation).

Everybody testifies to Demetrius, and so (continues the Presbyter) **does the Truth itself.** The latter phrase is remarkable. Its exact meaning is not altogether clear. The words, in another author, might be no more than a strong affirmation that the common opinion of Demetrius is the plain truth about him, and it may be that no more is intended here. But in these epistles we must always suspect that the word 'truth' has some more special meaning. It is indeed an unlikely suggestion that **the Truth** is here personified, and identified with God, with Christ, or with the Holy Spirit (in spite of John xiv. 6, 1 John v. 6). **The Truth,** in the language of these epistles, is the revelation of God in Christ. This revelation is appropriated by Christian faith, and embodied in Christian living. The Presbyter speaks of his 'children' as **living in the Truth.** Similarly, the First Epistle speaks of **practising the Truth** (1 John i. 6). As thus practised, the Truth becomes a matter of direct experience and observation, and provides a guarantee of the Christian standing of him who practises it. It may be that this gives the meaning of the expression in the present verse. The Truth itself testifies to Demetrius in the sense that his whole way of life so manifestly embodies the Christian ideal (as we might put it) that no one who is acquainted with him needs any further testimony. The Truth shines by its own light in all his actions.

The Presbyter, however, wishes to make it clear that he takes personal responsibility for his guarantee of Demetrius's soundness. No doubt Gaius will be impressed by the fact that

Demetrius is generally esteemed, and in time he will appreciate the self-evidencing integrity of his life; but meanwhile it will mean more to him that the Presbyter, whose judgment he is accustomed to trust, pledges his word in Demetrius's favour: **I testify to him too, and you know my testimony is true.** The phrase recalls the formula with which the Fourth Gospel is accredited in the editorial note appended to the last chapter (John xxi. 24). Who the 'we' are who thus attest the truth of the Fourth Gospel, we cannot say; but they were certainly not far removed from the circle of our Presbyter. Might we conjecture that he was himself the editor who wrote the note when the Gospel was published with its appendix?

EPISTOLARY CONCLUSION (13–15)

13 **I had a great deal to write to you, but I do not want to write to**
14 **you with ink and pen; I am hoping to see you soon, and we will have a talk.**
15 **Peace to you! The friends salute you: salute the friends one by one.**

13-14 In conclusion, the Presbyter apologizes for the brevity of his letter. He will be seeing his correspondent before long. Such apologies were more or less common form; but in this case it may well be that there were delicate matters to discuss which the Presbyter preferred to leave to a personal interview.

15 The greeting, **Peace to you!** was adopted by Christians from Jewish usage (cf. 1 Pet. v. 14). For the rest, the greetings follow the general model of contemporary correspondence. For example, in a first-century letter found at Oxyrhynchus we have 'Greet Ptolemas and all your people one by one' (*Oxyrhynchus Papyri*, II. 298: my translation); and in a second-century letter written from Rome: 'I send many greetings to your wife, and to Serenus, and to all who love you, one by one' (Milligan, *Select Greek Papyri*, No. 41: my translation). It is therefore quite beside the mark to infer (as some have done) that the party of the Presbyter was so small that it could (so to speak) be counted on one hand. His intention is simply to individualize for the recipients a courtesy which in writing must needs be left general.

Death
and the
Chaste
Apprentice

Also by Robert Barnard
in Thorndike Large Print

At Death's Door
The Skeleton in the Grass
The Cherry Blossom Corpse
Bodies

Death
and the
Chaste
Apprentice

Robert Barnard

Thorndike Press • Thorndike, Maine

Library of Congress Cataloging in Publication Data:

Barnard, Robert.
    Death and the chaste apprentice / Robert Barnard.
    p. cm.
    ISBN 0-89621-953-4 (alk. paper : lg. print)
    1. Large type books. I. Title.
[PR6052.A665D37   1990]   89-48536
823'.914--dc20   CIP

Thorndike Press Large Print edition published in 1990 by arrangement with Charles Scribner's Sons.

Large Print edition available in the British Commonwealth by arrangement with William Collins, Ltd.

Cover design by Jack Ribik.

This book is printed on acid-free, high opacity paper.

Note

The extracts from the supposed *The Chaste Apprentice of Bowe* are in fact taken from *A Trick to Catch the Old One*, *'Tis Pity She's a Whore*, and other plays of the Elizabethan and Jacobean period.

So don't blame me.

Death

and the

Chaste

Apprentice

The Saracen's Head

1

"Mad as a hatter," said Gillian Soames complacently, striding up the road from the underground towards Ketterick High Street. "Stark raving bonkers. Up the wall. Round the twist to an unprecedented degree."

Peter Fortnum, legging it beside her through the town, was surprised to see on her face an expression of quite sunny anticipation. After all, she was talking about Jason Thark, the producer-director of the play in which they both were to appear. The two had met on the underground, having previously done no more than swap words when they were in different productions at the Sheffield Crucible. Thus they were still in the earliest stages of mutual discovery.

Peter Fortnum was slim, fresh, and twenty-three. Gillian Soames was rather plain, beginning to be dumpy, and was a stage veteran of eight years in small parts. She had had her share of theatrical disasters and had gone on from them to other disasters or to the occasional minor triumph. She knew that this was a festival production, which would run its allotted course of twelve performances and never be heard of again, quite irrespective of the merits or otherwise of the production. Peter Fortnum was a nice lad, she was saying to herself, but you could spot the wetness behind his ears: He still believed that stardom might be just around the corner. Gillian knew that hard work was.

"So be prepared to swallow your artistic conscience," she added darkly.

"He's got a tremendous reputation," Peter ventured.

"Oh — reputation!"

Gillian's tone seemed to contain a limitless scorn for drama critics. Thus did Lady Bracknell dismiss cloakrooms at railway stations. Peter wondered whether Gillian wasn't, perhaps, a Lady Bracknell in waiting. But if she meant that directors' reputations were gained over the bodies of actors who knew better, then Peter could go along with that.

10

"People do say he does interesting things," he amended.

"The sort of director who gets that said about him," said Gillian, still with the same unruffled composure, "is the kind to run a mile from. What does it usually mean? If the play cries out for a simple, direct approach, he decks it out with moving sets, Wurlitzer organs, and so many spots it looks like the Battle of Britain. And if the play is weak and needs a bit of gingering up, he puts the characters in body stockings and sets it in the Gobi Desert. That sort of director's motto is 'Don't notice the play; notice *me!*' "

"Well, he can't play about much with an Elizabethan stage," Peter pointed out.

"That's true," conceded Gillian with all the reluctance of the born prophet of doom. "At least you wouldn't have *thought* he could. The critics will come down on him if he tries any modern tricksiness, that's for sure. Still — "

She stopped short in her stride as she and Peter noticed simultaneously a poster for the play in an arty little bookshop. They peered into the window, and Peter read out the title with a reverence the play hardly warranted:

THE CHASTE APPRENTICE OF BOWE

The poster was done in the form of a play-

11

bill — of the Restoration rather than any conceivable Elizabethan type. Peter's and Gillian's heads slowly dipped down as they read through the list of the players' names. There at the bottom they were: Peter Fortnum and Gillian Soames.

"At least we got on," said Peter.

"Which is more than the author did."

"It was published anonymously."

"Nobody willing to own up," said Gillian cheerily. "It does come rather into the 'justly neglected' category, doesn't it?" They resumed their lithe stride in the direction of the High Street. "Actually, I'd do a walk-on part in the worst play of Robert Greene just for the pleasure of working at the Saracen."

"It must be fabulous," agreed Peter. "Like getting back to one's roots — starting again at the beginnings of drama."

"Something like that," agreed Gillian, who distrusted enthusiasm.

"And actually staying there, too! I thought we'd be shunted off to some crummy bed-and-breakfast dive, with rooms at the Saracen reserved for the stars."

"That's not how they do things at Ketterick. The theory is that there *are* no stars — which is bullshit, but useful bullshit. Of course, a lot of the names have flats or houses in London, anyway. Some of the rest prefer to

12

take theatrical digs. I've got a poky room in north London which I've loaned to a friend for the summer."

"And I'm living out of a suitcase at the moment. I could have got cheaper digs, but just the idea of staying at the place . . . "

"Precisely. It has an aura. And at the Saracen's Head somebodies and nobodies rub shoulders and swap pints. That's something Arthur has insisted on from — Oh!"

"What?"

"Dear old Arthur. The landlord of the Saracen. I'd forgotten for a moment that he'd died."

"Was he nice?"

"The dearest old man. And one of the masterminds behind the festival. He treated everyone alike, from Hamlet to Second Gent. I suppose the place must have been sold or something. Anyway, we'll soon see."

They turned a corner into a wide but not too busy street, and Gillian pointed histrionically. "There it is," she said.

As if they had but one mind, they set down their cases and gazed.

Even from a distance, viewed through the clutter and bustle of an outer-London suburb, the Saracen's Head looked like something special, something rather out of the run of old English inns. You noticed first its long

13

frontage, which straddled a huge pair of gates. Through these, coaches had once rumbled to disgorge their passengers in the great yard beyond, for Ketterick had been a stopping-place between the north and Dover for fast coaches that had shunned the center of London. As you moved closer, you noticed that, apart from plaster over the half-timbering, it had been neither renovated nor tarted up, but had been left blessedly alone. The Saracen's Head had benefited over the centuries from a family of landlords who were quite remarkably slothful, men who could just about bring themselves to pull a pint but not much more. One of them, it is true, had in the mid-eighteenth century attempted something in the way of modernization, but fortunately he had died, and in his son the family inertia had reasserted itself. In the nineteenth century the railway had removed its principal function, and in the twentieth century hideous shopping precincts and malls had diverted a lot of traffic from Ketterick High Street. The Saracen's Head had slumbered on until it was rediscovered by architectural and theatrical historians in our own century. The sleeping princess had been reawakened by the kiss of the Ketterick Arts Festival.

As Peter and Gillian approached, past the modern facades of video shops and Marks and

Spencers, the great gates at the center of the facade were pushed open.

"Half past five," said Gillian, licking her lips with satisfaction. "Opening time."

Peter, seeing it for the first time, took in the details of the frontage as they stood on the other side of the road, waiting to cross. It was an untidy, welcoming facade. To the left of the great gates were the Massinger Bar and the Webster Bar. To the right, Reception and the Shakespeare Bar.

"The Shakespeare Bar's ours," said Gillian authoritatively. "Not that the festival ever does Shakespeare."

"No, we're stuck with *The Chaste Apprentice of Bowe.*"

"Anyway, they were just the Toby Bar, the Snug, and so on until the festival started. Even dear old Arthur wasn't averse to capitalizing."

They crossed the road, and from an unspoken wish they walked straight through the massive gates and into the great courtyard. Here they stopped, and Peter looked around with reverence at the open space within which they would be playing. Here the Lord Admiral's Men and the Lord Chamberlain's Men had played when forced from London's South bank by the plague or the hostility of City aldermen. The Saracen was, at ground-floor

15

level, the usual array of bars, dining rooms and kitchens, and the other inevitable offices of a large hotel. But at first- and second-floor level, on three of its four sides, it had kept the balconies from which the better class of Ketterick spectators had watched the entertainments provided by the traveling players. On the fourth side, the inn's proprietor of the eighteenth century, in that brief and regrettable spurt of energy, had bricked in the balconies and enlarged the bedrooms behind. Enough remained, with the row upon row of seats in the great courtyard itself, to provide sizable audiences for the Elizabethan and Jacobean revivals that were the staple of the Ketterick Arts Festival.

Even as they stood, silent, antennae atwitch to get the feel of the place, a couple of late workmen came out with two more sections of the stage. They began fixing them on to the section already set up, which was beginning to project out from the kitchens at the far side of the courtyard to form an apron stage. It was on this bare platform that the festival company had performed *The Devil's an Ass, The Faire Seducer, The Roaring Girls of Cheapside,* and other minor masterpieces of our drama. It was on this platform that Peter and Gillian would perform lesser roles in *The Chaste Apprentice of Bowe.*

"Our stage," said Gillian with satisfaction in her voice, and reverence too. "You're right. It's difficult to see what Jason Thark can do to bugger *that* up."

They watched the workmen and the embryonic stage, silent and companionable, united in some powerful but indefinable respect for their own art and its beginnings. Their mood was brutally shattered by an interruption.

"Would you be the operatic lady and gentleman?"

The voice had an Australian twang, and when they turned, they saw a bulky presence, now running to fat — an ex-rugby football player, perhaps, or the regiment's champion middleweight boxer. He was dressed in a suit of good cloth but baggy proportions, was balding, and his eyes were watery, shifting and ill focused. But what was most immediately off-putting was his manner, which was unpleasingly ingratiating, yet oddly combined with something cunning, something almost threatening. He oozed up to them, it was true, but his manner had as its subtext something of the bully, as if he were itching to get them under his thumb.

"I'm Des Capper, the landlord," he said.

"Oh." Gillian Soames hardly bothered to keep the layers of meaning out of her voice. After a moment's hesitation she shook his

17

hand because she could hardly avoid it. She did it in a manner that suggested she had already made up her mind he was a lousy replacement for dear old Arthur. "No, we're not the operatic lady and gentleman. We're both in *The Chaste Apprentice*."

Des Capper's face fell, and his manner lost several degrees of ingratiation.

"Oh. Suppose I should have known. The operatic people tend to come larger, don't they? It's the lung capacity that does it, you know — It's the lung capacity that makes or breaks a singer. You must be Miss Soames and Mr. Fortnum, then?"

"That's right."

"Playing Alison Greatheart and Peter Patterwit."

"Right."

"Most of the principals have been here a week or more."

"The leads always come early. We are not leads."

"Well, I'm sure you'll make something very nice of your respective roles," said Des Capper, leading the way towards Reception and making no move to help Gillian with her suitcase. "It's not the size of the role that counts, you know. A good actor can make a marvelous thing out of a juicy little part. I've seen it happen."

18

"We know," muttered Gillian. "We *are* actors."

"Just so long as you speak up and speak out," Des went on, disregarding her. "You can't get away with mumbling on this stage, oh, dear me, no."

"I have appeared in five of the eight productions here," said Gillian, acid-sweetly.

"Then you'll bear me out when I say speak up and speak out. The way some of these young actors produce their voices must have dear old Sir John Gielgud turning in his grave."

"He's still alive."

"That makes it worse. Personally I think it's all part of your mental approach to the part." Des, ensconced behind the reception desk, absently shoved little cards in front of them to sign as he continued to lecture them on their profession. "Have you tried yoga? There's many actors that do. I've got a terrific book of yoga exercises I could loan you. Incredible. They've changed my life, I can tell you. . . . What? Room numbers? Oh, yes. Have you filled in the cards? Fine. You're 227, Miss Soames, and you're 234, Mr. Fortnum. Close without being adjacent." He leered. "Can you find your own way? You should never pick up a heavy case like that, young man. You can do terrible damage to your dorsals that way. I've known people ruined by it, and an actor ought to be specially careful." He came round from behind the desk and put himself in a posture of demonstration. "What you should do is *bend* the knees slightly, go *down* to it, then lift it smoothly like *this*. . . . Got it? Don't mind me telling you, do you?"

By now the nature of the new landlord of the Saracen's Head needed no further defining in either of their minds. He was that most loathsome of God's creations, the Australian know-all. They both gave him smiles that scarcely rose to the level of the perfunctory and set off in the direction of their rooms.

Or roughly speaking in the direction of their rooms. The old inn was a maze of corridors, obscure passageways that ended in blank walls, inexplicable open areas that must once have served a purpose but which now seemed merely to be dumping places for unwanted pieces of furniture. The inn was innocent of lifts, which in any case would have been of limited use: The Saracen's sprawl was not vertical but horizontal. Discreet wooden arrows pointed in the direction of room numbers, which were allocated with the same beautiful lack of logic or pattern as the general layout of the place.

"I love it," said Gillian as they toiled back

along a passage that had led merely to a laundry cupboard. "Do you know, I've stayed here five seasons, and I still haven't fathomed it. And I still expect to hear Tom Jones and one of his doxies from one of the bedrooms."

But it was not Tom Jones that they heard.

"And if you upstage me again at the end of Act One, by God I'll have your guts for garters."

They were in one of those inexplicable open spaces, and the voice came from the bedroom or suite that led off from it. It was a male voice that was clearly accustomed to making itself heard in large spaces — a traditional theater voice. Gillian held up a finger and — still holding their cases, fearing they might have to make a hurried exit — they stood listening with the telling stillness of stage actors.

"Carston Galloway," whispered Gillian.

"I did not upstage you. You seem not to want to acknowledge that there *is* anyone else onstage."

"I am perfectly willing to cooperate with real company players. They wouldn't try to ruin each other's performances."

"Oh God, don't talk to me about your performance. Talk to your little backstage drab about that."

"Darling Clarissa," whispered Gillian.

"I suppose that *swoop* to the front was

21

something you arranged with dear Jason in bed?"

"Darling, we have *quite* other things to think about when we are in bed."

"Crap. Sex may be important to you — God knows, I've reason enough to know that it is — but nothing is more important to you than the shoddy little theatrical victories you arrange for yourself. So don't feed me that shit about sex being all in all."

"I love your exquisitely modulated guttersnipe language."

The Galloways were doing their daily exercises. They were famous in theatrical circles for the fearlessly open way in which they conducted their sex lives. The odd thing was that for all their openness and honesty, their emotional lives were just as great a mess as if they had been secret about it.

"I've always been so *sorry* for you," said Clarissa in a lethal purr. "There are so few female directors. And the ones there are direct practically nothing but all-female plays. It does frustrate your instinct to pay back in kind. So you have to content yourself with ingenues and assistant stage managers . . . nobodies. Still, I suppose they renew your youth, which heaven knows has lasted longer than most people's youth."

"My God! Coming from you . . . "

22

Gillian shook her head at Peter Fortnum, and together they stole down the corridor. A floorboard creaked under them, as floorboards could be relied upon to do at the Saracen when one was trying to be circumspect. It was unlikely that the Galloways in full flood would notice or care.

"Par for the course," said Gillian when they were out of earshot. "We can expect a feast of that in the next week or two. Ever worked with them before?"

"No," admitted Peter. "I've mostly been in pretty experimental stuff. Disused warehouses and upstairs rooms in pubs. That's not really their line, is it?"

"Oh, dear me, no. The thought of Clarissa in a Hackney pub is practically lèse majesté. Revivals of *Lady Windermere* or *The School for Scandal* — all powdered wigs and rustling taffeta — that's the Galloways' line. I believe Rattigan was about to write something for them when he died, and they certainly created some minor roles in late Coward. They're a practically extinct theatrical breed."

"The giant egos?"

"Well, that particular form of giant ego. Nowadays it takes different forms. The day giant egos are extinct in the theater we may as well all shut up shop and go home. . . . Good Lord, we're here. Do you think we'll ever

23

find our way here again — or find our way out, for that matter?"

They put their keys in their doors and swung them open. Each discovered they were in unlovely little boxes clearly furnished with castoffs from other rooms.

"It's all right," said Peter cheerfully. "I never expected anything better."

"It's *not* how dear old Arthur used to organize things. All the actors were given good rooms. Still, at least we've got a view of the courtyard and the stage."

They went to the window of Gillian's room. At the far end of the courtyard the stage was a little further towards completion — that great projecting space that would so cruelly expose any faults in their techniques, any immaturities or imperfections. Peter drew his eyes away, almost in fear. Down in the front part of the courtyard Des Capper was oozing forward again, this time to welcome a woman and two men, who had been disgorged from a taxi, and had come in to view the great space.

"Probably the operatic lady and gentleman," said Peter. "And if so, they're *not* large."

"Have you ever known that sort of blow-hard to get things right?" Gillian asked bitterly. "Is that young one Indian? He looks rather plump, an incipient fatty. No doubt Des Capper will put that down to his lung

24

capacity. Actually the woman looks decidedly presentable. I say — just look at Des! Look at the way he's fawning and scraping! It's a fair bet they're the stars of whatever it is, isn't it? Isn't he odious? Stomach turning! Look, he's even rubbing his hands. He's one of the most ghastly men I've met."

"He doesn't seem much of a replacement for your Arthur," agreed Peter. "I wonder why they appointed him."

"Appointed? I thought he must have bought the place or something."

"Didn't you see the plaque outside? It said the Saracen was one of the Beaumont chain of hotels. He called himself the landlord, but he must be some kind of manager."

"Really? Well, someone who's appointed can be sacked. The festival committee ought to do something about it. There must be some way he can be got rid of."

She said it casually. Others in the course of the next week or two were to say or think the same thing with more vehement emphasis.

The Shakespeare Bar

2

Gillian and Peter went out for their meal that evening. There was a little bistro called The Relief of Mafeking, Gillian said, where you could get a wholesome nosh-up for £2.95. In fact, they found the price had gone up way beyond the rate of inflation, as it did with most good things once they caught on, but it was a satisfactory bargain all the same. Even actors in work — and Peter was only intermittently so — had to watch their pennies.

"I never eat at the Saracen before I've got my first paycheck," Gillian explained over the chicken casserole, "and then only every three or four days. It's very pricey, though the food is marvelous." She added darkly: "Mind you, it's probably shark meat and kangaroo steaks nowadays."

She did not actually sing "Change and decay in all around I see," but the dust of mortality was definitely in the air. She had hit on the phrase The Great Australian Blight, G.A.B. for short, and she used it rather frequently in the course of the meal.

Later, with an agreeable sense of wallet and purse hardly at all depleted, they dawdled back to the Saracen's Head. They paused outside the Alhambra, a tiny theater, Victorian Moorish in design, a thing of many domes and minarets, which had been rescued from the degradation of Bingo when the festival first got under way. Here they inspected the poster for that year's operatic offering at the Ketterick Festival.

"*Adelaide di Birckenhead*," read Gillian, shaking her head. "Never heard of it. Not that that says anything. Since they did *Anna Bolena* five years ago I haven't heard of any of them. They deliberately go in for the unknown, as we do on the drama side. The critics feel they have to come if it's the first performance for umpteen hundred years."

"*Adelaide di Birckenhead* has just got to be early Romantic."

"I should think so. It almost always is. You're right. '*Opera semiseria di Gaetano Donizetti.*' I presume that means we only have to

27

take it semiseriously, which is a blessing. Who's in it? Oh — a Russian-sounding lady. She's never been here before. The tenor and baritone are old festival standbys, but they don't usually stay at the Saracen's. The American tenor's rather dishy, but the Mexican's a nasty piece of work. God — I'm dying for a drink. Let's get back and see if I can find anyone I know."

The fact that the Shakespeare Bar at the Saracen was the one used by the festival people had nothing to do with any desire to pay tipsy tribute to the Swan of Avon. All the actors and singers who stayed at the inn had rooms on that side, the side where the balconies had been bricked in. The rooms on the other three sides had to be vacated for the duration of the festival, on the orders of the fire chief, so that members of the audience seated on the balconies could have unimpeded exit in the event of fire (in which case they would undoubtedly have been lost and frizzled in the maze of corridors). The Shakespeare was a big, warm, scarlet-velvet bar, with sofas and easy chairs, and its only disadvantage, that particular year, was its closeness to Reception. Des Capper alternated between the desk and the Shakespeare, where he hovered from table to table like an unappetizing headwaiter, determined to give more of his personal attention than anyone actually wanted.

At the bar a gaunt, harassed woman with pulled-back hair was worked off her feet. As she waited to be served, Gillian was delighted to see that there was someone she knew there. Ronnie Wimsett had been in two earlier Ketterick productions with Gillian, and his Theodorus Witgood in *A Trick to Catch the Old One* the previous year had been much admired. He was a rather plain young man by actors' standards, though wholesome and presentable in a middle-class sort of way. One's first instinct on meeting him was to put him down as a bank clerk or a clothes store assistant. It was only after talking to him for some time that one realized this was the chameleon's self-protection. He had a talent for imitation and deadpan comedy that lit up his face and voice and a rubbery looseness of body that made him wonderful in farce. He was well into rehearsals, for he played the chaste apprentice himself.

"I shall say *nothing* of Jason's direction, nothing of his interpretation or of his understanding of my part in the play," he announced solemnly when Gillian and Peter had settled themselves down at his table. "Not because it's dreadful, you understand. But because you should come to your first rehearsal tomorrow with no trace of bias or *parti pris.*" He took a great draught of Saracen ale. "Let us instead while away the hours by ripping to shreds our fellow actors in this little-known masterwork."

Gillian smiled evilly, leaned forward, and the two went at it. Peter Fortnum, sitting on the edge of this gory arena, was interested and amused for a time, but his short career in the theater had left him with only a small circle of acting acquaintances, and after a time the names, their couplings and uncouplings, their tantrums and their delinquencies, began to pall. He was just beginning to wonder whether an obsessive interest in the marital affairs of the Galloways was not playing their game as they wanted it played when he heard muttered words of Russian from the table beside him. He pricked up his ears at once.

Peter Fortnum was grateful to his minor public school for two things, and for only those two: These were the opportunities he had been given in the annual school play and the chance to learn Russian. Quite apart from anything else, the latter had given him quite spurious claims on any small parts going whenever anyone decided to do a Chekhov or a Gorki. He swung his chair around, chipping in a few words, and in no time at all he was sitting beside the star of *Adelaide di Birckenhead* and interpreting for her as she made her first real effort to communicate with the agent who had brought her to the West.

Natalya Radilova was slim, dark haired, and beautiful. She was also very much at sea. It was only her second time in the West, and her attempts to discuss financial and other arrangements with her agent had been hindered by the fact that she knew no more than twenty or thirty words of English. She had in all their preliminary communications pretended to a "competent" knowledge of the language, but her letters to him had in fact been written by a friend.

"I've arranged all this with your Ministry of Culture," her agent said somewhat wearily.

"Arrange it with me again," said Natalya.

The agent, Bradford Mallory ("Call me Brad") was, like the Galloways, something of a theatrical throwback, though in his case, Peter suspected, it was much more of a conscious act, for it had the label "performance" stamped on it, as theirs had not. He wore a cloak, he said, "dear boy," and he occasionally patted the hand of the other singer on his books whom he had brought to Ketterick. This was the young man whom Mallory had apparently rechristened — "rather witty, wouldn't you say, dear boy?" — with the single name of Singh. An incredibly good looking young man, his Indian complexion had lightened from long, perhaps lifelong, residence in Britain. He said little, occasionally pouted, and sometimes smiled abstractedly at Mallory's affectionate advances. But what he did most often was to look at his reflection in the mirror on the wall behind Brad Mallory. When he had a clear, uninterrupted view of himself, he would put his chin up to pose in his most attractive position, pat his immaculately cut hair, adjust his tie, and then smile a catlike smile when the image presented to him was at its most pleasing. He was, Brad Mallory said, *the* coming countertenor, and he was to sing in the concert on the opening night of the festival.

As Peter Fortnum translated between Natalya and her agent — yes, she did know the role, yes, she did realize that, small though the theater was, the festival held a unique position in British musical life and success here could be a springboard for a very promising operatic career — he was conscious of a discordant presence in the vicinity, an intrusive note. The Australian voice has a cutting edge, admirable in the opera house but less well adapted to the social hobnobbing of a saloon bar. Des Capper was giving someone the benefit of his curious store of knowledge and opinions, which meant, in effect, he was giving them to everyone.

"Do you know that in Queensland they've got this new law forbidding hoteliers from serving sexual perverts?" There was a dirty little snicker. "Be a bit of a problem here in festival time, wouldn't it? Couldn't afford to lose half my customers." Peter half-turned his head and saw that it was the Galloways and Jason Thark whom Des was regaling with his muckiness. Peter's glance caught him gesturing in the direction of Brad Mallory and Singh, and he immediately changed his tone. "Mind you, I'm tolerant. Live and let live, that's my motto. I don't know if you've read about it, but it's been proved by scientists that sexual deviancy's purely a matter of brain damage during childbirth. Just like spastics. I know all about what causes spastics. Well, it's just the same with poofs, only more minor. It's like this . . . "

"Dear God!" breathed Mallory, raising his eyebrows to heaven with theatrical eloquence. "What have we done to deserve this antipodean clodhopper clumping all over our private lives and our personal sensibilities?"

He put his hand warmly on Singh's, but Singh's smile did not suggest that he had heard or, if he had, that he had understood. He said in an English that was perfect yet oddly inflected, addressing Mallory alone:

"Can we go up and watch the video? I've

got *Little Lord Fauntleroy*. You said we could watch it later tonight."

"And so we shall, dear boy, after one more little drinkie. It's my first chance to have a real talk to lovely, lovely Natalya, and she's full of questions that only I can answer."

Singh pouted but let himself be bought another sweet sherry.

Over at the Galloways' table, the theater's most glamorous couple had been stimulated by the company — though Des Capper was not in himself stimulating — to stage a public version of their afternoon row. It was a cleaned-up version, much more elegant, suggesting that they carried the idea of rehearsals and trial runs into other areas of their lives.

"We've never had any secrets from each other, nor from anybody else," Clarissa was proclaiming. "We take our pleasures when and where the fancy takes us. Of course it is a tiny bit unfair on Carston that all the people of real *weight* in the theater are men. Hardly any female producers, and the only kind of heterosex most of them are interested in is rape, and they're against it. And though Carston is not *averse* to men, as a variation, even he would hardly find the average impresario or producer attractive. Which leaves the balance of advantage very definitely on my side."

"And puts *me* very much in my place," said

34

Jason Thark with a wide, untrustworthy smile. He was, in fact, a not unattractive man — broad shouldered, commanding. But he was — and he let you know it — a man to keep on the right side of.

"Darling, I'm honest with you, as with everyone else. You're really rather attractive, and I'd have slept with you even if you hadn't been our producer. On the other hand, that does add a sort of spice . . ."

Des Capper, watching them, had assumed an exquisitely misjudged air of being a man of the world.

"I've known plenty of couples in my time who had what they call nowadays an open marriage," he put in, bending forward confidentially. "It's nothing new, oh, my word, no! I was in India just after the war, and what I could tell you about the Mountbattens' goings-on would make your hair curl!"

Clarissa regarded him with the sort of look she might use to wither a bit player who had interrupted her big speech five lines too early.

"Which is why Carston, poor darling," she swooped on, "does *very* much prefer that we get work as a *couple.*"

"Though that's not so easy these days," Carston confided genially. "Playwrights aren't writing bitch parts for women as they used to."

"And why he himself has to make do for his sexual adventures with" — Clarissa's smile widened triumphantly as they were joined at their table by an inconspicuous young woman — "*awfully* promising young stage managers like Susan here. Susan, dear, we were just saying what a *won*derful job you're doing."

In the face of a smile which resembled that on the face of the tiger that had just swallowed the young lady of Riga, Susan Fanshaw sat down and said nothing. She was getting good at doing that with the Galloways. She had bought her own drink — for Carston Galloway was not a generous lover — and she had noted Clarissa eyeing her as she stood at the bar. Knowing Clarissa, she had realized she would be a target as soon as she joined them. She sat down with a mixture of unease and defiance. Jason Thark was more used to the Galloways and their social style, and he sat there, slumped, gazing about him with an easy tolerance. Des Capper, on the other hand, was beginning to feel ignored and made motions of moving on.

"Well, it's been nice having a chinwag," he said with a little wave of his pudgy hand. "Better get along to have a chat with some of the others in my little flock."

"Darlings, I had no idea he was a *cler*gyman!" floated Clarissa's voice after him, exquisitely modulated so that he could not avoid just hearing. "I would have tried to be polite to him if I'd known."

Des Capper, lips tightening, settled himself down at the next table. Nobody made any move to admit him, but somehow he managed to get himself in all the same.

"All settled in nice and cozy?" he inquired to a quartet of frozen faces. "Are the Russian lady and the Indian gentleman finding everything to their liking? They've only to give a shout if not and I'll personally see that something is done."

"Singh is English." Bradford Mallory sighed. "As English as I am — and rather more so than you. Natalya has not, so far, been able to express any discontents she may have accumulated, but she has now acquired an interpreter, so if she feels you don't warm the samovar sufficiently before you pop in the tea bag, she will be able — thanks to our *char*ming young friend here — to expostulate with you on the subject."

Des Capper blinked, as if he had been hit with a dictionary. But he was unputdownable, at the same time giving the impression that he was registering all the snubs.

"Ah — Mother Russia." he said with a sigh.

"Motherfu — ? Oh, Mother *Russ*ia."

37

"Mother Russia. It's an expression . . . sort of a nickname. It's a country that has always held a fatal fascination for me. The Winter Palace, Anastasia, *Battleship Potemkin* . . ."

" 'Lara's Theme,' *Gorky Park*," murmured Brad Mallory.

"Exactly. It's a country of great elemental passions. I think I'd have been able to come to terms with it. The tragedy is, I've never been. I'd like to have told them a thing or two about how to run their agriculture. Ask the little lady" — he turned to Peter Fortnum, but he patted Natalya Radilova on the knee — "if they've ever been lucky enough to hear our great Joan Sutherland at the Bolshoi."

"Tell this stupid peasant to take his fat hand off my knee," said Natalya Radilova in Russian.

"Ah — she understood me. What did she say?"

"She asked you to take your hand off her leg," said Peter diplomatically.

Des Capper burst out into a chilling mine-host laugh.

"Well, well, well. No offense meant and none taken, I hope. I know they're a little puritanical still in these Iron Curtain countries. Me, I believe in being broad-minded. There's more than one kind of partnership, eh, sir?" Des gave a broad and repulsive wink

38

at Brad. "If you ask me, the Russkies could take a few tips from your country, young man," he added, turning to Singh, who was lost in rapturous contemplation of the mirror image of himself sipping sweet sherry.

"Singh is English," breathed Mallory.

"The Indians know a thing or two about sexual tricks, eh? Not that we were in a position to cast the first stone as far as moral habits were concerned. We, the Raj, the ruling class, I mean. As I was saying at the next table, I was there in '46-7, aide-de-camp to the Viceroy — "

"*Aide-de-camp*, now?"

"That's right. And some of the goings-on and permutations and possibilities that I saw while I was with the Mountbattens you wouldn't believe. Still, when you went out among the natives — as I did, because I've got what you might call an inquiring mind, as you may have noticed — you saw things you'd never even *read* about. Even an old soldier like me had his eyes opened, I can tell you. Ever since then India has always exercised — "

"A fatal fascination?"

"It has. It's been calling me back — "

"Please. That chair. Madam — you are my soprano?"

The voice — clipped, exact, icy — seemed to come from a great height. The young man

39

was no more than six feet, but he seemed as high as the Matterhorn, and as daunting. He took Natalya Radilova's hand and, bending over, implanted on it a kiss, much as if he were stamping her passport.

"Gunter Gottlieb," murmured Brad Mallory with a pretense of enthusiasm.

It was a name more often breathed with devotion, even fanaticism, but that was always by people who did not know him, or need to. Orchestral musicians usually crossed themselves as they uttered the name or spat. Gunter Gottlieb had only recently become a name to conjure with in British musical life. He had been appointed conductor of the Midland Symphony Orchestra at the early age of twenty-seven. It was not, then, an orchestra with a great name. Mahler said that tradition is slovenliness; with the Midland Symphony Orchestra slovenliness was a tradition. Not any more. In a matter of months that mediocre band had been transformed by a mixture of sackings, threats, taunts, hectoring, and rehearsals that became torture sessions lasting well beyond the limits of endurance.

Now Gunter Gottlieb's concerts had become the talk of the Midlands and beyond. London critics traveled to Coventry and said that the young Austrian's Mahler was definitive for his generation. Old men wept at his Brahms and Schumann. Young girls waited outside the studios and concert halls for his autograph, undeterred by the open contempt with which he treated them. One or two of them would be selected for brief and violent couplings with the great man by one or other of the two thugs who, in imitation of more established conductors, comprised his embryonic entourage. Already the first records were in the pipeline. He was the talk of the musical world. It was a pity, everybody said, that he was such an unadulterated swine, but his music — !

Gunter Gottlieb had been in Ketterick a week. Des Capper — even Des Capper — knew his man. Without a word he vacated his seat and evaporated. Gunter Gottlieb sat down, knowing the chair would be there. His attendant heavy fetched him a drink and stood behind the chair looking menacing, though no more menacing than his master. Gottlieb sat in his chair, his back straight as a Victorian spinster's, his body seemingly bent by two perfect right angles at the knees and the buttocks. He fixed Natalya Radilova with his glassy, inquisitorial stare.

"You know your part?"

"Yes," said Natalya after translation.

"Perfectly? Including my embellishments for the cabalettas?"

"*Yes,*" said Natalya.

"You are late," accused Gottlieb, tight-lipped and schoolmasterly.

"Natalya, as you know," put in Mallory with an expression of tired courtesy, "was called in to save some performances of *Norma* in Cologne."

"Performances at Köln are no concern of mine. The production of *Adelaide* is. I was not consulted about your late arrival. Next year, when we perform *La Straniera,* I shall be in charge of *ev*erything: schedules, sets, costumes, production — and singers. Especially singers." He smiled his sunset-over-the-gulag smile. "No production can be perfect unless one man has total control. I have made it clear to the committee that I must have that control."

"I have no doubt you will get it," Brad said with a sigh.

"Is that quite understood? Now let us turn to your *aria di sortita* in the first act. . . . "

He bent forward an inch or two, apparently in a gesture of intimacy, and went into lengthy instructions on how to phrase, project, and act during the heroine's opening aria. Any idea that this was hardly the time or place did not seem to occur to him. Peter Fortnum's powers as interpreter were taxed to the limit. Natalya listened with every ap-

42

pearance of attention. She was used to the ways of totalitarianism.

At the bar the gaunt, exhausted woman with the pulled-back hair, who incidentally was Des Capper's wife, was up to her eyes in orders. Des, however, was not in the business of helping behind any bar. He stopped by the table where Gillian Soames and Ronnie Wimsett were still deep in the entrancing business of character assassination. Nowhere, except perhaps the House of Commons, offers more scope for that sport than the theater, and they were set fair to continue until the call for last drinks.

"Everything all right here?" Des asked, clearly intending to muscle in. "Anything I can do for you?"

Gillian Soames raised her head, clearly about to say, "Yes — piss off." But Ronnie Wimsett, a peaceable young man, took her hand in his, gazed adoringly into her eyes in the manner of a second-rate tenor in Act I of *Bohème*, then turned to Des and sighed. "No — everything is just wonderful."

There was nothing Des could do but leave them to themselves. He threw some orders at his drudge of a wife, then pottered off to his little office behind Reception, convinced that that pair were resuming an affair of long standing. It was one of a series of assumptions, some true, some false, that Des Capper made about his artistic guests. These assumptions soon attained in his mind the status of facts, as the many harebrained theories he read about in magazines did. They were stored up and gloated over, for Des was convinced in his mind that knowledge was power. It never occurred to him that knowledge was also danger.

Open Stage

3

The nature of Jason Thark's directorial gloss on that year's Ketterick Arts Festival play became clear to Gillian the next day. On the way down to breakfast on that, her first morning of rehearsals, she stopped to study a large poster in Reception detailing all the major events and the backup arrangements. Among these latter was a lunchtime lecture on *The Chaste Apprentice*, to be given by the lecturer in Gay Studies at the local polytechnic.

Whether the chaste apprentice of the play was gay in the modern sense of the word was open to question. That he was dreary in any sense of the word was incontrovertible. Gillian mentally reserved her position on whether the gloss could be made to work.

Behind the grand apron stage, now finally assembled, lay the magnificent and sprawling kitchens of the Saracen's Head as well as a couple of private dining rooms. When the festival began, the actors would take over the dining rooms as well as a good half of the kitchens. Until then the actors tended to lounge around in the yard as the play was being rehearsed or camp in the dining rooms where they could talk and laugh and quarrel with more freedom. Today was the first full stage rehearsal, and Gillian experienced the familiar lift of the heart when Clarissa Galloway, as Lady Melinda Purefoy, came on with Peter Fortnum as Peter Patterwit to begin the play:

MELINDA: A private word, Sir, nothing else.
PETER PATTERWIT: You shall fructify in that which you came for: your pleasure shall be satisfied to your full contention: I will (fairest tree of generation) watch when our young friend is erected (that is to say up) . . .

The authorship of *The Chaste Apprentice of Bowe* was a matter of some lethargic scholarly dispute. It was variously attributed to Dekker and Chapman, to Beaumont and Marston, to Beaumont and Massinger, and to Heywood and Middleton. It was generally agreed that two hands were discernible in it, though only half a brain.

At the lower level of the play the story line concerns the attempts of two apprentices, Peter Patterwit and Matthew Cotter (who is really Sir James Cotterel in disguise), to persuade the third apprentice, Simon Clear, to lose his virginity. At the same time, Sir James is being sought by his true love, Lady Melinda Purefoy, whom a family feud is preventing him from marrying. On the other level, the apprentices' master, Ralph Greatheart, the goldsmith, is resisting his wife's attempts to marry off their daughter, Alison (Gillian's part, and a lousy one), to an elderly aristocratic roué, Sir Pecunius Slackwater. At the end of the play the chaste apprentice loses his virginity to a whore in Deptford, Matthew is unmasked as Sir James (much to the chagrin of Mistress Greatheart, who would have consigned her daughter to him had she known), and Alison is given in marriage to Peter Patterwit, who is thus much too well rewarded for all his dreadful jokes in the course of the play.

Jason Thark's notion of how to ginger up the play was evident from the moment Ronnie Wimsett took to the stage as the chaste apprentice. He had been instructed to deck out his performance with every gesture from the camp repertoire: the fluttering hands, the swooping voice, the wiggled bottom, the mincing walk. It was pure sixties camp, an exercise in behavioral archaeology: Thus are homosexuals *not* played on stage today, and thus do they *not* behave. But Ronnie was a superb comedian, and the performance in itself was a riot. Gillian could see Ronnie making a great effect with it, which he could never have done with the lines as they appeared on the printed page:

SIMON CLEAR: Why sure, Madam, I will do it straight

was no great shakes as a line, yet said with a spaniel wiggle, a lewd gesture unseen by his mistress, and with vocal leaps worthy of a Mozart soprano, it was a surefire laugh getter.

Gillian also saw, of course, that as an interpretation it was open to several objections: The apprentice was supposed to be a dull young man, so that every other line Ronnie spoke and half the things that were said about him by others were contradicted by his physical performance; this young man might be innocent of the knowledge of women, but chaste he could not conceivably be. In Jason Thark's reinterpretation the crowning episode with the whore of Deptford became no more than a brief shift of allegiance. Not that it mattered much; this was no masterwork. But homosexuals were these days as sensitive about their image as other minority groups.

They could take against the production, and — remembering the usual makeup of the festival's audience — Gillian could imagine them banding together to form a fair-sized picket.

The idea that there might be some element of exaggeration and stereotyping in this performance got through even to Des Capper. On the second day of stage rehearsals he oozed up behind Gillian and Ronnie, while up on stage Carston Galloway, as Ralph Greatheart, was having a tremendous row with his (stage) wife. Having so much experience with his real one, Carston was making a great thing of it, and Gillian and Ronnie were talking in their normal voices when Des came up behind them and thrust himself uninvited into their conversation.

"That's a real little gem of a performance you're giving there," Des nasaled out, clapping Ronnie on the shoulder. "Got all the mannerisms fit to kill. I was pissing myself laughing back there."

"Thank you," said Ronnie briefly, unwilling to be rude to a man in his own courtyard.

"I wonder — don't mind me saying this, do you? — whether you've quite got at the *psychol*ogy of the bloke. I wonder whether you're really living inside him yet, understanding what makes him tick. Ever heard of Stanislavski?"

"Didn't he compose *The Rite of Spring?*"

said Ronnie brusquely, and marched back-stage. Des nodded sagely.

"I think I got through to him," he said with grotesque complacency. "You could see he got my point. Though I think it was a quite different Stanislavski wrote *The Rite of Spring.*"

As the days of rehearsal flew by and the play took shape, both Gillian and Peter saw enough of the Galloways to wonder whether the balance of power — was that the word? of strength? of influence? — was quite as it had seemed to them on the day of their arrival. Gillian had seen the situation then as pretty much the same as when she had acted with them in a Haymarket revival of *The Rivals*, or two years previously here in Ketterick in *The Faire Seducer;* Peter, new to them, had seen it as the classic henpecked husband situation, though with a strong element of fighting back. Now they began to revise their opinions.

The first thing they noted was that Carston Galloway was giving a superb performance as Ralph Greatheart: warm, crusty, independent, salty. This was light-years away from the elegant, youngish man, cigarette holder in one hand, White Lady in the other, which was how the theatergoing public had hitherto seen him. Galloway was making the transition to being a good character actor. And like most actors, he knew his worth. Peter heard him one day when he took Jason Thark aside.

"Oh, Jason, that understudy to little Soames — is that still going begging?"

"Yes, we haven't got anybody."

"Then give it to Susan, will you? Susan Fanshaw. She's not really stretched by all these fiddling stage-management jobs."

Jason paused only for a second. "All right, Carston — gladly. Will you tell her?"

"If you like," said Carston, winking.

Whether Clarissa would ever make the transition to successful character actress could only be a matter for guesswork. What was sure was that she was not willing to make it yet. That really was the trouble: Melinda Purefoy was young love, she was romantic interest, she was dewy-fresh virgin. The actor playing Sir James Cotterel, with whom she was in love, was a public-school smoothie of twenty-six. Whereas Clarissa was — what? The reference books differed, or rather most of them kept silent, having no wish to give currency to Clarissa's blatant untruths. But the record of her career was public knowledge: She had made her West End debut in an H. M. Tennent revival of *Present Laughter* in 1962. Put her beside her supposed lover in the cruel light of day — which, after all, was what they would be acting under, with some blessed softening of evening light — and the gulf between them was brutally apparent. Put her, on the other hand, beside Constance Geary, a gin-ridden old bag whom everybody loved, who was giving a great performance as Old Lady Sneer, and you saw at once what Clarissa would become. Both were mature ladies at different stages of maturity. They were sisters under the gin.

Why she wanted to play the part was obvious — to prove she could still convincingly manage young women. It was as unwise an ambition as could be conceived, and how she had got the part was far from obvious. Gillian and Peter never saw any great evidence that her bedding with Jason Thark brought her tangible rewards in the way of added prominence or any shielding from his wrath. Could it be, then, that she had got the part because they wanted Carston for Ralph? Quite the reverse, in fact, of how she wanted people to see the situation.

Clarissa, however, was not to be underestimated, and she retained her unrivaled power of fuss making, which was legendary in theaters the length and breadth of the country. On Gillian's fifth day of rehearsals, during the midmorning break when everybody was in the little private dining room drinking coffee or something stronger, Clarissa burst in on them in a manner that certainly did not suggest she was going to ask whether anyone was for tennis. She used, in fact, her standard stage manner for delivering disastrous news or staggering developments.

"Really! It's too bad! Jason, you'll have to do something."

Jason was going over business with Ronnie Wimsett. He merely turned and raised a coolly inquiring eyebrow.

"It's that appalling Capper person. I've just been up to my bedroom — "

"Which one, darling?" inquired Carston languidly. "Ours or Jason's?"

"Ours, pig. And I found this . . . antipodean monstrosity poking around in my drawers."

"Underwear fetishist, would you say?"

Clarissa drew her hand across her brow. "God! Don't trot out all those ancient jokes, Carston. In the drawers of my dressing table. Actually poking and prying in them."

"Did you catch him in the act?" inquired Jason.

"Well, not quite," admitted Clarissa with a sigh designed to be heard in the dress circle. "One of those damned floorboards creaked just as I was opening the door. He'd got the drawer shut by the time I'd got into the room."

"What did he say?" Carston asked.

"He said he was just checking up on the maid's work." She put on a hideously nasal stage Australian accent. " 'She's new to the job, y'see, and I'd like to be sure she's up to the high standards we set ourselves at the Saracen.' "

Jason shrugged. "Seems a fairly foolproof explanation."

"Oh, does it? Well, let me tell you, the maid who does our room every day, including this morning, was here two years ago when we were in *The Faire Seducer*. I count her as an old friend. She's just thrilled by anything to do with the theater. I gave her a pair of my stockings when we finished here last time — they do so appreciate something personal, these people."

This artless revelation of Clarissa's rather blunted the impact of her indignation. The assembled company was so staggered that the Galloways apparently tipped the hotel staff with items of their castoff clothing that they were unable for a moment to focus their minds on Des Capper's iniquities.

Constance Geary sighed and said privately to Peter Fortnum: "I wonder if I could tip my maid with my castoff gin bottles." Then suddenly a thought struck her, and she spoke up. "Oh — I've just remembered."

"What?" asked several people.

"Yesterday morning, when I was in the bathroom — making the best, darlings, of what never was very much — the maid came in and started doing the room. I sang away like mad, to tell her not to interrupt my mysteries. When I finally emerged, blushing all too artificially, she wasn't to be seen, and the door was open. So I poked my shy, virginal little head out, and there she was with this anthropoid Australian at the far end of the corridor. She had my wastepaper basket in her hand, and as far as I could see, darlings, they were actually *counting* the half bottles of gin in it."

"Really!" said everybody, laughing as they were intended to do.

"Perhaps they were thinking of sending your score to the *Guinness Book of Records*, darling," said Ronnie.

"But isn't it such *fun?*" exclaimed Connie. "What do you think he does with his knowledge?"

"Enjoys it?" suggested Jason.

"Oh, I rather hoped he might feed it into a computer or something so I could become a statistic."

Clarissa was annoyed at losing the limelight and annoyed that Connie had defused any anger she might have generated against their prying Mine Host.

"You call this *fun?*" she demanded with a vocal swoop reminiscent of an eagle picking up a lamb. "Fun? To have this *grubby* little creature scrabbling around in our private lives?"

"Well it's hardly something we need to take seriously, is it?" Connie said reasonably enough. "It's a bit late in the day for me to go all coy about the fact that I spend much of my time pickled in gin. And you Galloways run much the most public private lives in the business."

"Carston and I have always been quite open about — "

"Yes, darling — spare us the party manifesto. Since you *have* been so open, what's the point in getting upset if this little Australian mole comes sniffing around in your underwear drawer? It's been washed in public often enough, heaven knows."

Clarissa shot her such a look that they resembled nothing so much as two old bags in early Coward. She held her fire only because she knew Connie was a redoubtable opponent.

"What's he doing it for, that's what I want to know?" she asked, looking around. "What does he want?"

"It's for the knowledge," Gillian said. "It's

56

a sort of instinct, and as Jason said, he probably just enjoys it — hugs it to himself, makes good stories of it after we're gone. He is unutterably loathsome, but he can hardly expect to be able to *use* things which none of us is trying to hide."

But Clarissa was far from being placated. "I think something should be done. You, Jason — you're the obvious one to do it. You could go direct to the festival committee. It's your first year here — you don't remember how wonderful it was at the Saracen in previous years. If something's not done quickly, the festival will lose all its spirit, all its old character. That man's got to *go*."

Jason took that point, at least, seriously. "I think, actually, you may be right. But the time to do something is not *now*. All we would achieve would be bad blood, recrimination, frustration. Not good for the show, for any of the shows. What might work is a collective letter, after this festival is over, from all the artists staying or working at the Saracen — a letter sent both to the festival committee and to the hotel chain that appointed him. Though what on earth possessed them to appoint him in the first place I can't imagine."

"Might one suggest blackmail?" said Clarissa sweetly.

"That's a point." Jason was thoughtful. "If

so, we've really got a problem on our hands. . . . Come on, boys and girls. Back to the grindstone. All onstage. We've really got to lick the brothel scene into shape."

Gillian had had to revise her opinion of Jason Thark as director somewhat. There were large areas of the play where he did, in everyone's opinion, excellent things. He worked tirelessly with Carston Galloway on the part of Ralph Greatheart, and together they created a rounded, human, and funny character from the bare bones of the script. He coaxed from Constance Geary, whose technique had been formed in proscenium-arch theaters, a performance that exploited all the potential of the apron stage. All the swirling crowd scenes, including the Deptford brothel one, went with great brio. The chaste apprentice as archgay seemed to Gillian funny but misconceived, and with Clarissa he could do nothing — but Melinda Purefoy was never going to be much of a part in anybody's hands. But all in all she had no doubt he was going to put together a real performance and probably have a critical success.

Of Jason as director, then, her estimate had risen. On Jason as a person she felt she could reserve judgment. On Jason's intelligence generally, her opinion took a nosedive one evening. (She was sitting with Peter, Con-

58

stance, and him at a table for four and telling them how much better the food at the Saracen used to be.) Suddenly Jason came up with one of his "ideas."

"I say, wouldn't it be effective if Singh could introduce each act with a few Elizabethan part songs?"

"With *what?*"

"Elizabethan part songs. I'll suggest it to Brad."

"I didn't know Singh was a ventriloquist," said Gillian. "I suggest you say Elizabethan lute songs."

"That sort of thing," said Jason blithely. "Something suitably bawdy could go down well."

Unfortunately the idea came to nothing. Singh had such songs in his repertoire and had performed them in Balliol College Hall and to other select musical societies. But on the first night of *The Chaste Apprentice* he would be performing Handel arias in an operatic concert in Town Hall.

"The opening concert of the festival," said Bradford Mallory. "A bit of a popular mishmash, to get audiences, but I've persuaded some of the London critics along to hear Singh. I am *not* having the dear boy dashing from one end of town to the other to fit you in. But he could sing on the other nights."

But Jason was only interested in the first night. That, after all, was the night the critics came. As with Brad, it was success with them that really counted with Jason.

"Rather typical," said Gillian. "And what appalling ignorance in somebody directing an Elizabethan play. I think he is essentially brilliant but vulgar."

She might, if she had thought about it, have admitted that this was a pretty good combination of qualities for the director of a minor Jacobean comedy. But Gillian was not disposed to like directors, and her nerves were just a little bit on edge as the first night of the festival drew nearer. So were all their nerves. The matter of Des didn't help to keep them calm. They were all watching him, wondering. More to the point, they felt him watching them. Few of them had any inhibitions about their sexual lives, though few would care to conduct them under the sort of spotlight the Galloways directed on themselves. But it can be that the most lavishly open people in fact have corners in their lives that they reserve from public scrutiny, and the grubby, obsessive nature of Des's interest made them feel threatened. It was a rare person who did not have a few private, personal things to be cherished in solitude, blushed about, cried over in the dark.

Who could be sure that Des, in his snuf-flings in the undergrowth, would not find some path that would show him the way to those personal walled gardens?

The Alhambra Theater

4

Five days before the festival was due to begin, in thin afternoon sunlight, Peter Fortnum made his way through the streets of Ketterick towards the Alhambra Theater. The afternoon session at the Saracen was mainly to be devoted to scenes involving the Greatheart family, and he was not required until later. There were great stretches of the play in which Peter Patterwit did not appear, and contemplating the arid desert of smutty facetiae and labored puns that constituted the dialogue when he did, Peter was inclined to think the audiences might wish those stretches still longer.

On days when he was free he had got into the habit of going along to the Alhambra to see if he could be useful, which meant, in effect, to act as interpreter. Today, however, he had a more specific mission. He no longer looked at the silver-blue-and-maroon Moorish facade, merely nodded to the stage-door keeper, and forged his way unhesitatingly through the maze of cold, painted brick passageways to the backstage area. Today was to be the first full stage rehearsal with orchestra.

As Peter slid into the wings, he signaled to Natalya.

"Ah — Peter," she said in a pause.

"Oh, Peter — great," shouted Terry Potts, the producer. "Sit there at the side in case we need you, will you?"

Glad to be recognized and useful, Peter sat quietly in the wings and peered out into the auditorium. He recognized the director of the festival casting a benevolent eye over the second cornerstone of his two weeks of events. He saw Brad Mallory, with Singh, sitting in the third row and looking out for the interests of his other client performing at Ketterick. Very much his secondary interest, thought Peter rather bitterly.

He turned his glance back to the stage area and took in his first view of the set. The festival organizers had gone back to a designing pair who had served them well two years before for Donizetti's *Il Diluvio Universale*. ("This is less a revival than a resurrection,

63

in the Burke and Hare sense of the word" — *The Observer.*) Now they had constructed a permanent set with fragmentary bits of castle dotted around. It was handsome and serviceable, and splashes of color were provided by tartan wall hangings, for just as Bellini had called his opera set in Portsmouth *I Puritani di Scozia,* so Donizetti had apparently been convinced (or preferred to believe for romantic/commercial reasons) that Birckenhead was north of the border. Indeed, to him or his librettist all England seemed to be an appendage of Scotland, which at least righted a balance, some might think.

"With passion," shouted Gunter Gottlieb, a domineering intensity oozing from every pore. "This man is your lover and your king! Thrill your audience!"

For upstage had entered the handsome figure of the Swedish-American tenor who was to sing Roberto il Bruce ("Broo-chay," as the language coach constantly insisted they all must call him). On stage Adelaide di Birckenhead, her husband Adalberto, and a motley collection of retainers and clansmen were about to launch into an exciting ensemble with choral backing. It was an ensemble that was later to serve for a vengeful heroine who had been abandoned in the catacombs in *Maria di Rudenz* and for conscience-tormented Christians and

Romans in *Poliuto*, proving that Donizetti certainly recognized a showstopping tune when he hit on one.

"Now — passion!" shouted Gunter Gottlieb. "Controlled, thrilling passion!"

Adelaide di Birckenhead had had a history even more checkered than most of Donizetti's immense output. Composed originally in 1825 for the soprano Ferron and the castrato Velluti, it had been put aside when the latter deserted the company for meatier pickings in London. Later, at the height of his powers in 1835, Donizetti had unusually found himself without a libretto. "For God's sake write me a libretto," he had gone around frenziedly wailing to all his poet friends, displaying all the withdrawal symptoms of today's druggies. To no avail. He had had to reset almost the entire text of *Adelaide*, recasting Velluti's part for tenor. Unluckily, he had promptly forgotten about it in the excitement of composing *Lucia di Lammermoor*. Part of the manuscript score had lain for years in the Sterling Library in London, while the rest had been discovered only the previous year serving as a doorstop in the Conservatory of Music in Naples. This was to be its first-ever performance.

The story concerned a crucial moment in Scottish history, which it travestied. It was said by one Italian commentator to have *"origine walterscottiana,*" a suitably vague description which obviated the need to ransack the works of the great unread Walter. The noble and patriotic Adelaide is unfortunate enough to be married to the skulking Adalberto, who supports the English tyrant Edgardo, who is busy suppressing the noble Scots. Adelaide is in love with the true Scottish king Roberto il Bruce, who is in hiding from the ravaging English armies. When he comes to *il castello di Birckenhead* in disguise, seeking succor, he presents her with a crisis of conscience which she solves spectacularly in the last act by hacking off her husband's head, then stabbing herself at the climax of a thrilling cabaletta. The stalwart clansmen of Birckenhead, typically willing to change sides at the drop of a coin, acclaim Roberto as their king.

The American tenor Krister Kroll stood at the Romanesque doorway at the very back of the stage, decked in furs left over from *Attila* ("proving that even Verdi nodded" — *The Observer*) in 1978 and tartan bought in bulk from the local Pricewise chain of discount stores. He was the only one in costume, because he said it was the sort of costume you needed to get the feel of. He was in the mold of so many American tenors: stalwart, clean limbed, and rather small of voice. He had appeared, pleasantly, in Rossini's *Torvaldo e Dorliska* ("a

66

stillborn curiosity" — *The Observer*) the year before. As he stood, dramatically, at the door- way, first Adelaide whispered her apprehen- sions at the sight of her lover, then her husband expressed his suspicions at the sight (in furs and tartan) of the handsome stranger. And then Krister Kroll launched himself into the great tune:

> *Io son pari ad uom cui scende*
> *Già la scure sulla testa . . .*

Even to Peter, sitting in the wings, it was an anticlimax: It was like being handed lemonade when you had expected champagne. He saw the festival director mask an expression of dis- may; he seemed to be wondering what sound, if any, would penetrate to the gods.

Gunter Gottlieb, with an impatient gesture, stopped the orchestra. Silently, pregnantly, he pointed with his baton to the center front of the stage. Krister Kroll looked uncertainly from Gottlieb to Terry Potts, the producer, in the stalls. Terry was already jumping out of his seat in agitation.

"But, Gunter, you can't have him there. He's just arrived, and he's apprehensive and agitated, uncertain of his reception. He can't just barge his way right to the center of things."

Natalya seemed to agree with him. She was

67

expostulating violently in Russian against the improbability of the thing, which Peter was just about, somewhat nervously, to translate when he saw that Brad Mallory, with Singh in tow, had come on to the stage and Brad was expostulating with her and calming her. He seemed to be able to do it without benefit of common language, but that was doubtless a necessary talent of agents.

None of which cut any ice at all with Gunter Gottlieb. He pointed icily once more to center stage. Nervously, Krister Kroll moved forward.

"Now again from the soprano."

The annoying thing was that the man was undoubtedly right. You couldn't have the opera's one big moment, comparable with the Sextet from *Lucia*, go by default because the tenor couldn't be heard. Now Kroll rang out sweet and true, lacking only that dash of kingly swagger and animal excitement that the part seemed to demand. In a conflict between what made musical sense and what made dramatic sense, the music had to win. And yet, and yet . . .

"Now," said Gottlieb, stopping the orchestra at the end of the number and gesturing to the producer as if he were a dog he was sending to retrieve a partridge, "now you rearrange the staging."

And with a sigh the poor man, knowing

when he was beaten, did just that.

"All right, if we must, we must. Yes, I know it's improbable, Natalya. I agree with you, darling. But you'll have to go *there*, center left, and . . ."

"I know how he feels, poor bastard" came a voice behind Peter's shoulders. He turned and was astonished to see the figure of Des Capper arriving in the wings. His eyes gleamed brightly with malice as he contemplated the scene. "Been a bit of a brouhaha, has there? Looks like it."

Peter, for some reason that he could not analyze, did not want to swap derogatory opinions of a fellow artist with Des Capper. Gottlieb was a bastard, but a brilliant bastard. He merely said: "They're just having to rearrange the positions a bit."

"Looks like there's been a good old-fashioned blowup to *me*. I know the signs. That swine has got the light of battle in his eyes. I know just how that producer must feel."

"Oh, yes?"

"*Just* how he feels. I've felt his nasty tongue myself. He's got no thought for the feelings of others. I'm sensitive. I don't like being spoken to like I was dirt."

Peter did not comment on Des's sensitivity. "What are you doing here?" he asked.

"Oh, I'm committee. Ex-officio as landlord of the Saracen. I've a right to go anywhere — "

He suddenly caught sight of Singh, still on-stage with Brad Mallory. "My! I see they had Indians in Birkenhead even then. Running the corner shops, I suppose."

Peter turned away with a grimace of distaste and didn't bother to correct him. He wondered about Des's right to go anywhere. It wasn't a right that any other member of the committee seemed to exercise. Peter turned back to the stage. Gunter Gottlieb, on the podium, was softly tapping his baton on the score. His expression suggested that he was long-suffering but had been pushed near the limits of even his saintly endurance.

"*Now,*" he said when Terry Potts paused for breath, "is all clear? We go from there to the end of scene."

It was only ten minutes of music, but it seemed endless to Peter. The ensemble developed into a big scene of suspicion and suppressed fears, with every character generously sharing his innermost feelings with the audience. The problems of balance were acute, not least because of Krister Kroll's sweet but small tenor, which was swamped by the larger voices around him. Again and again Gottlieb stopped the music, reorganized the singers, hushed the orchestra, subjected Krister Kroll to heavy, biting irony, lashed the other singers, and ridiculed members of his orchestra.

Even Peter felt himself sweating with tension. It was at the height of the unpleasant session, when the frayed tempers of singers and players were beginning to conquer their fear of Gottlieb and find open expression, that Peter from the wings saw Gottlieb's "heavy" sitting in the front row of the stalls, a slow, relishing smile on his face. He might not like music, but he certainly did appreciate aggro.

At long, long last Gottlieb called a break, and the tension dissolved. Peter's immediate visual impression was one of sweat. The orchestral musicians, jostling their way out through the door at the back of the pit, were shining with it, and one of the younger men seemed close to tears. The chorus members were bathed in it and wiping their foreheads, and the principals were drenched and close to the breaking point. Backstage everything became a jumble as singers and players made for the Green Room in search of cold drinks or chocolate to revive their strength. Peter was conscious of the Mexican baritone standing by a wall, clenching and unclenching his fists and muttering furiously to himself in the manner of operatic baritones. He was conscious in a far corner of the room of Krister Kroll being collared by Des Capper. Des had been in the Green Room when they arrived, making himself at home and waiting for a victim. The chain-saw voice cut through to Peter:

"You know, physiologically speaking there's no such thing as a small or a large voice. It's all a question of the diaphragm and the way you use it. If you'll take a tip from me . . . "

The American seemed to be a supernaturally nice person, for he was showing only small nervous signs of wanting to get away. Then Natalya Radilova arrived from the stage, and Peter darted away and took her aside.

"The message came through for you," he said in Russian. "It was 'Best wishes for rehearsals and the first night.' "

Natalya smiled, a smile apparently out of all proportion to the banality of the message. She squeezed Peter's hand, and they found themselves a private corner of the Green Room.

Once the chaos there had sorted itself out into groups, Peter and Natalya found themselves joined by Krister Kroll, still wiping the sweat from his open, engaging face.

"Who is that *creep* who got hold of me?" he demanded. "That schmuck? That smart-ass? I have never *heard* such crap as that guy was spouting."

"It's the landlord of the Saracen," said Peter. "A loathsome Australian by the name of Capper."

"I've known plenty of Australian singers," said Kroll, "and they've mostly been great people. But this, this — "

"It's not the nationality, it's the type. As with Gottlieb. Keep away from Capper. He's poison."

"Boy, am I glad I rented an apartment. I nearly went to the Saracen this time, to treat myself. But to have that creep giving me advice about breathing all day would — "

But he stopped, because heads were turning in the direction of the door, and conversation was stilling so that people could hear what was going on there. Gunter Gottlieb, alone of the performers, did not require sustenance or refreshment. His heavy had procured a soft drink for himself and was standing massively behind Gottlieb, doubtless to prevent a stab in the back. But Gottlieb had captured a prize: the director of the festival, who had been sitting in on the rehearsal after checking receipts at the box office. He had been hauled to the Green Room by Gottlieb with an end in view.

"Next year," said Gottlieb in his unattractive clipped tones, "we do *Fidelio*. People are waiting for my *Fidelio*."

"It's an idea," said the director in a practiced neutral voice. He was a local man, but one with long experience in arts administration. "Though of course we have tended to stick with the Italians. But next year's already tied up. We're doing *La Straniera*."

73

"I change my mind," said Gottlieb, putting aside *La Straniera* with a contemptuous sweep of the hand. "We do *Fidelio*."

"My dear chap, it's not on. Even if the committee were to agree — which I wouldn't bank on — it's still not on. You don't seem to understand the operatic world. All the worthwhile singers are booked up years in advance. All the principals for *Straniera* have been engaged. They'd hardly be suitable for *Fidelio*."

"I have my cast here," said Gottlieb, drawing a sheet of paper out of his pocket. "With alternatives if my first choices are not available. It is clear, yes? If you can get neither of them, you come back to me. Understood?"

"No, I'm sorry, old chap, it is not understood. There's no question of our upsetting our existing arrangements —"

It was at this point that Des bustled up.

"I wonder if I could mediate. As a member of the festival committee I think we ought to try to come to some compro —"

Gunter Gottlieb turned on him with a savage fury and pointed to the door.

"Out! Out! Out!" he bellowed. "I do not take advice from taverners! Get out and do not come near this theater ever again, is understood? You come near one of my rehearsals ever again and I have you removed, thrown out on your fat bottom. Is understood?"

Des had retreated three steps. When the heavy advanced from behind Gottlieb's back, he spluttered back any riposte and turned to slink out.

"No offense," he was heard to mutter.

Gunter Gottlieb turned back to the festival director, iciness reasserting itself.

"Is all your committee fools? They must learn to know their place. Now, as to *Fidelio*, I have a designer in mind . . ."

"Oh, my God," said Peter, pushing back his chair. "This bear garden makes life with Jason Thark seem a haven of rest. I must be getting back to the Saracen."

"Peter," wailed Natalya in Russian, "you're forsaking me. I have that dreadful finale to get through."

"Sorry, love. Duty calls. I was only given till four. They'll probably all be crying out for some fresh and engaging humor from Peter Patterwit. . . ."

But they weren't, and he spent most of the rest of the afternoon and early evening lounging around, not unhappy to have escaped from the Alhambra. Gunter Gottlieb's plans for the festival were inevitably the topic of conversation in the Shakespeare Bar that evening. Gillian and Peter went out and bought a Chinese takeaway, enduring with sweet smiles the murderous glances from Des

75

as they marched through Reception with the little cardboard boxes. Des, understandably, was looking murderous all evening. When they had eaten their fill in Gillian's room, they went down to the Shakespeare and found Natalya, Ronnie Wimsett, and Krister Kroll at a table together. The last named kept looking round nervously for routes of escape should Des feel impelled to come over and offer further advice on what he should do with his diaphragm. Gillian and Peter joined them, and soon they were well at it.

"It would change the whole character of the festival," Ronnie Wimsett said when he was told of Gottlieb's demands. He was a serious-minded, private young man, but he had come to feel passionately about the festival, to appropriate it in some way as a part of himself, as Gillian had. "The two things go together — Jacobean drama and nineteenth-century Italian opera. People like the music critic of the *Observer* sneer because it's not ear-wrenching stuff, but in fact it's wonderfully direct and passionate, really theatrical. And it's what people expect of Ketterick, what gives it its character. Give Gottlieb his way and it'll become just like any other festival. We'll be doing *The Marriage of Figaro* and *Pallyarse and Smellyhands*, and they'll be *his* *Figaro* and *his Pallyarse*. When that happens, we'll be just like any other festival. The next thing will be, he'll start dictating what plays are done, to tie in with *his* opera of the year."

"Still, the guy, though scary, has a way with him," said Krister Kroll ruefully. "What're the odds that Ketterick will *not* be doing *La Straniera* next year?"

"Never having heard it," said Gillian, "I can't weep bitter tears about the *specific* loss."

"Oh, it's great Bellini, and practically unknown. Even Beefy and Scrawny haven't recorded it."

Beefy and Scrawny, it was explained, were the currently highest paid tenor and soprano in the world.

"It's the principle I'm concerned about," said Ronnie.

"It's the personal level that concerns me," said Kroll. "It won't be the death of the festival if I don't come back, and I certainly won't while that monster is in charge. I'm a peaceful guy, but some of the things he said to me . . ."

Natalya Radilova, who was beginning to follow bits of conversation in English, went off into a bitter tirade in Russian. Peter paraphrased for her.

"She's complaining about my not being there when she did her big final scene this afternoon. He was vile to her apparently. It's a difficult scene — It's where she brings her husband's head in on a platter and goes mad over it."

"My God!" said Gillian. "I thought this was supposed to be '*opera semiseria.*' I'd really hate to see a serious one."

"No, that's just another example of the amiable Gunter's influence," explained Kroll. "There are two manuscript endings, and they'd chosen the first. In that, some functionary comes along and explains that for unspecified reasons Adelaide's marriage has been invalid all along. Adelaide goes off to be Roberto il Bruce's queen amid general rejoicing, with only the baritone throwing a fit. That Mexican is awfully good at throwing fits. Anyway, along comes Gottlieb at the first rehearsal and says: 'No, we do the second.' In that one Adelaide hacks her husband's head off and then stabs herself after some fearsome coloratura. That's what Natalya is having to do. The annoying thing is that, as usual, Gottlieb is right. It's a much more effective conclusion."

Natalya went on at length in Russian. Peter explained. "Natalya says it is ridiculously difficult to do because it's so way out — so gory and savage. The audience will reject it at the drop of a hat, because it just seems impossibly savage."

Once again a familiar voice came from behind Peter's shoulder. He was beginning to feel he had a minor devil following him around.

"You wouldn't say it was impossible if you'd seen some of the things I saw in 1947, at the time of independence. Some of those poor bloody Indians had been so hacked about that their own mothers wouldn't have known them."

"Was this when you were viceroy?" Gillian asked sweetly. But Des did not appear to be listening. He was gazing ahead dreamily.

"Oh, yes, I've seen some sights, don't you worry." His eyes were on a far table, where Gunter Gottlieb was pontificating to the Mexican baritone and Brad Mallory. "I learned all you need to know in India about how to even scores."

The Alcove

5

A mist hung over Ketterick and the London suburbs around it as the first day of the festival dawned. During breakfast, though, it began to lift, and by ten the town was bathed in gentle sunshine from a pale blue sky.

The visitors were arriving, that was for sure. By now Ketterick was securely established in the festival catalog, cunningly poised to take advantage of that moment, around May to June, when longen folk to goon on artistic pilgrimages. By car and coach, by late-arriving trains from Newcastle, Bath, and Manchester, even by bicycle they came, changing the character of the complacent suburb. Some of the visitors were regulars, with their diaries already filled in and their seats booked; some came on spec and sat around in parks and squares going through the festival brochure to see what they might take in. There was the *Play of Daniel* in the ruins of Walsey Abbey, three miles out of town; there was Bruno Brazen, the well-known American organist and showman in St. Margaret's Church; there was a wispy French soprano singing wispy French songs; there was Morris dancing in the Queen's Square and a superb black dance group from Leeds in the Civic Hall. Tonight there was *The Chaste Apprentice* at the Saracen's Head and a popular operatic concert. Both these events were booked solid, but for the disappointed there was a beer race in the Ketterick football stadium. There was — as there was on that other pilgrimage, to Canterbury — something for everybody.

At one time or another during the day most of the new arrivals strolled into the Saracen's Head to look at the wonderful courtyard and stage. One of the hazards of this was that Des Capper was liable to sidle up with a proprietary air and ply them with information, advice, and cures for constipation. One of the American visitors, a lecturer in Renaissance studies at Kent State University, called him "a true English innkeeper" and "a real Harry Bailly after Chaucer's own heart"; but most of the rest sensibly ducked off to one or other of the bars. These were kept very busy, and Mrs. Capper in the Shakespeare was rushed off her feet, though help from her husband got she none.

If they were lucky, these stray visitors saw scraps of last-minute rehearsal. In the true spirit of the Elizabethan troupe, the cast was quite unembarrassed about putting finishing touches to the performance before future members of the audience, who marveled at the contrast between their apparel of jeans and T-shirts and their talk of ruffles and cod-pieces. The brothel scene had caused particular difficulty, being such a whirl of activity, and the casual dropper-in might see Peter Patterwit open that unedifying scene with Doll, the whore, indulging in some typically sparkling Jacobean wit:

DOLL: You, goodman swineface.
PETER: What — will you murder me?
DOLL: You remember, slave, how you abused
    me t'other night in a tavern?
PETER: Not I, by this light.
DOLL: No, but by candlelight you did . . .

Oddly enough, such samples did not put off most of the visitors. Somehow the setting and atmosphere (or the "ambience," as several of them preferred to put it) were so exactly right for the play that many of them dashed straight off to the festival box office to see what tickets

82

were available for later performances.

If Des was a hazard for the occasional visitor, he was an ever-present danger to the performers and residents. It was, after all, his first festival, and he naturally wanted to see everything he could. Unfortunately, he wanted to be part of everything, too, and there was abundant evidence that despite his recent rebuff at the Alhambra, the start of festivities had gone to his head. He was liable to pop up everywhere, poking his nose in and having his little word of worthless commendation or erroneous advice to all and sundry. Few were polite back, but he gave no sign to their faces of having registered their contempt.

Constance Geary's part as Old Lady Sneer was not a large one. She played a cousin of Sir Pecunius Slackwater, dragged into the marriage negotiations. Her performance was already a matter of well-routined gestures and intonations, and she left it to younger generations to overrehearse. She sat around in various parts of the Saracen's Head, holding court and allowing visitors to buy her drinks. Sometimes she could be found on her own in the little alcoves and open spaces that the inn abounded in, quite happy with her memories and her gin bottle. She also noticed a lot more than might have been thought, though she would have been hard put to order it in any way in her mind. It was nearly lunchtime, in one of those alcoves, apparently deep in thought after a copious swig from her bottle, that she saw Des Capper coming.

"All on your own-e-o?" he asked with his horrible brand of jocularity.

"Trying to be," said Connie.

"They can get tiresome, can't they, actors?"

"*We* can. But then so can most people."

"What I mean is," said Des, leaning closer, Connie thought to catch the smell of her breath, "you can have too much of them. They tend to emote is how I'd put it. Those Galloways, for example. Always at it, aren't they?"

"At it? You mean like Alice?"

"At each other's throats might be a better way of putting it. Morning, noon, and night. And both of them having a bit on the side and talking about it openly. Jeez, I don't know; it's not my idea of a marriage."

"My dear man, I've known more different kinds of marriage than I've had hot dinners. There are as many recipes for a good one as there are for a bad one."

"What makes them stay together, that's what I wonder? Why stick it out?"

"I imagine it must be because they rather like it."

Des looked at her, then shook his head with

84

wonderment. "Then there's young Peter Fortnum. He's up to something, that I do know."

Connie Geary paused, looking at him contemplatively. She took her bottle out of her handbag, had a swig, and replaced it. Then she looked at Des again. "I presume we are now changing the subject, am I right? Because Peter Fortnum hardly comes under the heading of actors who emote. Indeed, he is an exceedingly quiet young man, which is pleasant but unusual. A youthful Alec Guinness, no less. So we are now discussing what he is up to, and I must confess I have no idea. Do you mean to ask if he is sleeping with the charming but impenetrable Russian lady?"

"Oh, as to that, maybe, but I think not," said Des, rubbing his hands together. "But there's something going on, and I think it might be a sight more interesting than them sleeping together."

"I'm glad to hear it. At my age there are a lot of things more interesting than sex, though I'm not sure there ought to be at theirs. Have you any idea what it is?"

"Oh, I've ideas all right. There's no flies on me, you know. I'll get to the bottom of it."

"This is fascinating," said Connie. She sat there hoping she would remember enough of this conversation for it to form a vital piece in the complaint to the committee when the present festival was over. She even decided to stop sipping from her bottle, to keep her head clear. "Is there anyone else at the Saracen in whom you are taking a special interest?"

"Oh, lots," said Des, leering. "A student of the human condition, that's me." He leaned forward. "Know how that Kraut conductor gets his girls?"

"He's Austrian. Not that anyone imagines *that* makes much difference after the Waldheim business."

"Right. Same difference, that's what I say. Well, do you know how he gets his girls?"

"Animal magnetism?"

"His heavy recruits them for him. Just like that. He puts the proposition, then they're taken up to his room for a quick you-know, then they're out. He picks them out from among Krauty's fans. Doesn't pay them, either. I expect they form themselves into a sort of club or have a special tattoo or something."

"I did hear whispers about that," said Connie with a shiver of distaste. "It *is* rather disgusting."

"And I'll tell you this: He likes them young. The younger the better."

" 'His favorite form of sinning is with one who's just beginning,' " sang Connie, from

86

the Catalogue Aria.

"That's it. That's just about it. If I could catch him with one who was below the age of consent . . . "

"Yes?"

"That would do the trick. . . . Trouble is, at that age they're not usually interested in classical music, are they? And the heavy tells me he's very careful."

"You'll have to find something else, then."

"Yes, I will, won't I?"

"And is there anyone else of us that you have your eyes on?"

"Oh, yes. Oh, there definitely is. No question about that. . . . " Connie sat there quiet, but a cunning expression came into Des's eyes. "But that would be telling, wouldn't it? You're not going to draw me out on that."

With a sigh, Connie took out her gin bottle.

"You know what that stuff does to your kidneys, don't you?" asked Des. He went on to describe it in detail before leaving with a wave and his favorite addendum: "Don't mind me telling you, do you?"

Onstage they were rehearsing a quarrel between Sir Pecunius Slackwater, suitor to Alison Greatheart, and the whore of Deptford, who was an old acquaintance.

SIR PECUNIUS: Out, you babliaminy, you unfeathered, cremitoried quean, you cullisance of scabosity!

WHORE: Good words, Master Slackwater, to speak before a maid and a virgin.

SIR PECUNIUS: Hang thy virginity upon the pole of carnality . . .

By the wall of the courtyard, Natalya, in slacks and jumper, was standing in a patch of sunlight near the windows of the Shakespeare Bar. She was beginning to tap her feet and look anxiously at her watch, but then she saw Peter Fortnum coming through the great gates from the High Street.

"Did you get through? Have they arrived?" asked Natalya urgently in Russian.

"No, there's been some confusion about times. The party's not due for another hour at least."

"Oh, my God."

"I think it's a genuine confusion. There doesn't seem to be any doubt they will arrive."

"I've got to go. I'm due at rehearsal in ten minutes."

"I know. I'll stick around and ring them again in an hour or two."

"Will you come and tell me?"

"Yes, if I can. I don't *think* I'll be needed to rehearse here, but you never know what people may take it into their heads to want to go over. But I'll try."

"Please come if you can. *Please*, Peter."

"Of course. You know I will. And it'll be all right."

He took her hand, but they sprang apart as they heard an involuntary cough close to Natalya's ear. Des Capper was standing just inside the open window of the Shakespeare Bar. From the expression of extreme frustration on his face it was clear that the fatal fascination that Mother Russia had always had for him had never induced him to learn her language.

In the street near the Alhambra Theater the big man with the Midlands accent was approached by a girl.

"Excuse me, but you're Gunter Gottlieb's bodyguard, aren't you?"

He looked at her appraisingly. "Something like that."

"It's just that . . . he's always in such a hurry after rehearsals . . . and I wondered if you could . . . get his autograph for me."

She proffered a book. It looked very new. The big man did not take it.

"Maybe I could . . . And maybe I could go even better."

"Really?"

"Maybe I could arrange a . . . meeting."

She smiled up at him, looking all of fifteen. "I wondered if you could."

"At a price, of course."

The operatic offerings of the Ketterick Festival were never premiered until the second or third night. Nothing was allowed to draw attention from that year's play. Maybe in future years Gunter Gottlieb would change all that, but he had not done so yet. By tradition the musical event on the first night was something undemanding: a Viennese night, a Gilbert and Sullivan evening, a nice bit of Tchaikovsky. This year it was a popular operatic concert. Gunter Gottlieb, needless to say, would have nothing to do with it.

Thus, the final rehearsal with the Midlands Orchestra in the Town Hall was under the command of a pleasant young man who had done well in a recent conductors' competition. They'd put together a very nice program, with an overture by Rossini, some ballet music by Verdi, and lots of standard arias. Natalya was singing *"Vissi d'Arte"* and the letter scene from *Eugene Onegin*, the Mexican baritone was spitting out Iago's "Credo," and Krister Kroll was singing an aria from *Faust* that the program, through slovenly proofreading, referred to as *"Slut! Demure, chaste et pure.*" Singh's arias had presented more of a problem, since the countertenor repertoire hardly counted as popular opera, but Brad had hit on two surefire Handel arias, and these he was to sing in the first half. Brad had insisted he was to *conclude* the first part of the concert, knowing that the scope for excitement and applause would be the greater if there was nothing coming immediately after.

Natalya was finishing the letter aria in a glorious flood of sound when Peter arrived at the Town Hall. He listened approvingly. He was no expert on music, but he knew a good sound when he heard one. It was a very informal rehearsal, and the Town Hall was dotted with people. Peter was pleased to note approving glances going from person to person. Natalya came off the platform and into the body of the hall, looking around for him. He put up his hand, and she came over to him.

"I got through," said Peter.

"And?"

"They'd just arrived."

Natalya did not allow herself any obvious expression of relief, but Peter could see her tension relax.

"All of them?"

"Yes, all of them. I spoke to him."

"Oh — marvelous."

"He sent his love."

91

"Only three more days now."

Onstage Singh had launched into Caesar's aria with horn obbligato from *Giulio Cesare*: "*Va tacito e nascosto.*" His rich, agile voice was filling the Town Hall effortlessly and was weaving brilliant patterns with the horn. Brad Mallory, sitting in the middle of the hall, looked to be purring.

"What an extraordinary voice," said Natalya.

"Quite amazing."

"What else did he say?"

Peter looked around, instinctively cautious.

"It's all right," said Natalya. "I'm sure that dreadful man doesn't speak Russian. I could see it in his face."

"No, I don't think so. Anyway, he's over there."

And as Peter launched into an account of what had been said on the phone, he looked toward the back row of seats where Des had ensconced himself, exercising in the absence of Gunter Gottlieb his right as a member of the committee to go anywhere and see anything. He was gazing ahead of him, almost dreamily, with a smile of pure, luxuriating pleasure playing on his lips.

The
High
Street

6

Performances of *The Chaste Apprentice of Bowe* began at seven o'clock. Everything at the Ketterick Festival began early, for many members of the audience were not staying in Ketterick but came from other suburbs and were nervous about traveling on bus or underground late at night. So at six the great gates of the Saracen's Head were closed, and the small door cut into the right-hand one was opened for the collection of tickets. Everyone, even those seated on the balconies, went through this gate, and the ticket collector stationed himself there from six onward. All the bars were closed to members of the general public until after the performance was over — enough to do to serve the players and the audience. Frank, the hotel's commissionaire, stood by the main entrance to the hotel, to the right of the gates, to stop anyone who might try to get into the play without paying by slipping through Reception and then through the Shakespeare Bar.

Once through the little door in the great gates, the audience, chattering and laughing and sure they were in for a rather special experience, separated up, some going to one or other of the bars, some to sit in their seats and read their programmes, some merely to sit and soak up the atmosphere of the great courtyard. Those who had seats on the balconies had directions on how to get to them on the backs of their tickets — directions which mostly added to their confusion, so indescribable were the complexities of the Saracen's Head.

Behind the stage, in one half of the enormous kitchen, and screened off from the rest, the actors changed. The women had the private dining room next to it, but coming and going between the two was frequent and unrestricted. Costume was important in the Ketterick plays, for splendor and variety of dress provided the feast for the eye that compensated for an otherwise bare stage. No producer — not even Jason Thark — had yet suggested a modern-dress production at Ketterick, and anyone who did would have been firmly rebuffed. The stage demanded ruffs and bodices, buskins and codpieces.

Fish was being served in the dining room that night. The smell penetrated into the dressing rooms and provoked feeble witticisms like "Odds fish!" A limited meal was provided for the few residents not involved in the play and the richer members of the audience. Late-night snacks would also be served after the performance: lasagne, fish pie, or risotto. Most people, though, contented themselves with drinks.

They were pleasantly busy in the Shakespeare Bar. This meant that Win Capper was run off her feet. Hair drawn back, unhealthily sallow, she somehow looked like a woman who had been run off her feet since girlhood.

"Des," she called, unusually daring, when she saw her husband going around the bar doing his Harry Bailly act among the early arrivals for the performance, "do you think you could come behind the bar and help out for a bit?"

Brad Mallory, sitting at the bar, thought this must be an unprecedented request. He had never seen Des giving a hand at anything around the hotel except Reception. Certainly Des received the request gracelessly, casting his eye up to heaven and taking his time in getting behind the bar.

"Des," said his wife, working on an order for three different beers, "you're going to have to come and help at Interval. I'm not going to be able to cope."

"You'll have Dawn from the kitchen to help you," said Des, pouring soda into a whiskey in an infuriatingly leisurely manner. "There are three other bars for people to go to, for Chrissake."

"The Shakespeare's the biggest and most popular. There's only twenty minutes, and people have to have time to drink their drinks. You'll have to come and help."

"All right, little lady," said Des, leering around at a sea of proffered fivers. "Your wish is my command."

"No, I *mean* it, Des. I need you here."

"And I'll be here. Am I in the habit of not meaning what I say? . . . I ask you, Mr. Mallory, don't I usually mean what I say? Now, what can I get you?"

Outside in the main entrance Frank, the commissionaire, was getting bored. There was a steady queue waiting to go through the little door into the courtyard, but nobody was attempting to sneak past him into the body of the hotel to get an illicit view from somewhere or other. This was not surprising, as he was six feet two and built like a barrel. The only resi-

96

dents in the hotel at the moment were the festival people, in the rooms over the Shakespeare. Any other would-be guest who had arrived in Ketterick without a bed was turned away by Frank with a word, courteous but final. In fact, there was nobody manning Reception, because there was no point in it. Des had assigned the girls there to other work for the duration of the festival. Frank thought it very dull, really. Still, soon, when the play started, he could walk along and have a chinwag with Bob, the ticket collector on the gate. They were good friends and usually talked the play away during festival time. Unless, this year, that Australian twerp should take it into his head to put a stop to it.

The poncy Mr. Mallory — Frank had got *his* number — had come mincing out of the Shakespeare and now came through Reception, looking pale but not interesting. He nodded to Frank as he came through the main entrance and headed off in the direction of the Town Hall, clutching his cloak around him. A *cloak*, for God's sake. . . . Des Capper came out almost immediately after.

"I've been helping in the bar," he announced to Frank, as if it were a newsworthy event. "Helping the little lady. Now they're all taking their seats. I think I'll slip in at the back and watch the first few minutes.

Mind you, I think I've got *this* play's number, by seeing the rehearsals. It's no literary masterpiece, you take my word for it. Still, as a member of the committee, it's as well to see how the audience is taking it."

And he rambled through the little door into the courtyard. Frank gave a meaningful stare, of skepticism verging on contempt, at Bob, standing in the street by the door and taking tickets. So long a stare was it that he nearly missed seeing a young woman going through the main door of the hotel. He hotfooted it back to the door and into the open area around Reception, but by this time the young woman had crossed it and had gone, not to the Shakespeare Bar but to the stairs leading to the bedrooms.

"Can I help you, miss?" Frank called.

The girl turned round. She was a cool, fresh little thing, in a bright summer frock — and not much else, Frank guessed. Frank was an ex-soldier and experienced in such matters. A tingle stirred his old blood. She looked about fifteen, he thought, but when she spoke her voice was not a schoolgirl's.

"No. No, I don't think so."

It was an attempt — and not a bad one — at upper-class impertinence. Frank bristled.

"The play's about to start, miss, and the bars and dining rooms are shut, and — "

"But I'm not going to the bars or dining rooms, am I?"

"Would you mind telling me, miss, where you are going?"

She left a cool pause before she replied. "No, I don't mind. I'm going to see Gunter Gottlieb. You know, the great conductor."

"Ah." Frank did know. There had been other young ladies. "Mr. Gottlieb's not occupied with festival stuff, then?"

"No, evidently not, I should have thought. I have an appointment with him."

"I see. Very well, miss. Sorry to have troubled you."

She smiled at him, a practiced ingenue smile. Then she turned and went up the stairs. Shaking his head gently, Frank went back to take up his position outside the main door. The evening was clear and sunny, and both Ketterick folk and visitors were strolling along the High Street, window-shopping, eating ice cream, flirting and hoping to be flirted with. The odd car drove past, but no heavy trucks. They were banned from the center of Ketterick during the hours from seven to ten at festival time. Only heavy trucks could have made any impression through the massive gates of the Saracen's courtyard. Cars, Frank knew, made no disturbance at all.

A fragment of the play wafted out to him.

That meant the ticket gate had opened:

RALPH GREATHEART: I hope to see thee one o' the monuments of our City, and reckoned among her worthies, when the famous fable of Whittington and his puss shall be forgotten, and thou and thy deeds played i' thy lifetime by the best companies of actors, and be called their get-penny . . .

So the first scene was over, and Carston Galloway was on, inciting the chaste apprentice to City greatness (with Ronnie Wimsett looking and acting about as unlike a City worthy as it was possible to get). Frank had timed things in dress rehearsal, and he knew this meant the play was ten or twelve minutes in. Turning his eyes, he saw that Des Capper had emerged through the little door in the gate and was now closing it.

"Ah, well, it's going very much as I expected," he said judiciously when he came up to Frank. "Quite nicely on the whole. Whether that mob knows what they're laughing at is another matter, but so long as they think they're enjoying themselves, that's the main thing. Make 'em laugh, make 'em cry, eh? I haven't read up much about this opera they're doing yet, but I expect it's the same principle

100

there. That's show biz, the world over. . . . Well, I'll maybe look in during the second half to see how it's going. Meanwhile, I'll be in Reception if I'm wanted, Frank."

"Right you are, sir."

"Or up in the flat. Call up the stairs if I'm wanted. Keep on the door the whole of the first half. We don't want any gate-crashers seeing the play for free."

"Right. Oh, by the way, there was a young girl, sir . . . "

"Oh?"

"But she was a guest of Mr. Gottlieb's. . . . "

They looked at each other, and Des laughed lasciviously. "Someone should have told me that at festival time this place doubles as a brothel."

He winked and chuckled, as if that were a high honor. Then he went in and turned towards the reception desk, apparently in high good humor.

For a few minutes Frank stood just inside the door, looking out, hearing Des fiddling around on and under the desk. Then Des went into the manager's room behind. Frank nonchalantly went through the door into the street and stood for a few minutes there. The characters had changed a bit from a half hour earlier, but the activities were much the same. As a spectacle it lacked variety. So, giving a

101

nod to his friend Bob, who was standing by his little door, they met halfway, towards the end of the hotel wall. From here they could both keep an eye on their respective doors, yet there were no open windows to inhibit them from launching into a fine old discussion. Men, contrary to general belief, are much the best gossips, and the festival and its artists always provided these two with ample manure to spread. Every year it was the same, and they went at it with a will.

The first interruption came when they were just five minutes into their chat and hardly beginning to disentangle the marital and extramarital affairs of the Galloways. The girl who had gone up to Gunter Gottlieb's room came prancing out again.

"*Good*-bye," she called, waving.

"Well, *she* didn't take long," said Bob.

"They never do," said Frank. "It's in and out."

"Perhaps he pays them by the minute."

"And perhaps he doesn't pay them at all. We'll come to Mr. — I beg his pardon, *Herr* — Gottlieb in a minute. But as I was saying . . ."

In the Town Hall concert the Mexican baritone was giving the audience his Iago. It was a part to which he was suited, if you

102

regarded Iago as a snarling, spitting, teethbaring villain who could never have convinced anyone for two minutes that he was a good chap. But his enunciation of belief in eternal nothingness was getting through to Brad Mallory. At any rate, he was sweating. Sitting there in his aisle seat, he was sweating profusely. What was next? The march from *The Trojans*. Then little Natalya in the letter scene from *Onegin*. After that would be the time to slip out. Anyone who knew him would assume he had gone backstage to congratulate her. Or to spur on Singh, who was on soon after. There was that phone box just outside the Town Hall. Please God it would not be occupied.

Brad Mallory sat on and sweated. Never had the Trojan March seemed so long.

Frank and Bob had a long, uninterrupted chat during which few of the performers staying at the Saracen came off unscathed. It was only at a quarter past eight that Frank looked at his watch and shook his head.

"Blimey. Quarter past eight. Interval in fifteen minutes or so, I should guess. Better get back to my post."

He looked around him, like a diver coming up for air. Approaching along the High Street was Bradford Mallory, clutching his cloak

103

about him, though the evening was still warm.

"Concert over, Mr. Mallory?" Frank asked, back at his post at the entrance. Brad Mallory fluttered.

"The first half. That was all I'm interested in. Singh sang divinely! He had a phenomenal success!"

"I'm glad about that, Mr. Mallory." The romantic figure, having poked his head into the Shakespeare and then come out again, disappeared up the stairs. Frank repeated sardonically under his breath: "I'm *very* glad about that!" Then he went outside again and made a gesture to Bob at the ticket door which said, as plainly as talking, "These artists!"

Behind the stage, in the screened-off part of the kitchen that was the men's dressing room, the members of the cast that were not onstage sat in dim light, listening to the performance.

"It's going well," said Gillian Soames.

"Very well," said Ronnie Wimsett. "They're laughing at the jokes."

"And at a lot of things that aren't jokes at all."

"That's natural," said Jason Thark pedantically. "We get further and further away from the Elizabethan language. I sat through a performance of *Macbeth* last year and real-

104

ized I understood less than I did when I saw it as a teenager."

"That's because nowadays we play the Bard complete and gabble him," Connie Geary pointed out. "In the past they cut him and spoke him properly."

"At least no one seems to have taken offense at the chaste apprentice," said Ronnie. "That's a relief."

"That's because we made him so far out he was a parody of a parody of a homosexual," said Jason, still with his schoolmasterly manner, which was perhaps a sign of nerves. "That was my intention all along."

"The amazing thing is, they're even laughing at Peter Patterwit," said Connie Geary in her rich, throaty tones. "He's the sort of Elizabethan character who makes me groan and switch off the moment he sets foot onstage."

They were silent, listening to Peter Fortnum, who was doing his stuff onstage.

PETER PATTERWIT: Why, sure my blood gives me I am noble; sure I am of noble kind, for I find myself possessed with all their qualities: love dogs, dice and drabs, scorn wit in stuff-clothes, have beat my shoemaker, knocked my seamstress, cockolded my pothecary, and undone my tailor. Noble? Why not?

"He's doing a good job, that lad," said Carston Galloway. "He's got the projection for it, so he gets the meaning across, however feeble it is."

"Oh, God," said Connie Geary suddenly and loudly.

"Shhh," said Jason.

Connie was rummaging frantically in her bag, which she carried around with her everywhere.

"Darlings, I've never done *that* before. I've run out of gin. Somehow or other I've forgotten to put my second half bottle in my bag. I was sure — "

"Do you want me to get some more for you?" asked Peter Fortnum, who had just come offstage and was beaming with pleasure at the experience of an audience that was with him. "I'm not on again before Interval."

"But *can* you?"

"Of course. I can go through the kitchen and dining room and into the Shakespeare Bar. Or shall I go up to your room and get you a half bottle?"

"Darling, could you? You angel. Because we have *hours* to go yet, and bar measures go very little distance. The halves are all set up on my dressing table like a line of soldiers.

Here's my key. It's the first floor."

"I'll find it," said Peter.

But the Saracen has ways of defeating people who say that. At any rate, he seemed to be away an awful long time, and when he returned, Connie was wailing that she felt like the Sahara Desert at the height of the season. Peter was out of breath and explained that he had got utterly and completely lost. By then Carston Galloway was onstage, with Mistress Greatheart, Alison, and Sir Pecunius Slackwater in a tremendous quarrel scene that concluded the first half. The Interval was upon them, and the audience sounded good-humored and nicely thirsty as they hotfooted it to the bars.

In the Shakespeare Bar tension had been rising as the Interval approached.

"Well, the glasses are all ready," said Win Capper, looking at her watch. "Interval's supposed to be at half past. Fifteen minutes to go, if they stick to their times. *Which* they won't, knowing these artistic people. No consideration, as a general rule. Still, I think you could go and get the snacks from the kitchen. Here, take this tray."

Dawn, roped in as the best of the dining-room staff, trotted off to get the little plates of savory this-and-thats which were to be set out

107

on bar and tables in celebration of *The Chaste Apprentice's* first night. When she got back, she found that Win had poured out a large number of red and white wines and some gins and whiskeys.

"They're the staples," she said. "You can't go wrong pouring them in advance. And we'll be rushed even with Des here. If they want ice, they'll have to serve themselves with it. Now let's put the snacks out."

In the event, Interval started only three or four minutes late. "I expect Des is watching from the window," Win said, "and he'll dash through when it starts." But when the great mass of the audience from the courtyard began to stream into the Shakespeare, saying things like "It's *awfully* funny, isn't it?" and "I never expected to understand so much," Des still hadn't arrived. Win and Dawn had no option but to begin taking orders and serving them in double quick time, seeming at times to have four hands each, and needing six, and taking the next orders while giving change from the previous one and totting up prices in their heads and being at both ends of the bar at once. And when they collided over the red wines or the whiskeys, Win would mutter to Dawn: "Where is Des? He promised faithfully he'd come. There's much too many of them for the two of us to cope with. Where *is* Des?"

Reception

7

They didn't find Des until long after the play was over. As soon as the audience had been summoned by bell back to the courtyard, Win sent Dawn off with two trays of glasses, to pile them into the dishwasher in the kitchen. There wouldn't be time to do all of them by hand, she said, and she was right. The concert ended at nine-fifteen, and as the Town Hall was only five minutes away, it was not long before some members of the orchestra staying at the Saracen drifted in, and then soloists. Natalya had walked back with Singh. They had not been able to communicate very much, but since Singh was wrapped in a cloud of self-approbation brought on by a gaggle of critics, arts administrators, and early music enthusiasts who had fawned over him at Interval, and since even Natalya was quietly hugging herself at the warmth of her reception, they had been companionably quiet.

Singh had gone straight to the rooms *en suite* that he shared with Brad, but they soon joined Natalya in the Shakespeare. Now they were both positively purring with delight, though Natalya thought she had never seen Brad's hands flap more nervously. Singh had been offered a prestigious engagement for the next Bach Festival and had been urgently pressed to take the role of Idamante in a new Welsh National Opera production of *Idomeneo*. Natalya congratulated them but would have been more interested in offers that would display her own talents. After a time, she left them to their delighted self-absorption and watched the closing stages of the play from the window. The second half of the play was shorter, being mainly Deptford and whores and rollicking fun, but it ended with a great scene of reconciliation and matrimony, which was guaranteed to send audiences out with a warm glow. By five to ten it was all over, and the actors, with Jason, were receiving delighted acclamation from the audience. The great gates were opened, and critics scurried away to telephone in their reviews for the later editions. Then the Shakespeare was bustling once more.

"I suppose we can cope," said Win to Dawn, "since we did at Interval. There's not the same rush now. There's over an hour

110

to closing time."

It was always pleasant at the Saracen after the play was over. Some of the actors, still in costume, usually mingled with the audience, as Peter Fortnum did now, though he confined his attentions to Natalya Radilova, going off with her into a corner and having a long and serious conversation. Constance Geary was in the Shakespeare, too, letting longtime admirers buy her drinks. Before long Krister Kroll arrived — the general public being admitted after the play was over — wanting to talk about the concert. He had changed into casuals and looked very handsome, but after trying to break into the rapt little duo of Mallory and Singh, he gave up and went over to join Peter and Natalya. He was welcome, because he was the sort of person who always was welcome.

In another corner Gillian, Ronnie Wimsett, and Jason Thark were going over the performance blow by blow. Gillian was just deciding that they were doing this mainly as a boost to Jason's ego, rather than with any thought of revising or strengthening the production, when a thought struck her.

"I say, the Great Australian Blight's not here. I'd have expected him to be worming his way around, calling Stanislavski to our attention or telling us to speak up and speak out."

"Probably got other fish to fry," said Ronnie Wimsett. "Some agreeable little piece of blackmail or something."

"I suppose it's too much to hope that he's had a heart attack while executing some particularly problematic yoga exercise?" hazarded Jason Thark.

Gillian suddenly noticed that Win Capper was collecting glasses and ashtrays at the next table, and she kicked the other two. When Win turned around, she smiled and said: "I'd have thought your husband would have been here, Mrs. Capper, to tell us how we'd done."

She had nothing against Win Capper, but the faint spark of malice in the last words was irresistible. It eluded Win Capper.

"I'd have thought he would've myself. I was expecting him at Interval, but he never showed. Rushed off our feet we were. I expect he's got something on."

"I expect *so,*" said Gillian.

Win had spotted the great bulk of Frank, the commissionaire, standing proprietorially by the door of the bar.

"Frank, you seen Des?"

Frank's forehead creased. "Saw him during the first half, Mrs. C. He went in and watched the play for a bit."

"Haven't you seen him since then?"

"Only when he came out. He went into

112

Reception, said he'd either be there or up in the flat if he was wanted. He said he might look in on the second half, but he didn't. He's not in Reception now. Want me to call up the stairs?"

Win considered. "No. Better not. He'll have something on. He hates being disturbed when he's got something on."

"I *bet* he does," muttered Ronnie Wimsett as Win moved away.

At eleven o'clock Win called "Time," and at ten past she flicked the light switch two or three times. The townspeople and festival-goers had drifted away, but the performers were reluctant for the evening to end.

"Don't they have any all-night bars in this place?" demanded Krister Kroll.

At the bar Win contemplated the second mountain of dirty glasses and ashtrays.

"It really is too much," she said to Dawn. "I think we should count this as a special night and leave everything till morning. I'll ring Des and tell him."

But when she dialed the flat number on the telephone behind the bar, she got no reply.

"But if he's not in the flat, where *is* he?" she said in bewilderment to Frank, who had just come into the bar again. "I just hope he's not *ill* — but Des is never ill. He's so conscious of health things."

113

"That sort's sometimes the first to go," said Frank with gloomy tactlessness. "Would you like me to go up and have a look."

"Oh, dear . . . Well, I think *I'd* better go. You know how Des is — But if he's not in the flat, I don't know where to look. . . . "

She bustled off, distractedly poking at a stray strand of hair. Everyone left in the bar had been pushing back their chairs, preparatory to going to bed or continuing the parties in their rooms. Something made them wait. It *was* odd that Des had not been around after the show — *his* show, or so he had often seemed to believe. From his table in the corner with Natalya and Krister Kroll, Peter could see through the glass door of the Shakespeare Bar. He saw Win go out, saw her cross the hotel entrance lobby, saw her go around the reception desk and into the manager's room behind. Then he could see no more, but could only wait. It was not a long wait — less than a minute — before he heard clattering footsteps falling over themselves on the stairs and cries, cries that continued as Win stumbled through the manager's room and out into Reception, her face twisted in horror, her hands bloodstained.

"Oh! Oh, my God! He's dead! He's been killed! Frank! Frank! Call the doctor. No. Call the police. Someone's killed my Des!"

The Manager's Office

8

In the car from the Police Station, coming from the other side of town, Superintendent Iain Dundy gazed gloomily out over the dark, nearly deserted streets of Ketterick. He was a man in his mid-thirties, with a broken marriage behind him, a reputation for fairness, and a long fuse to his temper. He was already possessed by the conviction that on this case he was going to need it.

"I've always thought of myself as an unprejudiced man," he said apropos of nothing to Sergeant Nettles, who was driving. "I've never had any sort of a 'thing' against homosexuals, never hated blacks or Indians. Most of the Japanese I've met seemed perfectly charming, though I've never been able to understand a word they've said. I've had a holiday in Germany and quite like the people, and most of the American tourists we get here seem pleasanter than you're led to expect. I even once had a friend who was a Northern Ireland Protestant. . . . But I do hate arty people. I admit it. I can't stand them. They touch a nerve in me. I've had a feeling ever since this festival started up that one day I was going to get stuck with a case chock-a-block full of arty people. And I wouldn't mind betting this is it!"

His expression became positively dyspeptic as the police car drew up outside the main entrance to the Saracen's Head.

It was difficult, the Saracen residents found, to know what to do after Win's spine-chilling reappearance. Of course, she had to be seen to first. While Frank made an imperative phone call to the police from the reception desk, Gillian helped Dawn, the stand-in barmaid, to get Win into the Shakespeare and settle her onto the sofa. But when Frank came back with a portentous expression on his face, as if the world's cares were now on his shoulders, and when he had announced that the police were on their way and had peremptorily forced on Win a stiff neat brandy, there really seemed nothing left for the rest of them to do.

Actors do not commonly feel themselves *de trop*, but that was how they felt now. Win, after all, had never seemed particularly to take to their company, and she obviously would be more at ease with her own kind, whatever that was. She was moaning, "Oh, it was horrible," and crying intermittently, but she was calming down. To leave might seem like copping out, but to stay and gawp would surely be vulgar — since Sir Henry Irving, the British actor, has above all things eschewed vulgarity. They cleared their throats awkwardly and skulked off.

"We'll be in our rooms," said Jason, "if we should be wanted," and Frank nodded importantly.

That wasn't how it worked out, though. Singh certainly went to his room; he said to Brad that he wanted to see the late-night movie, which was *The Texas Chain-Saw Massacre*. Gillian went rather green at that, but Brad Mallory murmured fondly: "Oh — the young! They have such wonderful powers of recuperation." Though in fact Singh had given no sign of having anything to recuperate from. The rest of them seemed instinctively to cling together. The thought of solitary bedrooms was uninviting. They lingered in one of the large, open spaces on the first floor, which had a window looking out onto the High

117

Street. From there, silent, they saw the police arrive — first the detectives, then a uniformed constable, who took up position outside the main entrance, then several more from the uniformed lower ranks. The actors had an odd sense of passing almost imperceptibly from one drama into another. This second one was certainly not going to be amusing.

"If only," said Ronnie Wimsett, "if only we knew exactly *when* he died."

"Why?" asked Gillian.

"Because, dear dumb cluck, if he died during the play and if he's up there in his flat, you must see that no one of us could have done it."

"I never considered for a moment that one of us could have," said Jason Thark. The silence that followed this was one of relief, as if Jason's position as producer gave him some sort of authority in police matters as well. That his statement was untrue, however, he immediately revealed by his next. "I suspect that we can narrow down the time much more closely than merely that of the duration of the play. Because when I was getting my drink after the show, poor old Win was wondering where Des was, and that girl from the dining room — Dawn is her name? — said rather sharply: 'It's no good him showing up now. It was during interval that he was wanted and when he said he'd be here.' So I rather suspect

118

that the police will find that he's been dead some time."

"Which will let us out," said Ronnie Wimsett.

"We-e-ell," began Gillian, but she was interrupted by footsteps on the stairs. And not just footsteps. The carrying voices of the Galloways were unmistakable.

"It was Des, dreadful Des" came Clarissa's voice.

"Are you quite sure?"

"I heard the commissionaire, or doorman, or whatever you call him, say it to the constable by the main entrance. 'His name is Capper, or was. Des Capper.' Unless he's gone out of his mind, the police are here because somebody's dead, and that somebody is Des Capper."

"Well, I'll be damned" came Carston's impeccably well bred tones.

They emerged blinking from the stairwell: Clarissa, Carston, and Susan Fanshaw, who characteristically was saying nothing. When they had got their bearings, Clarissa stared triumphantly at the assembled cast of *The Chaste Apprentice of Bowe*.

"There! You see? Everyone's here and discussing it, aren't you, darlings?"

"We are," admitted Connie Geary. "But where have you been that you missed the fun?"

119

"Oh, my dear, such a miscalculation! I wouldn't have missed being first to hear of dreadful Desmond's death for the world if I'd known! But how could I? We went to the Webster."

"Why on earth did you do that?"

Clarissa had her audience and, as was her wont, immediately began acting a big scene, though it was a little enough matter she had to tell of.

"Well, darlings, after the play and the curtain calls — only there is no curtain, and I *do* find that awkward! — Carston and I changed, because the fact is we do feel it a *tiny* bit unprofessional to mingle with the dear old general public in costume — " She gestured round at Ronnie and Peter, still in their apprentice's costumes. "Call us old-fashioned if you like."

"Old-fashioned," said Gillian, and was rewarded with a dazzling reptilian smile.

"So when we were ready, we collected Susan Fanshaw, my husband's *sweet* little mistress, who had had a heavy evening seeing you'd all got your swords and cudgels with you and that your wimples and codpieces were straight, or whatever codpieces are supposed to be, and we went out into the yard, and there were *fans* waiting for us, still waiting after all that time. . . . Well, we saw you all in the Shakespeare, and we thought we ought to *spread* ourselves around a bit so as to be fair, so we took the fans into the Webster and let them lavish on us the best hospitality their purses could buy. Poor dears, they loved it!"

Susan Fanshaw looked at Clarissa (from behind her) with an expression of the utmost contempt on her face. Clearly she had been embarrassed by their sponging. Carston did not notice the glance and took her hand absentmindedly.

"Anyway, the consequence was, you missed all the excitement," said Brad Mallory. "Win's announcement was a real Act One curtain, I can tell you."

"Darling, don't tor*ment* me! I would so have enjoyed it. Because the fact that he's been murdered — I take it, with all those police, murder is in question? — "

"Apparently," said Jason.

" — the fact that he's been murdered does seem a singularly apt retribution for his grubby little interference into my private life."

"Don't say that to the police," said Carston, sighing. "They might scent a whiff of megalomania. Or paranoia. It takes an odd kind of mind to find death an appropriate punishment for rummaging around in someone's drawers."

"Carston, of *course* I am not so stupid as to talk like that to the dear policemen. Naturally I shall tell them what an *in*teresting little man he was, with his homely medical advice and his en*tranc*ing accent and his *fas*cinating memories of the last days of the Raj. I shall say that in the short time we have been here I had come to number him amongst my *dear*est friends."

"Don't overdo it the other way either, Clarissa," said Jason in a tired voice. "The police are trained to smell rats." He added, rather insultingly: "And the last thing I need at this stage is to lose one of my leads."

"Fortunately I've always found the police to be charming and *most* respectful," said Clarissa, hardly hearing. "I've always got on famously with them."

"Don't I remember," said Carston.

"This is all getting way off the point," said Gillian. "When you came, we were trying to establish when he'd been murdered. We rather think it must have been before Interval."

"Before about eight-thirty, then?" asked Carston.

"That's it. Or a few minutes after. We were running ever so slightly late."

"And it must have been after — oh — seventen, seven-fifteen," contributed Carston.

"Oh?"

"Because he was standing at the back during the first scene and into my bit in the second scene. I've got good long sight, and there's a moment when I peer into the audience, trying to see Sir Pecunius arriving from the Palace of Westminster. I saw him at the back then, and I saw him leave, which almost put me off my stride. So it was after that."

"Brilliant!" said Ronnie, rubbing his hands. "So we have a *terminus post quem* and a *terminus ante quem*. And they let all the actors out entirely. Because we'd have had to go through the kitchens, which had a card game going on in them, then through the dining room, which had most of the staff there, judging from their faces at the windows, then through the Shakespeare into the foyer. No way anyone could do that and then murder Des without being seen. Anyway, we were all behind the stage when we were not on it."

His words fell on an embarrassed silence. Gillian looked down at her hands and then dared to look up at Peter Fortnum. She found that Jason and Connie were looking at him too, and Natalya was looking at them and frowning in puzzlement.

"Well not quite *all* the time," said Peter, brazening it out.

"Come along, let's go to bed," said Connie briskly. "They're going to want to question us in the morning. Let's leave the question of my gin till then. We'll go to bed and think things through."

And that was exactly what they did. Some of them had a great many things to think through.

While the actors and musicians had been chewing over things in the alcove, Superintendent Dundy had been sweating his way through some preliminary questioning of Mrs. Capper in the little manager's office behind the reception desk.

No, Mrs. Capper had said, she didn't mind talking. Would rather, really. Would rather go to bed knowing she'd got it over. And if she talked it through with him, perhaps the memory of poor Des lying there with the dagger between his shoulder blades would become less horribly vivid.

So talk she did, with Iain Dundy keeping her, at the start, on fairly neutral background topics.

"When did we come to Britain? Let's see, it was the time of the miners' strike — not the last one, the one before that. Seventy-four, was it? I remember because there was no electricity most of the time, and lots of the industries were shut down, and the shops, and I wanted to go home after I'd been here a cou-

124

ple of days, I can tell you."

"Home?"

"New South Wales. Des was manager of a very nice hotel in Dubbo. I wish we'd never left. People don't go sticking knives into each other in Dubbo."

Dundy let pass this romanticization of her past. "Why did you leave?" he asked.

"Just chance, really. There was this English hotelier stayed with us, got pally with Des — everyone got on well with Des — and offered us a job. Des thought if we didn't go then, we never would, though it wouldn't have broken my heart if we never had. This was back in — oh, seventy-three, it must have been. So eventually we came over, and Des became bar manager of this big hotel in Bournemouth. Then it was manager of the Excelsior in Carlisle, then here. All of them hotels in the Beaumont chain. Des was very pleased to get Ketterick. It's what he called a prestige hotel in the group, and it gave him a bit of a stake in this festival that's going on now."

"You weren't so pleased?"

Win Capper shrugged. "Drinkers are pretty much alike wherever you are, that's what I say. And the people who go on about what a lovely hotel it is don't think of the amount of walking that's involved!"

125

"But what about your husband? Had he enjoyed his time since you both came here?"

"Oh, yes. Happy as a lamb with two tails. All this airy-fairy arty stuff was meat and drink to him. But of course Des was a very well read man."

"And he got on well with people?"

"Oh, yes! Des was always good chums with people right from the word go."

"Why was that?"

"Well, he never put on airs. He was always chatty and always had an appropriate word for everybody. As I say, he knew an awful lot. He had an inquiring mind."

Iain Dundy wondered whether an inquiring mind was really likely to make a hotel manager popular. Des Capper was dead, after all. Perhaps he had pursued his inquiries in foolish or dangerous directions. He said: "You mean he was interested in everyone?"

"Well, I meant more that he knew what everybody was interested in, so he was on their wavelength and could talk with them. Like about acting and singing with this lot now. He could give them tips, little bits of advice. And I think he was very useful on the festival committee. He'd really wised himself up on the play they're doing, and he was starting to read up about this opera with the silly title. He said he had to be clued up, so he could discuss with the people staying here. He was very thorough, was Des. And a walking encyclopedia sometimes!"

More like a barroom philosopher, Dundy guessed, and a know-all to boot. Des sounded quite unbearable.

"So what exactly happened tonight?" he asked.

"Oh, Lord . . . I wish I could forget it. . . . We opened at six, but just for members of the audience, because we don't open to members of the public until after the play's over. We were quite busy. I was behind the bar, and Des was going around talking to people in the Shakespeare, as he usually did. I had to call him over to help me, and I told him we wouldn't be able to cope at Interval time without him. He said he'd come. Then of course the audience started drifting out into the yard to take their seats, and Des knocked off. That was the last I saw of him until — "

"Did he say where he was going?"

"He said he might go and watch the play for a bit from the back. Frank — that's the doorman — says that's what he did. Dawn and I were busy in the bar, so I didn't think about him until he didn't turn up at Interval."

"You and this other barmaid — Dawn is it?"

"Yes. She's one of the waitresses, and very capable."

"You were together in the Shakespeare Bar the whole time until Interval?"

If Win Capper understood why he was asking this, she gave no sign. She just answered obediently, as if she were a child in class answering by rote.

"Dawn went to fetch the snacks from the kitchen. That took three or four minutes, I should think. Otherwise we were together the whole time."

"And you had to cope together at Interval?"

"That's right. We were so rushed that I didn't have time to ring around for Des."

"And after the interval you didn't get worried?"

"I knew he would have come if he could." She dabbed at her eyes, which were very full. "I didn't *think*. How could I? And I knew we could cope after the show, because most people go straight off home. Dawn told me that; she'd helped out previous years. Anyway, after the interval we got everything shipshape again and got the glasses washed, and then, when the concert finished, people started coming in again."

"When was that?"

"Twenty, twenty-five past nine. The Town Hall's only five minutes away, and some of the residents came straight back here. Our interval had finished a bit before nine — ten or five to. Then, of course, when the play ended, towards ten, we filled up quite considerably."

"Tell me about finding him."

"Oh, my God, do I have to? You've seen — " She swallowed at the memory.

"Try to do it quite objectively, as if it were someone else involved, someone else's body."

She looked up at him as if hardly understanding, but then she swallowed again and tried.

"We were quite busy until just after eleven, but after I'd called 'Time' I realized I hadn't seen Des since before seven. And that wasn't right. He'd have wanted to go round the Shakespeare and talk to people after the play, see how they thought it had gone. I wasn't exactly *worried,* because he could have been in the Webster or the Massinger, but the Shakespeare is very much *his* bar and the easiest to get to from Reception and the flat. And then Frank said he hadn't seen him since soon after the play started. That didn't seem right, either. So I rang the flat, and there was no reply, and then I *did* start to wonder."

"Did your husband have any history of illness?"

"No, always fit as a fiddle. Like I said, he

129

had this thing about health and lots of little tips about how to keep in shape. He read up on it you know. . . . Still, he is over sixty. . . . *Was* . . . So you do think about heart attacks. . . . Anyway, I went to the manager's office, and he wasn't there, and I opened the door that leads up to the flat and called — "

"Was the door unlocked?"

"Yes. It usually was, except at night. So I went up the stairs and opened the door into our lounge, and — well, there he was. You couldn't not see him."

"Was the body exactly as it is now? Did you disturb it in any way?"

"No. Or not much. You see, I screamed, and then I knelt down and looked at his face, so I maybe touched his shoulders. But I know a dead body when I see one. And there was the knife between his shoulders — "

"You recognized the knife?"

"Oh, yes, it was a knife that Des brought back from India years ago. Had it before we were married. It was always on the little table by the sofa."

"Had you or your husband ever entertained any of the present festival guests at the hotel in your private flat?"

"Not that I know of. Why would we?"

Why indeed? Dundy thought.

"Did you notice whether anything else had

been disturbed in the flat?"

"No, I just got up and . . . ran downstairs. Screaming. It was so horrible."

Iain Dundy looked at his watch. "I think that's all we need from you tonight, Mrs. Capper. Have you got anything to make you sleep?"

"Not personal. Des didn't approve of things like that. But there'll be something around somewhere in case one of the hotel guests asked for it."

"Then I suggest you take it. You'll be able to use one of the hotel rooms to sleep in, won't you? Oh — one last question: Did your husband, to your knowledge, have any enemies?"

She looked at him, wide-eyed.

"Oh, no. Des didn't have an enemy in the world. Anyone'll tell you the same."

He jumped up and opened the door for her, and she walked across the foyer to where Dawn was waiting for her by the door into the Shakespeare. At the sight of a friend and female sympathy, Win tottered a little as she walked and then crumpled into her arms, to be led inside.

"Excuse me, sir."

Dundy swung round and saw that there was a young man standing talking to the constable at the main entrance. He had an air of fledgling copper about him, but he wasn't a

131

policeman Dundy knew. This he was sure of because he was black, and black policemen were rare enough to notice. When he raised his eyebrows, the young man came over.

"They sent me from the station, sir. I'm Metropolitan CID, but I was there visiting a mate from training days. They thought I might be useful because I was in the audience tonight."

"Here, for the play?"

"That's right, sir."

"You might well be useful. Are you free at the moment?"

"Free for the next forty-eight hours." He held out his hand. "I'm Peace, sir. Charlie Peace."

The Hotel Staff

9

"I don't know how much help I can be," said Charlie Peace as Dundy gestured him to the vacant armchair in the small office. "The bloke on the door says he was killed in the hotel here."

"That's right."

"I can't say I registered much from inside the hotel while the play was going on. Women collecting up glasses in the bar, staff watching the play from the dining room — not much more than that."

"Why were you at the play?"

"Came with a girlfr — Well, a girl. Student at London University. She asked me along, and I came to see if she was really interested or whether it was the okay thing these days for girl students to have a black boyfriend."

"And which was it?"

"We said polite farewells at the gate." Charlie's mouth expanded suddenly into a great, generous grin. "Plenty more where that came from."

"But you've got a clear idea of the play itself?"

"Oh, yes. It wasn't half bad, really, and one or two good laughs. Oh, I remember what went on onstage. It's what went on behind the stage that you'll be interested in, won't it, sir?"

Dundy sighed. "It will. Most of that will have to wait till tomorrow, though. Shall we contact the Yard and see if we can use you for a couple of days? Then you might get days off in lieu."

"If you could," said Charlie. "Days off have been pretty scarce as long as the football season's lasted. Are you going to be doing anything more tonight, sir?"

"Well, there was one thing. . . . Did you notice that doorman chappie, Nettles?"

"Oh, yes, sir. Know him by sight. Probably even exchanged a few words, back in the days when I was on the beat."

"My guess from the look of him is that beneath that old-soldier exterior there lurks a leaky-mouthed individual who'd tell you his life story for the price of a pint."

"I think that's probably true, sir. The bloke on the door says he's already had his war memoirs."

"He didn't give him his boss's life story as well, did he?"

"Afraid not. But he did say the place had gone to the dogs since he took over."

"Right. That sounds like an antidote to Mrs. Capper's 'not an enemy in the world' delusions. Let's have him in now."

"Is that what she said?" asked Frank, the doorman, shooting a cynical smile across the manager's desk at Iain Dundy and taking in Nettles and Charlie as he licked his lips in anticipation. "Life and soul of the Shakespeare, popular with all and sundry?"

"That's pretty much what she told me," said Dundy, looking straight at him.

"Balls," said Frank succinctly. His mouth was still working with relish at the prospect of character assassination ahead, and there was a glint in his old eyes. "Balls with the best of intentions, I don't doubt. I'm sure she believed every blessed word she spoke. But it's balls nonetheless."

"Not popular?"

"About as welcome as the death-watch beetle."

Frank expanded in his chair in the manager's office. This was the life. This was something to take home to the missus. A murder investigation and him in on the ground floor. Key witness, in fact, by reason of his position outside the main entrance. *And* he could tell them a thing or two about the hotel, the superintendent would find, a thing or two that he wouldn't hear from anyone else. There wasn't much that had escaped him in the last week or two.

Iain Dundy looked at Frank skeptically: his big body expanding with self-importance, his furry mustache twitching with relish at the idea of being part of a murder inquiry. He had been through the events of the evening with him, when he had last seen Des, and so on, and that had been moderately satisfactory. Now he was getting on to the nitty-gritty, which was hearsay and conjecture, and all the more enjoyable to Frank for that. He'll tell me everything, thought Dundy, but will that everything be right? He looks like the sort of man who turns suggestions into conjecture and conjecture into fact in the twinkling of an eye. Basically a stupid man but possibly to be trusted on the things he knows best. And he must have come to know Des Capper pretty well.

"Mind you," Frank resumed, "fair's fair.

136

He came after poor old Arthur Bradley — Know Arthur, did you? Most everyone did hereabouts. Him being so popular and the perfect gent, it would have been difficult for anyone coming after. This one no sooner showed his nose and everyone was asking why the devil he'd been appointed."

"You mean, if he was unpopular in the Saracen, it wasn't altogether his fault?"

Frank scratched his ear in puzzlement. "No, I don't altogether mean that. What I suppose I'm trying to say is that no one could have been really popular, but he sank plumb to the bottom of the charts. And that was because of what he did and the sort of man he was."

"Maybe you'd better explain," suggested Dundy.

And explain Frank did. Explained Des's manner — the oozing, oleaginous manner that hid the desire to dominate. Explained his know-all ways that made him believe he could pronounce and advise on all subjects under the sun. Explained that on his daily rounds as manager of the hotel he made it his business to gain knowledge of his guests rather than to minister to their comfort. And Frank went further. He made it clear that if it struck Des's fancy to use his knowledge, gain a covert pleasure by flaunting it, then that is exactly what he would do.

"To take a case in point," Frank concluded, still expressing the utmost pleasure in his narration by the whole set of his body. "This happened several weeks ago, but I actually saw it, and I can vouch for it. There was this bloke, late middle-aged, who'd been here before with this dolly-bird, who he'd signed in as *Mrs.* Williams, or whatever it was. This time he had a middle-aged lady, one on the sour side, or that was how she looked, and she was also Mrs. Williams, obviously the real one. He was a fool to do it, but there you are — some people *are* fools. Now, dinnertime it was, and I had to deliver a telephone message to the next table, so I saw this as it happened. Des Capper was doing his rounds — the head-waiter does *not* like him doing it in the dining room, but he hadn't a hope in hell of stopping him — and he went up to the Williams table, obviously singling it out, and with his usual dripping-oil manner he said: 'Good evening, Mrs. Williams. Everything to your satisfaction, is it? This is the first time we've had the pleasure of welcoming you to the Saracen, I think?' And after the usual courtesies, he turns to her husband, and he says: '*Mr.* Williams, on the other hand, we have seen before. Though that time, if I remember rightly, you were . . . on your own, weren't

138

you, sir?' And he puts his hand on the man's shoulder and applies a bit of pressure."

"Ouch!" said Iain Dundy.

"It was *daft,* that's what it was. One way to make sure that bloke was never again seen at the Saracen with or without fancy woman. There's hotels where a man like that knows he's safe, and there's others, and Des Capper had put us into the second category with a vengeance. But you see the sort of man he was, don't you? He couldn't resist that little display of — what shall I call it? — intimate knowledge, power over the man."

"And I suppose that at festival time there were plenty of things going on in the hotel that Mr. Capper could feed on?"

"Was there ever! *I* get a kick out of the goings-on at festival time, I can tell you. So you can guess what Des Capper was like. Went poking his nose in everything, giving advice here, a little bit of reminiscence there, and sniffing out intimate secrets all over the shop!"

"Which was not popular with the guests, I imagine?"

"They were getting up a petition, that I *do* know."

"A petition?"

"To get a change of manager by next year. Des unsuitable in view of the central position of the Saracen in the events of the Ketterick festival — that kind of thing."

"Hmmm. Interesting. Have you any idea what kinds of thing Capper had found out in these nosings around?"

"Ah — there you may find Win knows more than I do." He winked. "Pillow talk. Though mostly when he spoke to her it was to give orders. As far as him and me were concerned, we didn't swap information. I like to know what's going on as much as the next man, but with me it's just a case of 'That's the way the world goes.' With him it was something more . . . something nasty. Mind you, as often as not he'd know I knew, and I'd know he knew, if you get me. As in the case of Mr. Gottlieb — I beg his pardon: Herr Gottlieb."

Iain Dundy sighed. At last we must be coming to the arty ones, he thought. "And who is Mr. Gottlieb?"

"Some kind of musician. Conductor, I think. Travels around with a couple of heavies. And this is the grubby bit, which is what Des enjoyed most, because he really had a nose for the grubby: They pimp for him from among his fans. It's almost like them pop stars back in the sixties. He had one of the little groupies visiting him tonight, and Des commented on it when he came back from watching the play."

140

"So there were visitors to the hotel during the first half of the play?"

"Just the one. Just her. Between her going and Mr. Mallory coming back from the concert, there was nobody."

"Capper was interested in the girl, was he?"

"You bet. He was interested in anything connected with Gottlieb. Probably goes back to the war or something, though he always says he was in India and the Far East. Mind you, so far as I can see, everybody seems to hate Gottlieb. But with Des it seemed to have a special edge."

"But he never talked it over with you or told you why?"

"No, he just winked when I told him about the girl."

"Anyone else he was interested in?"

"Oh, everyone. His little antennae were always a-twitch. But not everyone gave him the sort of raw material he was interested in. There were the Galloways, of course — "

"Ah, *them* I've heard of," said Dundy. "May even have seen them on tour or on television. Definitely a couple, aren't they? Melissa is her name? And — "

"Clarissa and Carston. Yes, they act as a team, as often as not, and they were here a couple of years ago, when they created the same sort of brouhaha. They *act* as a team,

141

but they don't act like a team, if you get my meaning, sir. Not offstage. She's sleeping with the producer, and he's sleeping with an assistant stage manager, and everyone has to put up with a running commentary on the whole business from dawn to dusk, which is part of some sort of nonstop row they're having."

"A row about that?"

"I don't think so. No, according to the room maid they're completely open about that. But they spend their time sniping at each other nonetheless, and they give the impression that's as much habit as anything else."

"Maybe it is. On the other hand, there could be a specific reason, and Capper could somehow have got wind of it. Anything else?"

"One of the older actresses drinks. Who doesn't these days? A fair bit of A sleeping with B. Not all that interesting. Then there's something interesting happening around the Russian lady."

"Oh?"

"Something hush-hush."

"Do you think she wants to defect?"

"Maybe. I expect that's probably it. But if so, she's a long time about it. What's to stop her defecting now if she wants to? Anyway, there's something going on between her and one of the younger actors. Peter Fortnum, his name is, and he speaks Russki. Of course, it could be just good old-fashioned sex, but it looks like something more, *too*. If she's wanting to defect, I'd have thought Mr. Mallory would be in on it, too, but though this Fortnum is always making hush-hush phone calls and going to and fro with messages, I haven't noticed that Mr. Mallory is involved in any way."

"You mentioned Mallory before. Who exactly is he — and what?"

"A poncy agent. He acts for the Russian lady and for a superponcy Indian boy who apparently sings with that choirboy's voice I can't stand. He was at the concert tonight, of course."

"But did you say he came back at Interval time?"

"That's right. He said he left at the *concert* interval, and he got back to the Saracen sometime before *our* interval here. Around eight-fifteen, I'd say. He'd heard Singh — that's the name of his poncy Indian boyfriend, if you'll believe it — do his bit and came away. 'Singh sang divinely,' he said. That was all he was interested in."

"So the only outsider who came into the hotel during the first half of the performance — say, from seven to about eight-thirty — was the girl for this German conductor?"

143

"That's right. Austrian, I think he is, if you're getting technical."

"Otherwise there was Des Capper coming out to watch the play from the courtyard and then going back in again?"

"That's right. And going on about how he was going to serve in the bar at Interval, as if it was the height of bloody condescension on his part to serve in his own pub."

"And then just Mr. Mallory?"

"Right again."

"Now, you were talking, I know. Can you really be quite sure that no one could have got past you?"

"Sure and doubly sure. Bob and I talk every year during the play, but both of us keep our eyes open. It's our job to stop gate-crashers, and we do."

"What about the other entrances?"

"Well, obviously there are other entrances on a normal day. Each of the three bars has one, for instance, and there are doors into the kitchens. But naturally, when the play is on, you can only keep open manned entrances, and that means the one in the central gate. All the others are locked, and I watch the one into the hotel and Reception."

"That was the regular procedure each year, was it? Not something Mr. Capper had organized?"

144

"No, no, I've been doing it for years now. And as I say, generally me and Bob at the ticket gate meet halfway and have a bit of a natter, because we can't watch the play even if we'd wanted to, which we don't. But we keep a sharp eye on our entrances. You couldn't have it getting around that there were ways of slipping into the plays without buying a ticket."

"Well, if that's true, it does narrow the field a bit. And the field could do with some narrowing." Iain Dundy sighed and looked round at Nettles and Charlie, sitting quiet and respectful in the background. That young Peace looked as if he was following well. He was on the ball and was going to be of help. Dundy looked at him as he said: "Anything else, I wonder?"

Charlie cleared his throat. "Just one thing, sir. I was here with a girl for the performance, as you know — "

"That's right," put in Frank. "Saw you going in."

Charlie smiled at him ferociously, as if daring him to voice the thoughts that had gone through his mind at the time. "Well, I thought you should know that we went into the Shakespeare Bar at Interval, and the door out to the street *was* locked, because we thought of going outside to get some air. At

145

the time I wondered about fire risk. As it was, we had to go out into the courtyard again, which was very crowded, what with the seats and all the people."

"Right," said Iain Dundy. "So that confirms what has just been said."

"That's right, sir. There was just a question in my mind about the key. It wasn't in the door, of course, or we could just have turned it and gone out. I wondered who had it."

"It would be Mrs. Capper," said Frank promptly. "And the barmen in the other bars would have had theirs with them, too, while the play was going on. I think it's the headwaiter who sees to the back kitchen door. The drill was that they would open up just as the performance was ending."

"Right."

"The chief fire officer has okayed the arrangement," said Frank self-importantly. "The fact is, we can get the big gates open in a matter of thirty seconds, so the major part of the audience would be out in the twinkling of an eye. The balconies are not high, and there are rope ladders on every one."

Dundy nodded. "Well, I think that's it — for the moment only, of course. I'll want to check up on details later. I wonder if that girl Dawn is still around. If she is, maybe I could just tie up a few loose ends with her before

146

everyone goes off to bed."

"She was getting poor old Win Capper off to sleep," said Frank. "She's a very conscientious girl. She may have waited to see if she was wanted."

And she had. She had started cleaning up the Shakespeare, but one of the constables had said she'd better not do that in case there was anything there that might be important in the way of evidence. So she had sunk down into a chair in the foyer and lit a cigarette. She was a smart girl, with normally dancing eyes and a humorous expression. Now she was tired to the point of exhaustion, but she tried to pull herself together enough to answer Dundy's questions.

"The last time I saw Mr. Capper? Let me see, that would be before the play started. Mrs. Capper had got him to help behind the bar. Not that he was much help, I imagine — all talk and very little action."

"You didn't like him?"

"Nobody did," said Dawn blithely, with the confidence born of a feeling that no one was likely to accuse *her* of murdering her boss. "I don't want to speak ill of the dead, but it doesn't do to tell lies about them, either, does it? He was damn-all use about the place, and that's a fact. Win did all the work, and she was nothing better than his slave."

"Nevertheless, Mrs. Capper got her husband to promise that he'd be there to help at Interval?"

"That's right. I came in just as they were talking about it, so I overheard. He was trying to wriggle out of it: 'You'll have Dawn to help you.' As if two was enough when they're crowded five or six deep waving five-pound notes at you! But he hated *serving*. He liked swanning around — that was all *he* was good for."

"And as it turned out, Mrs. Capper had only you for help, and you were with her all evening?"

"Yes, as it turned out. We coped at Interval. In point of fact, if you've got a third who doesn't do much but get in the way, he's more of a hindrance than a help. And Win had got a lot of glasses poured out in readiness while the first part was going on. So it was hectic, but we managed."

"But you *were* with Mrs. Capper all evening?"

Under Iain Dundy's calm, clear gaze, Dawn faltered as she understood what he was getting at.

"What you're saying," she muttered, "is that in this sort of case it's always the husband or wife who's suspected first. Though in fact Win thought Des was God's gift, poor cow."

148

"I'm not *saying* anything. I'm just trying to get at times."

"Yes, well — I filled the dishwasher in the kitchens with glasses in the second half. There were just too many to do in clear water in the bar, like Win normally would. That took me — what? — ten minutes."

"And in the first half?"

"I just fetched the snacks. . . . They were something a bit special, a sort of free extra because it was the first night. There was a bit of balancing plates on the tray and that, but it couldn't have taken me more than five minutes. Less, if anything."

Iain Dundy gave a meaningful look at the other policemen that said, Five minutes would be enough. But Dawn, under inquisition, had regained some of her perkiness, and she noticed the look. She said, smiling sweetly: "And when I came back, Win had poured out drinks for Interval, like I said. While I'd been away, she'd done about fifteen white wines, about ten reds, and the same number of whiskeys and gins. You try doing that in five minutes and killing your husband!"

"Couldn't they have been done before you came on the scene?"

"Where would she have kept them? The white wines would have to have been kept in the fridge. I was in and out of the fridge during the first half of the play, getting ice and whatnot. There were no ready-poured glasses of white wine there; that I can tell you for sure."

Charlie cleared his throat. "Excuse me, sir," he said. "My girl had white wine at Interval. First thing she said when she sipped it was 'Lovely and cool!' "

Charlie's imitation of upper-class girlhood was perfect. Superintendent Dundy sat looking gloomily ahead of him. To Sergeant Nettles his expression said as clearly as words: It's the arty types we're going to be stuck with.

Finally he shifted in his chair and turned to Dawn with a smile. "Thank you, love. That'll be all for tonight. I think we ought all to go home and get an hour or two's kip."

The Dining Room

10

The headwaiter supervised breakfast next morning. This was not something that he did very often, but he did it the day after Des's murder. He had heard about the killing the night before, of course, as he and his staff were waiting for the last of the supper-takers to leave. Dawn had been the first to bring the news, and further snippets of information had been gleaned (by guile) from the many policemen infesting the Saracen's Head. The kitchen and dining-room staff had been thunderstruck and hadn't enjoyed anything so much in years. They had quite lost the desire to get rid of the eaters and go home to bed. In fact, they had related the news to favored eaters with varying degrees of subtlety. ("I'm sorry the service has been a bit erratic tonight, but you see, the manager's just been murdered.") The headwaiter participated in all their contradictory emotions, though on a loftier plane, of course, and he had made do with a very few hours' sleep in order to be at the Saracen early, apparently to ensure that the dining room's high standards of food and service were in no way compromised by the untoward little incident of the night before.

Incidentally, he also intended to be the first to inform the headquarters of the Beaumont hotel chain. It is in the nature of headwaiters that they like to be the first with news, however hushed, regretful, or reverent the tone of voice in which they choose to broadcast it.

Thus, when the various members of the cast and other residents of the hotel came down severally to breakfast, they found eggs scrambled to a nicety, kippers beautifully frizzled, the traditional fry-up traditionally fried up. What was different was the atmosphere. They all dallied over their breakfasts for a start, hoping that someone else would come down with a new theory they had thought up in the long watches. All the play people sat at adjacent tables (not something they normally did) and exchanged intimacies and abrasions across the gaps, while the orchestral players and odds and ends sat as near them as they decently could and listened unashamedly, as did the unusually attentive waitresses, who fussed unconscionably around the tables in the hope of picking up something new.

"The point is," said Jason Thark, still in the magisterial mood of the night before, "that it would be quite impossible for any of us to go through the dining room here without being seen. Let alone the kitchen, let alone the Shakespeare Bar, but the dining room would have been quite impossible. And we would have had to go through all three to get to the stairs that would have taken us up to the first floor. No — Ronnie was quite right: We're out of it."

"There was just one thing," said Ronnie, "something I've been thinking over during the night. When I was playing onstage, I was conscious of faces in the windows of the dining room watching the play. . . . *Were* you?" he asked, swiveling round in his chair and transfixing the waitress, who was dawdling round with a toast rack in her hand as an excuse. She blushed.

"Well, some of us was watching."

"Never all of you?"

"No. Some of us watched some of the time. But you couldn't hear, not through the window, so you couldn't follow what was going

153

on, though it looked a good laugh and you had us splitting our sides, sir."

"But some of you didn't watch at all?"

"No, sir."

"And where were the ones who were not at the window?"

"They were around the table by the door into the kitchen having a bit of a giggle and a gossip, sir."

Ronnie leaned back in his chair, satisfied.

"So I was right. Nobody could have got past."

"There was also some poker playing in the kitchen," volunteered the waitress, unwilling to lose the limelight now that she was used to it.

"Right. Them we could see from our part of the kitchen. I admit that they most probably wouldn't have noticed if anyone from the cast had tried to sneak past. But the gag — Sorry, collection of staff by the door into the kitchen would certainly have noticed anyone, wouldn't you?"

"Well, I expect so, sir. We did see this gentleman" — she gestured at Peter Fortnum — "go through and then go back again. Not that it meant anything, I'm sure."

She retreated rather suddenly from the table, as if she had all but accused Peter of murder. She left some embarrassment behind her as well, though not in Jason Thark, who was impervious to any such human emotion.

"You see? She noticed. *One* of them would certainly have noticed if our murderer had tried to go that way. And apart from Peter, who was not to know that Connie would run out of gin, so I see no significance in his trip, nobody did."

For one moment this made everyone feel better. For only a moment.

"Oh, *come*," said Clarissa Galloway, putting back on her plate a delicate triangle of toast. "I really wouldn't have expected you to be so deficient in logic, Jason, my pet. For a start, Peter could have made sure Connie would run out by nicking a half from her bag. She said, if you remember, that she had never forgotten to have one there in reserve before. Secondly, he could have been intending to use some other excuse but seized on this when he heard Connie's laments. Of course, Peter *dar*-ling, I'm not saying that any such thing happened, merely that we must, above all things, remain *log*ical, because we can be sure the police will."

"I quite understand," said Peter, tight-lipped.

As soon as he saw it was nine o'clock, the headwaiter ceased supervising the mundane business of distributing breakfast goodies and slipped into his little office in the corner of the kitchens. Somebody would now be in at the head office.

The Beaumont chain had hotels from Aberdeen to Bodmin and from the sublime to the disgusting. Its headquarters was in Kensington, and when the headwaiter made it clear that this was a matter of the utmost urgency, he was put through without further ado to the managing director's office.

"He'll not be in until ten or so," said the great man's secretary. "He's been at Brighton with his son — he's a spastic and takes a lot of looking after. Where did you say you were speaking from?"

"The Saracen's Head, in Ketterick."

"Ah, yes. One of the jewels in our crown."

"Precisely."

"Haven't you got that festival thing on there at the moment? I hope it's not causing any problems."

"No, or not directly. It's the manager. Mr. Capper . . . "

"Ye-es?" Did the headwaiter detect a note of wariness, or at least of circumspection?

"He's dead. Murdered."

"Good God! Have you called the police?"

The headwaiter raised his eyebrows to heaven. "It happened last night. Of course,

156

the police have been here since then. That's all taken care of."

"I shall inform the managing director the moment he comes in. He'll be most upset. He knew Mr. Capper personally. And he won't like all the publicity there'll be. It will clash horribly with the Saracen Head's image."

It was the headwaiter's opportunity, the reason he had been so keen to relay the news. His voice took on tones of the most magisterial: "If you will allow me to say so, the whole Capper appointment clashed with the Saracen's image."

"Ah . . ." There was silence at the other end, as if the secretary were not used to being taken down a peg or two by employees from the suburbs. "You thought so?"

"I would say the whole hotel thought so."

"As far as this office was aware, he was doing an excellent job. He rang up last night, you know, to say that the play was going well. The duty man left a note for the managing director. He was first-rate like that, at keeping in touch. He must have been murdered after that."

"He must indeed. At what time did Mr. Capper make this phone call to your duty man?"

"The note is dated seven-thirty."

"I shall certainly inform the investigating officer."

"I hardly think — Is that necessary? Do we really want to involve Head office? Well, you must use your discretion. . . ."

"The main thing now is," interrupted the headwaiter, who had every intention of following his conscience and doing his duty as a citizen, "that we get a temporary manager as soon as possible. You do have qualified people who are between assignments, I suppose?"

"Oh, yes. Of course."

"The play isn't on tonight. It's the first night of the opera. After that the play runs every night of the festival except Sunday. It's essential we have somebody here by tomorrow. And preferably someone who could learn the ropes tonight."

"It's a tall order. But I'll list the possibilities and show them to the M.D. as soon as he gets in. I suppose Mrs. Capper isn't in a condition to — "

"Mrs. Capper is not the managing type, and by all accounts she is in no condition at the moment to do anything. It would hardly be seemly in any case even to have her helping behind the bar, whatever her mental state."

"No. No, of course not. Well, I'll try and get a lightning decision and ring you as soon as I have any news. Meanwhile, soldier on, eh?"

The discussion was continuing in the dining room. Breakfast had never taken so long, but the kitchen staff was not complaining. The waitresses were picking up an unending stream of fact, conjecture, innuendo, and downright falsehood, and they were regaling it to the cooks, who were putting their own interpretations on them. ("You mark my words!" the head cook kept saying after each particularly bizarre leap of the imagination.) Before long, they all felt, they would be ready to make an arrest, even if the police were not.

"Right," Ronnie Wimsett was saying. "Peter's absence is not in dispute. He went to get gin for Connie. We all find it pretty impossible to get to our own rooms — *still*, after a fortnight here — so it's not surprising that he found it difficult to get to Connie's."

Peter, and Natalya, too, sat stewing over their tea, looking straight in front of them.

"The question is, could any of the rest of us do it? Now, to my mind, going through on the Webster and Massinger side of the hotel is simply out. For one reason, at some stage you would have to come *out* — either into the courtyard or into the street. In the courtyard you have audience who would see you, including twelve standing-room customers at the back, by the main gates, whose vision you would have to cross. On the other hand, if you go out into the street, you still have to get back in past hawk-eyed Frank on the main entrance. Impossible — right? That leaves the route via the kitchens and the Shakespeare, which is inconceivable for reasons we've already gone into. So all in all — apart from Peter, and sorry about that, old chap — there simply seems no way any of us *could* have done it."

There was silence after this, though one or two, notably Susan Fanshaw, looked unhappy. Indeed, she started to speak but cast a half look in the direction of Carston Galloway and cut the sound short in her throat.

"Well, that settles it," cooed Clarissa. "We'll explain it to that rather *mel*ancholy looking policeman, and it will leave him free to direct his attentions elsewhere."

"After all," said Ronnie Wimsett, "we've been here for a couple of weeks or so, but Capper's been manager for months. Who knows what backs he's put up in his time?"

"The main thing is," said Carston, pushing back his chair and making to get up, "that we're all in the clear and can now get on with our business."

Brad Mallory's drawl broke unnervingly into the general euphoria. "Anyone would think," he said, "that the Saracen's Head was a one-story building."

He was sitting slightly apart, at a table for two, which Singh had just left. There was silence for a moment after his words, but then Ronnie Wimsett broke into it confidently:

"No, no, old chap. I've thought of that. To get to the stairs in the foyer outside the Shakespeare you still have to go through the kitchens, dining room, and the bar itself. And on the other side the stairs are between the Massinger and the Webster and you'd have to go through the one and could be seen from the other. No, that doesn't wash."

"Brad doesn't relish his position," said Clarissa in serpentine tones, "of being one of the few actually in the *hotel* part of the Saracen at the time of the killing."

Brad's smile in return revealed that he was hardly to be outdone in the friendly-snake department.

"Quite true if Des was killed after eight-fifteen. Yes, I could in fact have returned from the concert and gone straight upstairs and killed him. In *fact*, I went to my room, but I could just as easily have gone along to his flat. But what if he was already dead by eight-fifteen?"

Clarissa shrugged. "So what? It leaves us exactly where we were. Apart from young Peter, none of us could have gone through to the front part of the hotel."

Bradford Mallory, no less than Clarissa, could relish a big moment. "I seem to remember," he said, almost dreamily, "from one of my visits to your delightful play in rehearsal, a moment . . . a line — what was it? 'What mean these sudden broils so near my doors?' Something like that!"

" 'Have you not other places but my house, to vent the spleen of your disordered bloods?' " went on Gillian Soames, as if this were something she had been itching to bring up for hours.

"I know what you're going to say," said Clarissa Galloway with all the considerable force at her disposal. She had put her hand over the breakfast table and covered her husband's in a display of solidarity. It was a revealing gesture, which suggested that their instinct was to draw together at moments of crisis. She also revealed that this was something they had discussed overnight. Brad Mallory ignored her and went on in his dreamy fashion.

"It was, if I remember, a speech of Ralph Greatheart, at night, quieting the riotous behavior of the apprentices . . . and appearing to them in his nightshirt . . . appearing — and this is the point — *above*, on what we may call the upper stage. In fact, appearing on that part of the balcony over the center of the stage. Is that not right, Miss Fanshaw?"

"Yes," said Susan, tight-lipped.

"And my impression is that this scene occurs — what? — about an hour into the play?"

"Something like that," agreed Susan.

"And that with Ralph Greatheart on the balcony there is his stage wife and his daughter Alice — dear Gillian."

"Right," agreed Gillian.

"And did you, Miss Fanshaw, accompany them to the first floor to see that all was well?"

"No, I checked costumes and props at the bottom of the staircase as they all went up."

"The staircase," said Brad.

"I went up," said Jason Thark, hurriedly, before anyone else could mention it. "It was a tricky scene, and I went and stood in the bedroom behind."

"That's right," said Carston, "and you — " He shut up suddenly.

"I think, you know," said Brad, "that the police had better look into that scene and that staircase and who was there for that scene and who might have used the staircase before and after."

"There goes your alibi for all of us," said Gillian to Ronnie. "Somehow it always did seem too good to be true."

The Manager's Flat

11

The residential quarters of the manager of the Saracen's Head consisted of four rooms immediately above the entrance foyer and reception desk. They could be reached by a small staircase from the manager's office behind Reception or by a door from the maze of corridors and open areas on the first floor — a door that led directly into the sitting room. Des's murderer could have gained or been given access to the flat from either of these.

Superintendent Dundy had sent Nettles off to talk to the kitchen and the cleaning staff. Nettles was an excellent chap, but he did tend to chat, to comment, to make his presence felt. Dundy liked to sniff out a place in silence — walk around, get the feel, sense a personality. Then he would look around and think of what was missing, what was out of place. So he said to Charlie, down in Reception: "Let's go up and quietly get the lie of the land, shall we?" Charlie nodded, and together they ascended the stairs and went to work.

The manager's living quarters — or dying quarters, as they had so soon become for Des Capper — had been inhabited for twenty years by "dear old Arthur," as Gillian Soames and others always called him, and his impress was still on them. His had been the choice of furniture, his the choice of the pictures on the walls. It was mainly in the extras and inessentials that Des and Win had made their tenure felt. Or that Des had made his tenure felt.

The photo of the hotel in Dubbo, squarely in the center of the sideboard, had Des standing by the wrought-iron pillar of a wonderful nineteenth-century structure, looking loathsomely proprietorial. Win was not to be seen. Perhaps she was behind the camera, but as it seemed a highly professional photograph — you could feel the flies, smell the sheep-dip — this was unlikely. Probably she had been behind the bar as usual. The books all seemed to be Des's, too: *The Homemaker's Medical Enquire Within*, *The Secrets of the Tarot*, Desmond Morris, *Reader's Digest* evaporated books, L. Ron Hubbard, and Arthur Hailey.

165

Even the *Jane Fonda Exercise Book* belonged, Dundy guessed, more to Des than to Win. There were newish paperbacks of several biographies of the Mountbattens, presumably purchased to give corroborative detail to Des's recent incautious claims, which Dundy had heard about from Frank. There was also *Heat and Dust* and a popular book on Indian religions.

Des's research for the festival took in heavier tomes. From the Ketterick Public Library he had borrowed a thick book on Donizetti by William Ashbrook and a volume on Elizabethan and Jacobean comedy. The latter had been much renewed, with dates handwritten in. The former was a new borrowing, with a return date ten days hence. They both sat on a small table by the biggest armchair. Charlie took them up and skimmed through the sections on *Adelaide* and *The Chaste Apprentice*.

Iain Dundy was over by the sideboard, getting whiffs of Des's personality. There was a pile of old records there — Mantovani, James Last and the Beachboys — but the record player did not look as if it had been touched since they had moved in. The *Mirror* and the *Sun* of the day before were beside one of the easy chairs, and some old *Penthouses* were stacked under a coffee table. The racing pages of the newspapers were marked for possible

166

bets. In one of the papers something was cut out; it seemed to be the regular medical column. Iain Dundy raised his eyebrows and went on.

Win's influence seemed mainly to consist of dainty linen and lace mats on the dressing tables, sideboards, and occasional tables, such as the one on which the knife had lain. Probably also hers were the antimacassars on the backs of easy chairs and sofa. Leaning against the sofa, Dundy found that the covering was slightly damp. The furniture in the room was all solid, capacious and worn, and had no doubt served "dear old Arthur" for years, until it had now gained this light accretion of alien personality from the new managers. No doubt it was like this when a stately home was taken over by new stately owners.

The body had by now been taken away, though chalk marks and tapes marked where it had been, and Iain Dundy could remember it very well. The sitting room in the manager's flat was a large one, with the main bedroom leading off at one end, kitchen and second bedroom leading off from the other. The sofa and the easy chairs were clustered around a fireplace, with a small dining table and two chairs positioned by the window that overlooked Ketterick High Street. This left a goodly space at one end, where the stairs

167

down to the ground floor and the door out to the corridor were. It was in this open space that Des's body had been found. It had pitched forward, its head towards the door into the corridor, its back decorated by a knife between the shoulder blades. The table on which had rested the knife had been in that open space too, just behind the sofa. One could still see the imprint left by the handle of the knife on the embroidered table mat it had rested on. Anyone, on an impulse born of overwhelming nausea or provocation, could have taken it up and stabbed the loathly Des with it on the spur of the moment.

Did the position of the body tell one anything? Could Des have been starting towards the door when he was stabbed from behind? Possibly. Equally, he could have been standing in thought, facing in that direction, and propelled sprawling forward by the force of the blow from behind. There was nothing particular to look at on that wall apart from the door and a reproduction of Morris's *Queen Guinevere* beside it. But a man in thought does not need anything to look at, and Des, Dundy suspected, was a man with a variety of projects demanding thought.

Did he, Dundy wondered, keep all these projects in his head, or did he keep some written record, however vestigial?

Dundy and Charlie spent over an hour circling the flat warily, like two animals careful not to invade the other's territory. Then Nettles came up after a not very rewarding session with the domestic staff, and inevitably they all settled down to an interim comparing of notes. Dundy came out at once with the question of Des's projects and his thirst for scraps of knowledge.

"I don't think there can be any doubt," he said, "that he was a man who loved information. First of all, just information. Have you met people like that? Do they still exist in your generation? They'll bring it out anywhere, anytime: the age of the pyramids, the average number of eggs a chicken lays a year, the estimated population of China in the year 3000. Totally out of the blue they'll come out with it — some real conversation stopper. And like as not they'll just think they've floored you and congratulate themselves on their cleverness."

"I know that sort of bloke," agreed Nettles. "The sort who makes you slope off to the saloon bar if you hear his voice coming from the public. But in his case it shades off into something much more nasty, doesn't it?"

"Apparently. But I think it starts off as this sort of desire to accumulate out-of-the-way information. The sort of fact you got in the old Ripley "Believe It or Not" column or as a little paragraph in the *Reader's Digest*. That sort of interest is rather boring but totally innocent. When it spreads itself out and becomes a desire to collect information about living people, that's when it becomes dangerous. And so far as we can see, Des's magpie instincts about information also embraced people — the guests at the hotel and very probably the staff at the hotel as well."

"What I'm trying to get a handle on," said Charlie, "is the point of it all. I mean, with some people it can be just accumulation for the sake of accumulation. I wouldn't think it was that way with Des Capper, would you?"

"No," said Dundy emphatically.

"Then was it for pure, straightforward blackmail? Was it for chuckling over and poking ribs — as in Frank's story about the man who'd brought his bird here? Or was it something more subtle than either?"

"Yes, that is the question, isn't it? I suppose the murder gives us the answer to that, if we're on the right track." Iain Dundy paused and scratched his ear. "But perhaps it's not completely clear-cut, not as neat as you put it. You say: Did he accumulate grubby bits of information just for the sake of it, did he chuckle over it, or did he use it for blackmail? Perhaps the answer is: All three. It's not necessarily either/or. If the information was not usable, he just enjoyed having it. If it was usable, he had to decide what use to make of it."

"And there was one other possible use for it," said Charlie thoughtfully.

"What's that?"

"Revenge."

Dundy nodded.

"There is also this question of how he got appointed here," said Nettles. "It's something the staff keep bringing up. He wasn't just awful; he was the wrong type."

"We'll have to start looking at that," agreed Dundy. "If he was as unsuitable as Frank and everyone else imply, then the question of blackmail must surely arise there."

"And if it arises there, then the chances are that it has arisen again now," said Nettles.

"Yes, though let's remember one thing: That would be blackmail for personal advancement. It could be done very subtly. Just a whisper and a nod. It could be done so indirectly as hardly to be blackmail at all."

"Though not by this Capper character, surely, sir, if what we've heard of him is to be believed?" objected Charlie. "Hardly a subtle character, by all accounts."

"Probably you're right. But still, it is one further step to blackmail for money. A further and a very dangerous one. But if he was blackmailing one of the festival guests here, what else could it be but blackmail for money?"

Charlie coughed. "What the class newspapers call 'sexual favors,' sir?"

"Well, maybe," said Dundy. "I haven't had a very strong sexual whiff from this case yet. More a matter of sheer black bile, as far as Capper is concerned. But we'll have to talk to people and find out if that was one of his interests. I presume there are some reasonably attractive women around connected with the play in one way or another. His wife would be the last to know — or, on the other hand, she could be leading us on in a big way, don't forget. Still, I would like something just a little more definite than sexual favors."

"There's nothing written down, is there, sir?" asked Nettles. "No kind of record of the little things he found out?"

"That's what I've been wondering. Nothing's been handed over by the technical experts, and we haven't come across anything today. I wonder if he was the sort to write things down. What impression do you get?"

The other two frowned, then shook their heads.

"No impression, sir," said Charlie regretfully. "Could have been a real little Samuel Pepys. Could have kept it all in his head."

"The sheer *amount* he seems to have accumulated might be a hopeful sign," said Nettles.

"Yes, and at least that generation's more likely to write things down than a younger one," said Dundy hopefully. "Youngsters these days need a keyboard connected to a screen if they want to remember anything. I suppose the first thing is to organize a search of all the obvious places — desks, drawers, sideboards, and so on. You take the big bedroom, Peace, you take the small one and the manager's office downstairs, Nettles, and I'll take this room and the kitchen. If we get no results, we'll start thinking of hiding places."

And so they got down to it. But of results in the obvious sense, there were none.

There were just a few things that they thought it worthwhile to collect up and mull over afterward. Des had apparently eaten All-Bran for breakfast and taken Ex-Lax regularly. He had used a mouth spray against bad breath, and an antiperspirant. His teeth were his own, but he used a toothpaste designed to remove heavy stains. There were many used packs of playing cards and a backgammon set. There were road maps with routes laboriously marked out, perhaps by Win. The routes, mostly from Carlisle, had not taken them to well-known beauty spots or places of tourist fame, not to Wordsworth's Cottage or Castle

173

Howard. They had been exclusively to towns. When Dundy compared them to a leaflet downstairs on the reception desk, he found that they were all towns that boasted hotels in the Beaumont chain.

No harm in that, of course. Doubtless the Cappers would have got a reduction on their stays. But the fact that most of the routes were from Carlisle made Dundy wonder if they had been prospecting during Des's previous job, deciding which of the hotels they — or rather *he*, surely — was going to blackmail himself into the managership of.

On a personal level the only haul they got was a few letters and postcards. There was little any of them could make out of the postcards: one of the Alhambra with "Fantastic place — Kevin" on the back; one of Michelangelo's *David* with "Christ what a nancy boy, eh? Jacko." The postmarks were from the fifties, and they were addressed to hotels in Parkes and Coonabarabran, New South Wales. The only reason the policemen could see for keeping them had to be the pictures.

The letters were marginally more revealing. Three of them were from Des's mother. The latest, very feeble and practically without meaning, was addressed to Des and Win after their move to Britain in 1974. The earliest had also been addressed to Des in Britain — in fact, to a street in Pimlico. The date was December 1945, and it expressed the wish that he had waited until things were more settled before going "home":

But then you always did what you want, but I hear such dreadful things on the wireless and wonder and with everything so short there are you getting enough to eat?

The other was addressed to Private Capper, of the Second Borderers, serving in India, apparently stationed near Bombay. So Des's army career had begun *after* the Second World War. Not the impression he had given Frank, the doorman. The letter expressed bewilderment as to why he had joined up:

You always were a mystery to me, but one blessing youll be nearer home so when the three years are up you can come back, this is where you really belong son I hope youve learnt that by now with all love Your Ever Loving Mum.

The only other letter of interest was from India, dated 1947, and addressed to Corporal Capper, stationed in Hong Kong. After jocose preliminaries, it said:

You lucky bastard, getting out before it all turned nasty. My God, the things I've seen, but I expect you've heard from some of the boys, and you can believe it. Don't write and tell me you're living the life of Riley in H.K., Des, because I don't want to know. You always were the kind of crafty bastard who could slip out from under.

Not this time, thought Dundy.

"Well," he said, shaking his head and looking at the meager haul. "This is the sum total of finds of interest, and I can't say it gets us much further. No written notes of discoveries, no written evidence of any blackmail attempts. What does that mean? That he didn't write anything down?"

"Could be," said Nettles. "If he was a serious blackmailer, it would be much the wisest thing."

"Yes . . ." said Dundy. "Somehow the vibes I'm getting from this man don't suggest that he would always do the wisest thing. . . . But maybe I'm getting him entirely wrong."

"I may be wrong, too, sir," said Charlie, "but the vibes I'm getting suggest that he was a very *obvious* man, for all his cunning. As I said before, not subtle at all. Awful in an obvious way . . . obvious minded, somehow."

176

"Sort of second-rate brain?" suggested Dundy.

"Yes, or third. You know, the sort of person who thinks it's true because he's read it in the papers. Quotes *Reader's Digest* as if it were the *Encyclopaedia Britannica.*"

"Oh, God, yes."

"That's how I see him. And I wonder — if he's taken notes of any sort, then it seems to me he's probably hidden them in a very obvious place. I mean the sort of places old ladies hide things, the places that are always the very first ones that the experienced burglar looks in."

"Kept under the geranium pot, do you mean?"

"Yes. Laughable, and a bit pathetic. Where in the house do old people hide their little bits of money, their pension books, their savings certificates?"

"The backs of cushions," said Nettles promptly. "Behind the books in the bookcase. Under the sofa cushions. Under the mattress. In the tea caddy. On top of the kitchen dresser."

"That's the sort of place. I just wondered, sir, whether it might be worthwhile looking there."

In the event, Charlie turned out to be right about the obviousness of Des's mind. Des and

Win had gone in for Scandinavian-style beds, with the (hard) mattress laid straight onto a board. Good for the back, as Des would no doubt have told many a bar customer at length in his time. His notebook was pushed under the mattress, on top of the board. Apparently Win Capper had not had the aristocratic sensibilities of the princess who could not sleep on a pea. The notebook was on her side.

But there was no doubt it was Des's. Dundy took it downstairs and compared the handwriting with his entries in the hotel register. It was Des's hand, all right. Or fist, more likely. Because the little notebook, bound in green plastic, was mostly a jumble of jottings in no particular order and dubiously legible in places. These ill-spelled notes were *aides-mémoires* in the strictest sense. They seemed to be scribbled down pretty much anywhere, just as he felt the urge to commit things to memory. So that "Geary — gin?" came two or three pages after another note that read: "Geary — ten half bottles in six days *known*." There was, then, no sequence or continuity, and Dundy and his two assistants had to get from it such isolated nuggets as they could. If they were baffled, it had to be said that Des was frequently, too. His bafflement expressed itself in such diagrams as:

SUSAN F.   JASON T.

Underneath the diagram there was scrawled the question "What gives???"

Question marks, in fact, were very frequent. There were "Gillian S. — Ronnie Wimsett??" There was "Fortnum — Natalya R — phone calls — where? — expensive — what's up? Defecting?" Later, presumably connected with this, there was "Why Mallory not involved?" Mallory also appeared in "Mallory — Singh???" Underneath which was written: "Where?"

But there was one page in the book where there seemed to be some sort of organization, where the information seemed grouped around one central figure. There was a note that said: "Girls — young." Then he had added: "Constant supply — recruited by bodyguard. Bodyguard paid by the girls? Age?" This last word had been underlined many times. At the bottom of the page there was an enigmatic "HAD 9." What could that mean? That he'd had nine such assignations with classical music groupies to Des's knowledge? But there was a shaky arrow leading to the side of the page that suggested that this entry related to something on a previous page.

In any case, it was overshadowed by an entry in red: Stretching from the bottom left hand corner to the top right, misspelled but sharp in impact, in letters that bit deep into the page as if they had been scrawled in a fury, there was the legend:

GET GOTLIEB

"I think we may have struck gold," said Iain Dundy.

People Talking

12

For the actors it should have been a day of delicious anticlimax. It should have been a day for reading the early reviews, letting off a bit of steam, of shopping for unnecessaries. But it wasn't like that at all.

Reviews there were, luckily. Reviews that praised the "tireless energy" of the *Apprentice* cast, the "mature warmth and humanity" of Carston Galloway's Ralph Greatheart, and "the sense of a send-up of a parody" behind Ronnie Wimsett's chaste apprentice. The music critics had done their bit, too. There was acclaim for the "incredible and flamboyant richness" of Singh's voice and for the "golden opulence and vivid femininity" of Natalya in the letter scene. All these were lapped up, swapped, discussed, and disputed, though not by Clarissa Galloway, whose Melinda Purefoy was not mentioned at all.

But it was all, somehow, a bit academic. A bit of a sideshow. Because at half past eleven the superintendent, who had only been glimpsed hitherto walking purposively around the hotel, began interviewing people who he thought might be of help to him. And since the staff of the hotel had all been together at the crucial time and had been given a thorough going-over by one of his men, that left the actors and the residents. And of course, it was all quite ridiculous, but . . . but one really had to decide how much to tell him, didn't one? And one had to decide which of one's fellow actors one could talk to about how much to tell him. Probably it would be mostly routine, wouldn't it, and rather dreary, but then there would be those areas . . .

And it *was* mostly routine, this preliminary round of interviews. But there were areas in which Dundy and his men found tiny nuggets of interest.

"But I *can't* see," said Clarissa Galloway, "why we can't be interviewed together. We do everything together. Except sleep together, sometimes, but that goes in waves."

She crossed a shapely black-stockinged leg, doing it *at* Charlie Peace, as being the youngest man in the room. His eye gleamed with a spark of amused appreciation. Iain Dundy's mouth tightened. Of course with these arty people it all came back to sex in the end.

"I'm afraid interviewing you together would be quite against regulations," he said.

"It must be terrible to be so *bound* by regulations," said Clarissa with stage thoughtfulness.

"You say you do everything together, but in fact you weren't playing husband and wife in this play, were you?"

"Good God, no. Ralph Greatheart is an *ancient* character."

"Do your parts link up? Are you together onstage a great deal in the course of the evening?"

"No, we have a scene together at the end of the first act, but then we're hardly onstage at all together until the last act."

"Then were you offstage together a lot?"

"Oh, yes, a fair bit."

"Talking together in the dressing rooms behind the stage?"

"Well, I don't re*mem*ber talking together," said Clarissa, again with that contrived thoughtfulness. "But of course terribly a*ware* of each other. *Al*ways terribly aware. It's what distinguishes us as a partnership."

And that, Dundy suspected, was nothing but the truth, in spite of the stagy manner in which it was delivered.

"I see. While you were backstage, were you aware of anyone leaving the dressing room — the two dressing rooms, rather, in part of the kitchen and the private functions room — to go into the main part of the hotel?"

"No, I can assure you Carston didn't. As to the others — Well, of course there was young Peter Fortnum."

"Ah."

"*Quite* a talented beginning. Plays Peter Patterwit and has some quite *fright*ful jokes, which is almost inevitable in this kind of comedy, but he carries them off rather well. . . . "

"Yes, I'm sure. But it was his trip into the main part of the hotel you were going to tell me about."

"Was I?" She smiled dazzlingly at the three men. "Well, if you *want* to hear about it. It's surely of no importance. Let me see . . . He came offstage — it was towards Interval time, perhaps a quarter of an hour before — and Connie Geary was complaining that she'd run out of gin. She's a dipso, poor old thing, though quite a happy one, which is a blessing when you see the other kind. Where was I? Oh, yes, Peter Fortnum had just come off, and he wasn't due to launch any more of his *leaden* innuendos at the audience until after the Interval, and he said straightaway that

184

he'd go and fetch her a half, which is what he did. Actually, it *did* seem to some of us that he was gone an awfully long time."

"I see," said Iain Dundy. "Well, no doubt it's something I shall be able to follow up. Now, about the dead man himself — what were your impressions?"

She leaned forward. She had decided that honesty would be the best policy and sincerity the best manner. She delivered herself of a great deal of sincerity.

"Quite frightful! A squirt, a pusher, a bore. And of course dreadfully inquisitive! I don't expect *that's* news to you, is it? He made no secret of it. Now when you've been a *star* for ... some years, as I have, as Carston and I have, you get used to inquisitiveness — from fans, from the press, and so on. But quite naturally some of the others here aren't *used* to it in the same way and react very badly to prying and snooping. I think you'll discover in the end that that's where the answer lies. His snooping was the death of him."

And a very satisfactory end, too, her dazzling smile to all three men seemed to imply.

"My movements?" said Brad Mallory. "My dear man, they are an open book and vouched for by thousands. I was in the Town Hall. I had a seat in the back row — in case I was needed behind the scenes. I had people beside me who would certainly remember me even though I didn't have any conversation with them. I should think Frank, the doorman, noticed me when I left, and I remember speaking to him when I returned at Interval."

"You actually left the concert at Interval?"

"Ex*haus*ted by the splendor of Singh's performance."

His hand flapped, like a vulture's wing.

"And you came straight back to the Saracen?"

"Yes."

"And then?"

"*Straight* to my room — to recover some degree of equilibrium."

Unvouched for by thousands, thought Dundy.

"Ralph Greatheart is, I suppose, the biggest part in the play," said Carston Galloway judiciously. He made it sound as if he were calculating the number of lines rather than being immodest. "I *think* it's bigger than the apprentice himself. So I'm onstage a great deal of the time. Last night, when I wasn't onstage, I was in the improvised dressing room backstage."

Iain Dundy was conscious of movement behind Galloway in the cramped quarters of the manager's room, which had been put at his disposal to conduct the interviews in. It was Charlie Peace, who had been making signs and who now cleared his throat.

"Yes, Constable?"

"If I may, sir, there's one question I would like to ask the gentleman. I should say that I happened to be in the audience last night. There is one time, isn't there, Mr. Galloway, when you actually appear on the balcony? You and one or two others?"

"That's right. The upper stage. I included that, of course, when I talked of being onstage."

His manner was that of one rebuking an inattentive schoolboy. Nevertheless, he hadn't mentioned it, Dundy noted. If Peace hadn't been in the audience, would it have come up? He shot a grateful glance at Charlie, then took over the questioning again.

"This upper stage, sir — is it part of the regular balcony around the courtyard?"

"That's right. Divided off from the rest of the balcony by a couple of makeshift partitions."

"And reached through a bedroom?"

"That's right."

"And how, sir, did you reach that bedroom?"

"We went up a little service staircase in the corner of the kitchen. Apparently it's one that's used by the cleaning women and sometimes by the maids when they're taking up breakfasts in bed or room orders."

"I see. You say *we* went up, sir. Could you tell me who the other actors were who were on with you?"

"Oh, yes. It's a scene where the Greatheart family have been woken up at night by the horseplay of the apprentices, which of course has been taking place below on the main stage. It's a fairly traditional situation — "

"And your family in the play is — ?"

"Joan Carley, who plays my wife — my stage wife — and Gillian Soames, who plays my daughter. Oh, and I think Jason Thark, the producer, followed us upstairs to see how the scene went."

The wonderful casualness of these arty people when they lob their grenades, Dundy thought!

"Ah, he would remain in the bedroom, I suppose?"

"Yes . . . Though now that you mention it . . . "

"Yes?"

"I seem to remember, as we all went into the bedroom, sounds from the corridor — almost like a row." He passed his hand over his forehead in one of those stage gestures that he and his wife specialized in, which set Dundy's teeth on edge. "No, it's too vague. Remember I was about to go out onto the balcony. It's a scene that calls for a lot, vocally and dramatically, so I was only thinking of that. You'll have to ask Jason."

And you've made quite sure that I do, thought Dundy.

"This Jason Thark is the man your wife says, er . . ."

"They've been sleeping together since we got here," said Carston indifferently.

"I see . . . And did you all go back to the kitchens together after the scene was over, sir?"

"Er, no. The ladies, you see, go twittering off quite early in the scene, after a drunken obscenity from Matthew Cotter, one of the apprentices — only it's an obscenity nobody understands any longer, so it rather misfires. After they go, I have several more minutes haranguing the lads; then I go in."

"And last night they'd already gone downstairs?"

"Yes."

"And then did you go down with Mr. Thark?"

"No . . . No, Jason must have gone down by that time. I went down to the kitchen alone."

"I see. About what time was this scene, Mr. Galloway?"

"Oh, good Lord, one doesn't notice times. Well on in the first half but not Interval by a long chalk. I may say that I spoke to little Soames the moment I got down to the bottom of the stairs. Asked her how she thought it'd gone."

"And you couldn't put a time to it, roughly?"

"Oh, say, five to eight, or eight — something like that."

"I see. Thank you."

Iain Dundy did not have to look down at his notes to remind himself of the police doctor's preliminary estimate of the time of death. He thought it had occurred at some time between eight and a quarter past nine.

"I was in my bedroom," said Gunter Gottlieb. "I plan, I read the score, I *hear* the music to myself. So do I *feel* my way into the performance tomorrow — that is, tonight. Even Donizetti — which is piffle, pure piffle! — even Donizetti has to be *felt*, experienced, heard inside."

"I see," said the superintendent, feeling an intense dislike for the lean, arrogant figure sitting opposite him. "So you were here in the hotel, alone in your room, all evening?"

"Yes. Oh — one moment. A girl came."

"A girl? Her name?"

Gunter Gottlieb shrugged.

"I don't know."

"What did she come for?"

"Sex. We just have sex; then she go."

"I see. Was she a prostitute?"

"Certainly not. I don't use prostitutes."

"How did you meet this young lady, then?"

"Meet? I not meet her. I have sex with her. My bodyguard, Mike, he got her for me."

"I see. He made all the arrangements?"

"Yes."

"When was this? How long did it take?"

"It was, oh, seven something. I suppose altogether it took about twenty minutes. It usually does."

"I see . . . " Iain Dundy sighed internally. He was being very honest, this repulsive man. Was a lack of hypocrisy to be commended in a matter like that? he wondered. "Tell me, Mr. Gottlieb, can you think of any reason why Mr. Capper should feel a particular dislike for you?"

"Who?"

"Des Capper, the dead man."

Again Gottlieb shrugged. "I have no idea."

"You did nothing to him?"

"I was quite unaware of his existence."

Dundy felt quick glances in his direction from both Nettles and Peace. That was a lie, surely. The hatred of that "Get Gottlieb" scrawl could only have come from some incident the man would be sure to remember. Did the lie spring from his prodigious arrogance? Or was it a clumsy attempt to disguise guilt?

"Oh, he was the most *horrible* little man," said Gillian Soames. She had decided that Iain Dundy was just the kind of man she liked and was talking a lot to cover the fact. "Well, not little at all — all too large. You know the type — the sort of man who, the moment he puts out his hand to shake yours, you know you don't want to touch. Shiversome. Yukky. But I'm talking nonsense. You must meet a lot more of that type than most of us."

Iain Dundy had relaxed considerably. This was the sort of witness he liked: nervous, for some reason, but direct, reliable. Not arty at all, he told himself.

"Oh, I don't know," he said expansively. "Most of the people we meet are pretty average individuals. But it's interesting you should say that. When you connect him with the kind of people I meet, do you mean you thought there was something . . . criminal about him, right from the start?"

Gillian considered. "No, that would be going too far. I just took a dislike to him. Later on, when one heard of the man's snooping activities, one did start wondering what was the end in view."

"What snooping activities were these?"

"Oh, it was Clarissa who made the big fuss. He'd been snooping around in her room, she said, looking in drawers and so on. Occasion for big scene. But I'm sure on this occasion Clarissa was telling the truth. In fact, the more one took notice of him, the more he seemed to be snuffling around after information that might prove useful to him."

"May I test him on something?"

"Go ahead."

"He thought you might be having an affair with someone called Ronnie Wimsett."

Gillian laughed uproariously. Iain Dundy felt obscurely glad that Des Capper had been wrong, which was odd, because he had not yet swapped a word with Ronnie Wimsett. Behind Gillian's back a tiny glance passed from Charlie to Nettles and from Nettles back to Charlie. They recognized a sexual spark when they saw one. They were seeing one now.

"I take it he was wrong?"

"Of course. Want to know how he got the idea?"

"Yes."

"He was going round from table to table in the Shakespeare, pushing himself into all the conversations. That was my first evening here. When he got near our table, Ronnie and

I held hands and looked into each other's eyes to keep him away. Somewhat surprisingly, it worked."

"Couldn't see below the appearances, eh?"

"Well, with the performance Ronnie and I put on, that's not surprising. I was just surprised he thought being in love was a sufficient reason for his staying away. But often he got things wrong even when nobody was trying to mislead him. Like when he oozed up to Peter Fortnum and me the day we arrived and assumed we must be 'the operatic lady and gentleman.' The fact that we were gazing reverently at the stage should have told him that we were actors. Still, it doesn't do to assume that everything he thought he'd found out was wrong."

Dundy sighed. "No. The likelihood is that in one case he hit the jackpot. And a lot of good it did him. Now, can we talk a bit about that scene in the play that takes place on the balcony?"

Gillian crinkled her forehead. "Yes, I assumed you'd want to talk about that. It's funny, you know, but we discussed and discussed how we — the actors — *couldn't* have done it, and yet we never thought of that scene or never admitted we realized its significance."

"It seems to me," said Dundy, "that you never thought of the staircase, either."

Gillian smiled at him self-deprecatingly. "You must think us very dim. But in fact there were a number of people sitting around the bottom of that staircase all the time, so it would have been pretty difficult to slip up it without being noticed. That scene, of course, was different; that was legitimate business."

"Can you tell me exactly what happened?"

"I'll try — as I remember it. I think we gathered at the foot of the staircase and all went up together. That was Carston, Joan, myself, and Jason following. I remember Carston being first into the bedroom and then being in there with him and Joan just before going out onto the balcony. . . ."

She became silent.

"You don't remember Mr. Thark being there?"

"No. I have to be honest, don't I? I remember, just before we went on, hearing voices in the corridor. Angry voices."

"And the other voice?"

"Well, it *could* have been Des Capper."

"You can't be more definite than that?"

"No, it wouldn't be fair to."

"And when the scene was over?"

"Joan and I came out first. Joan went down, and I watched a minute or two more of the scene through the window. Then I went down, too."

"Do you remember when Mr. Thark and Mr. Galloway came down?"

"No. I went to talk to Connie Geary. Jason may even have been back in the kitchen already. But I'm afraid I didn't notice at all."

Charlie Peace cleared his throat. "Mr. Galloway remembers coming up to you after he came down, miss. To ask you how you thought it had gone."

Gillian frowned. "Oh, yes. I think you're right. He did come up at some stage. I'm sorry I can't remember exactly when."

"You're a good, careful witness," said Dundy.

Or a clever one, thought Charlie.

"I sang," said Singh.

He looked towards the mirror at the far end of the manager's office and was annoyed to find it angled to reveal whether there was anyone standing at Reception outside. So it was reserved for Iain Dundy to gaze on that smooth light brown skin, those doelike dark eyes, those perfect girlish features, that plump, underexercised body. Singh brought back all his distrust of "arty" people that Gillian Soames had done so much to banish.

"Yes, I realize you sang," he said, his irritation showing through for the first time that day, perhaps because subconsciously he was judging Singh to be as yet a person of little importance in any world. "I gather your arias were towards the end of the first half, is that right?"

"*At* the end. So the applause could go on."

"I see. So that would mean you were singing from just before eight, maybe, till about — what? — ten past?"

Singh shrugged. "Probably."

"What were you doing for the rest of the time?"

"I was sitting in the room for the artists. All the time. They were asking me about my voice, my technique. It is very extraordinary. And at Interval there were impresarios and theater directors talking about possible offers of engagements. I was never alone."

He smiled a catlike smile. The pleasure seemed not in having an alibi but in being so sought after. If what he said was true, and it seemed likely, Dundy thought he would not need to interest himself very much in Singh. It would in any case be impossible to be as interested in him as he was himself.

"Darling, it would be totally irresponsible of me to say *any*thing," said Connie Geary. She smiled at him with the art of one who had once cared if she pleased men. "I am a totally reliable actress: I get on and off the stage

197

when I should, and I never slur my lines. But apart from that I live in a *haze*. If you ask me 'Was he or she around at such and such a time?' I can only give you an impression. *If that.*"

"I see." Dundy sighed.

"And that wouldn't be fair."

"No. It's a pity, because you were around in the kitchen most of the time."

"Yes, I was. I only have three scenes, though *very* meaty ones. But I can't tell you anything definite about what went on backstage because it wouldn't be right."

"Do you remember sending Mr. Fortnum for more gin?"

"Oh, yes, though I don't remember when."

"Do you remember whether he took a long time?"

"Darling, it *seemed* an age!"

"Sure I took a long time," said Peter Fortnum.

He was firm spoken and fresh faced, and all Iain Dundy's experience told him he was about to tell lies. The same half look that had passed between him and his men when Gunter Gottlieb was talking now passed again.

"Why should it take so long? The maids say you ran through the kitchens and dining room."

"Superintendent, would you like to try an experiment? Send one of your policemen here to find room 146 and see how long he takes."

Dundy smiled. "I may do that. But it wouldn't be quite the same thing, would it? My men have probably never been in the residential part of the hotel. You have been here nearly a fortnight."

"It doesn't help," protested Peter. "You never get used to it. You think you've got it taped, and then it throws down a nifty one and you're lost again. And anyway, my room is on the second floor, and Connie's is on the first. I just got lost looking for it."

"Miss Geary's room is, as you say, on the first floor. It is also not that far from the door into Des Capper's flat. Did you go anywhere near that door?"

"No."

"How can you be so sure if you were lost?"

An expression of irritation crossed Peter's face. "Not knowingly, I mean."

"Did you see anyone while you were searching for room 146?"

Slight but perceptible pause.

"No."

"Well, well." Iain Dundy shifted in his chair. There were lies being told here, but for the moment they were not nailable lies. "Let's get on to something else. I believe you've been

199

helping a bit as translator for the Russian lady."

Another tiny pause.

"That's right."

"Including at rehearsals for the opera — whatever it's called?"

"*Adelaide di Birckenhead.*" Peter pronounced the name with relish. "Yes, I went along there when I could."

"Tell me, can you give me any reason why Des Capper should feel particularly bitter about Herr Gottlieb?"

Peter settled back more easily in his chair. "Oh, yes. Yes, I can. It was just a few days ago, actually. I was in the wings, and there had been one of Gottlieb's scenes. You've talked to Gottlieb?" Dundy nodded. "Then you can probably guess what they're like. Icy, premeditated murder. I don't think Des Capper saw the scene; otherwise he might have been more careful. Most of the cast were onstage, and Mallory and Singh had gone up, too. Capper came up behind me, saw Singh onstage, and made some remark about not realizing there were Indians in medieval Birckenhead. 'Running the corner shops, I suppose.' " Peter's imitation, like Gillian's earlier, brought the dreadful Des momentarily but vividly to life. "Typical barroom joke, and just the sort of thing that Des would think was clever."

"Just one moment. What was Capper doing backstage?"

"Exercising his right as a member of the festival committee to go anywhere and watch anything. I gather this is a right nobody else exercises. Anyway, eventually there was a break — God, we needed it! — and when I got to the Green Room, there was Des already there, irritating the hell out of everyone, particularly the poor American tenor who had been the main victim of Gottlieb's scene. . . . That's when it happened."

"The incident?"

"Yes, the row. Gottlieb was having a discussion — No, Gottlieb was *telling* the director of the festival that he intended changing the opera scheduled for the next festival to *Fidelio*. It was typical Gottlieb unreasonableness. The director was beginning to get a bit heated when Des stepped forward. Trying to mediate, so he said."

"Ah, and Gottlieb — ?"

"Bawled him out. Sheer barrack-room stuff. Get out, don't come near my rehearsals again, that kind of thing. If it had been anyone else, there'd have been applause."

"And how did Des Capper take it?"

"With Gottlieb you don't have much choice. He slunk out."

"Meditating revenge, do you think?"

"I know so. He practically said so later, said he'd learned all he needed to know about revenge in India in 1947. Des tended to go on about India."

Iain Dundy sat considering. Then he threw a bouncer.

"Tell me, sir, why have you been making so many expensive phone calls since you came here?"

Peter Fortnum blinked at the change of subject but had his answer — Dundy could have sworn to it — prepared.

"My girlfriend is in Germany. She is with a theater company in Stuttgart."

"She must have very good German."

"She is advising on costumes. For a production of *The Merry Wives of Windsor*."

"It's remarkable that you can afford all these calls. You're a young actor, and I believe you have quite a small role."

"Is it so remarkable?" Peter asked. "With a name like Fortnum?"

Superintendent Dundy reminded himself that from one point of view all an actor's performing life is living a lie.

"You're damned right I wasn't going to tell you," said Jason Thark. "And don't, for God's sake, ask why not, because it's bloody obvious, isn't it?"

"Well, let's get the facts clear first, shall we, sir? You went upstairs with the three actors who were about to appear in the balcony scene."

"That's right."

"But you never followed them into the bedroom?"

"No, because I saw Des Capper coming along the corridor. There was something about him — something pushy and self-satisfied — and so I lingered by the door. I'd heard about a set-to between him and Gottlieb at the Alhambra. He had the cheek to say, 'After you,' and make to go into the bedroom as well."

"Which in a way you might say he had a right to do," said Iain Dundy in fairness to the dead Des.

"In a way. With any other manager I might have admitted the right: it was his place, as the Alhambra wasn't. But give Capper an inch and he took a mile. He'd been barging in everywhere pretending he had a right as a member of the festival committee. Next thing would be he'd demand to sit onstage, as the noblemen used to. So I gave him the rounds of the kitchen and told him to stick to his quarters."

"How did he react to that?"

"How do you think? He bridled, muttered,

threatened, but in the end he trotted off."

"And you, sir? What did you do?"

"I was rather pleased with the whole affair, quite frankly. It made a good addition to the 'grand remonstrance' that the cast and I were going to address to the festival committee when the festival was over."

"Grand what, sir?"

"A sort of general complaint by the actors and the other people staying here. A letter to the powers that be in the Beaumont hotel chain and to the festival committee as well. So I went away to one of those little alcoves the place abounds in, one where there was a writing desk, and wrote down the threats that Capper had made and the ridiculous rights he claimed."

"I see, sir. Do you still have this memorandum?"

"Yes, as a matter of fact I've got it on me."

As he took it, Dundy was under no illusions. The memorandum could have been written ten minutes ago.

"Any thoughts?" Dundy asked his men when at last they were alone.

They looked at each other.

"On the face of it, Mallory seems the best bet," said Charlie Peace slowly. "Alone in his hotel room from around eight-fifteen till Interval time and after. If we take it Capper was killed by Interval, that gives him a quarter of an hour to do it in."

"Oh, and by the way, he poked his head in at the Shakespeare Bar on the way up," said Nettles. "Dawn told me that. Perhaps he wasn't just *exhausted* by Singh's performance, after all."

"Looking for someone?"

"Dawn couldn't say, of course. He said nothing. But maybe he was looking for Des."

"And maybe he found him," said Dundy.

"I'm not sure, on thinking about it, why I picked on Mallory as the best bet," said Charlie. "After all, there are at least three others who had good opportunities to get at Des as well. Carston Galloway after the balcony scene — and *didn't* the Galloways chuck around innuendos about the other actors? Then there's Fortnum, of course, when he went to get the gin. And Gunter Gottlieb any time after his girl left. He, in a way, had the most opportunity and was the least accounted for."

"Yes, but can you see anyone arranging an assignation like his was just before committing a murder? If, of course, he did intend committing it. The trouble is, we know of no reason for Gottlieb to kill Capper. He'd seen him off. It would make more sense the other way round: Gottlieb as victim."

"A highly popular corpse," commented Nettles.

"One thing, though," said Charlie thoughtfully. "If the key to all this is in Des's determination to 'Get Gottlieb,' then it may be we're paying too much attention to the play and not enough to the opera. Perhaps we should forget the actors for a bit and take a look at the singers."

The Director's Office

13

"Anyone for the opera?" asked Dundy.

Evening had come, and weariness set in.

"Er, my wife has just had a baby," said Nettles.

"Of course. I'd forgotten."

"It is the fourth, but I'd quite like to see it."

"Oh, Lord. Haven't you seen it yet?"

"Only got the message as I was coming in this morning." Nettles shrugged. "Policeman's lot. Policeman's wife's lot."

"What about you, Peace?"

"Try anything once. But we're not going to get seats, are we?"

"We'll try to get them to slot us in somehow."

Dundy had begun to feel that the line of

207

interviewees would stretch out to the crack of doom. It was all too much. There were others to interview, but they could wait: One of them needed a Russian interpreter. Ronnie Wimsett seemed to have been onstage much of the evening, and never on the upper stage. Gunter Gottlieb's heavy would at least have made a change after all the arty people, a reversion to familiar territory after uncharted shores. But he couldn't see that Gunter's girl was of much significance. She had apparently come and gone well before the earliest time the murder could have been committed. And it hadn't been anything more than a quick dip, for either of them, so far as he could see.

Sitting for a moment in the little manager's office, Nettles having scurried off, Charlie standing waiting for some action, Dundy meditated on the unattractive figure of the world's next "great conductor." He realized that all such figures had two sides, the artist and the private man, and that with Gottlieb the private man trailed badly last. He wondered briefly at such an unadulterated swine being the mediator between great composers and the ordinary man. He seemed to remember that a lot of musicians had behaved very badly in Nazi Germany. Then he shook himself and put aside the thoughts as unprofitable.

"I'll ring the festival office," he said. "See if

something can be arranged."

"Well, of course," said the voice on the other end of the line, "the director of the festival is very busy, because it is the first night of the opera. That's what he's doing at the moment. He's down at the Alhambra seeing that the critics get their creature comforts and welcoming distinguished guests: Lord Harewood is coming, and Lord Goodman, and all sorts of people like that. On the other hand, I do know that he's very concerned about this murder, concerned that it shouldn't cast a cloud over the festival. . . . "

"Ha!" said Dundy to Charlie as they collected together their notebooks and got ready to leave the Saracen for the first time that day. "Cast a cloud over the festival! Murder never casts a cloud over anything! As far as the mob coming here is concerned, it'll be a great bonus. Murder is the great British spectator sport, the ultimate in good clean fun."

Walking past the copper on the door and out into the pale evening sunlight, they found they had to cope with cameras and media persons stationed outside. One reporter looked pointedly and hopefully at their wrists ("Black held in Aussie slaying"), while another pursued them along High Street with questions. "Wrong man, sorry," lied Dundy, and they managed the rest of the five-minute walk in peace.

By now it was nearly seven o'clock, and the audience was flocking around and into the blue-and-maroon little theater, splendid, yet slightly dotty. Charlie looked at the audience curiously. It was certainly not like the Covent Garden audience — not dressy and ignorant. Charlie had got the measure of a Covent Garden audience in his younger days, when he had done duty for a ticket tout in Floral Street on a Pavarotti night. This audience was very different. There was the odd sprinkling of black-tie-and-long-skirt couples, but in general this was a young people's festival and a mecca for enthusiasts and cranks. Dress was casual, even colorful. Dundy, too, watched them for a moment; then they both slipped through into the foyer. Here Dundy gave a discreet message to one of the attendants, to be passed on to the director. Then they made for a deserted corner to wait for the rush to subside.

"My mother used to play Bingo in a place like this," said Charlie cheerfully. "This one's gone uphill."

The director Dundy could point out to Charlie, having seen his picture in the *Ketterick Evening Post*. He was a comfortable, candid-looking man, with just a hint of being worried out of his life, which Iain Dundy could quite understand, granted what much

210

of his life must be like. He was standing by the stairs welcoming faces in the audience that he recognized. There were many of these, for the festival thrived on its regulars, and they seemed as pleased to see him as he apparently was to see them. The audience was as comfortable looking as the director. They were mostly discussing the singers and waxing lyrical about the particular canary they fancied.

"It's a bit like a sports meeting," said Charlie. "People comparing Cram with Coe."

"And going all the way back to Bannister," agreed Dundy. "Some of these people sound like canary fanciers from way back, or gramophone freaks who collect seventy-eights. It wasn't like this in the old days. They've built up these audiences, just as the Saracen has."

For Dundy had been to the festival opera years before, when he had had a wife to buy tickets and the tickets had miraculously coincided with an evening off. The opera had been Donizetti then, too — *Don Sébastien, Roi de Portugal* ("like listening to a mouse trying to roar" — *The Observer*). Dundy had rather enjoyed it, but he remembered the audience's commentary as being more bemused than in-formed.

Eventually the forward-moving stream thinned, the director's genial greetings became fewer, and the noise of the orchestra's tuning up penetrated through the doors into the auditorium. Last-minute arrivals, scuttling through, managed no more than a smile and a nod at the director. He looked towards Dundy, raised his eyebrows, then nodded up the stairs. Dundy and Charlie went over, and all three went on thick red pile up to the circle, then through a door that led them into a maze of corridors out of bounds to the general public. Eventually they came to a door labeled "Festival Director," and Charlie and Dundy were ushered into a tiny but cozy office with a desk piled with reference books and telephone directories and with room in front of the desk for only a couple of chairs. The walls were decorated, like London Italian restaurants, with publicity photographs of opera singers.

"I have a little office at the Saracen as well," explained the director, making them comfortable and pouring them both neat whiskeys from a bottle in the filing cabinet. "But somehow it's been less pleasant working there since poor old Arthur died."

Dundy was willing to hear just one more verdict on the unlovable Des.

"The new manager?" he asked. "Our popular corpse?"

"Exactly. I'm sure you've got the general idea by now. An appalling know-all, a peddler

212

of folk wisdom and quack remedies, a one-man popular informer."

"And a great collector of inconvenient information about people," added Dundy.

"Yes, I — " The director hesitated, looked at Dundy, and then plunged in. "I suppose you remember the case earlier this year when my daughter was accused of shoplifting?"

"Yes, I was sorry you got all that publicity. I wasn't involved."

"Of course not. I don't blame the police. But she'd just lost a baby, had postnatal depression — Anyway, it made a good story for the local papers, and damn the consequences for her. It was all perfectly public, but what made it worse was Des coming up at the first committee meeting after the magistrates' hearing. 'Terribly sorry to hear about your little family trouble. As a father myself I can sympathize.' All done in a nicely raised voice. I could have — Well, no, I couldn't. But I *felt* like it then."

"I had no idea Capper had children."

"Nor had anyone. Maybe it was just a fiction to justify the sympathy. If he has, he seems conveniently to have cast them off, or it off, somewhere along the line."

Dundy looked at Charlie. He knew that both of them were toying with the entrancing notion of Des having fathered Singh during his time in India. Dundy shook his head and put the notion from him. Singh was about twenty years too young.

"You have no idea how he came to be appointed?" he asked.

"None. It's something all of us on the committee have discussed, I can tell you. We could only assume some . . . hold on the chairman or managing director of the Beaumont chain."

"Blackmail, you mean?"

The director looked mildly horrified, as if such a thought had at least not been put into words hitherto.

"Oh, come, come," he said. "It didn't have to be anything so dramatic. He could have done somebody some . . . service."

"Saved his son and heir from drowning?" said Dundy cynically.

"That sort of thing. Saved his life in the disturbances at the time of Indian independence. He waxed very eloquent about his experiences at Mountbatten's right hand."

"Hmmm," said Dundy. "Very *Jewel in the Crown*. As a matter of fact, I wouldn't mind betting Capper got his notions of what happened at independence time from that TV series. He wasn't in India at the time; he'd gone on to Hong Kong. You mentioned his characteristic as almighty know-all and crush-

214

ing bore. But it wasn't those in particular that annoyed the festival committee, was it?"

"No, though it was embarrassing, because he was pig ignorant, and we had to find ways of listening to him pontificating about things he knew bugger-all about. No, it was his pushiness and his prying that touched us on the raw. He took it as his right to go everywhere, poke his nose in everything."

"Did he have such a right?"

The director shrugged. "In theory, maybe. No other member of the committee would have *thought* of exercising it. But Des went everywhere, got to know everything, and *gave his advice.*"

Dundy waved his hand in the direction of the auditorium, whence pale echoes of vocal glory penetrated even to the director's office.

"I gather on occasion he poked his nose into rehearsals of the opera we can hear now."

"Oh, yes. I don't know how often. I was down here one day watching rehearsals and waiting to see that swine Gottlieb afterwards. There was a nasty moment, with Gottlieb humiliating the tenor, who had to be brought to the front of the stage if he was to be heard, and Mallory having to placate the soprano. The producer was rearranging positions, and suddenly I saw Des was there in the wings. I remember my heart sinking and thinking:

215

Des is all we need at this stage."

"We've heard about this little episode," said Dundy. "And about what happened afterwards in the Green Room."

"Do you remember exactly what Gottlieb said to Capper?" asked Charlie.

"Pretty well. 'I do not take advice from taverners' —I remember that. 'You come near one of my rehearsals ever again and I have you . . . thrown out on your fat bottom.' He has the men who could have done it, too."

"Did Capper say anything?"

"Nothing to the purpose. 'Sorry, I'm sure,' or 'No offense' — something like that. He just slunk away."

"But hoping to get his revenge," said Dundy. "We've evidence of that. He didn't like public humiliation."

"Who does? But with Capper it would have been a strong emotion, I'm sure. He nursed grudges."

"Yes." Dundy looked at him straight. "Tell me, if you were out to 'get' Gunter Gottlieb — "

"As, God help me, I may be yet."

" — how would you do it?"

The festival director considered. "I think my first reaction would be to say: hit him professionally."

"Ah! That's what I wondered. Because he is, shall we say, vulnerable, on his personal side, too, isn't he?"

"Girlies," said the director, shaking his head. "I know. It's something I've had to be very aware of. It's the popular press I fear: Royals and vicars and people in the arts world — those are the ones the tabloids have a particular down on. He seems impregnable, but that could be his Achilles heel. That's why I had a word about it with his minder — "

"Ah! You did that?"

"It seemed the sensible thing. I discovered that he was thick as two planks, but he had learned enough about the law to know how to keep on the right side of it when he had a mind. So I made it clear to him: nobody underage. And preferably nobody local. I think he's been recruiting from the groupies who followed him from Coventry and from people here for the festival. Gottlieb's needs are occasional and brief."

"So that's made him pretty near impregnable on the personal side, you think? That's why you'd go for him on the professional side if you had to?"

"Yes, because odd though it may seem, the festival is important to him. It's part of his overall strategy, and he wants to be a success here, make it *his* festival."

"How did you come to appoint him?"

"That's easily explained. It seemed such a

coup! He came with the Midlands Orchestra last year and gave a quite wonderful concert. Mahler and Beethoven — the most thrilling Seventh you can imagine. Our regulars were over the moon: It was the sort of glorious music making they heard in their dreams, one of them said. Our regular opera conductor was off to be resident chief of one of the state orchestras in Australia, so there was a vacancy to be filled. Not expecting him to accept, we approached Gunter Gottlieb."

"And he accepted?"

"Not immediately. He thought for three days, then accepted provided he had charge of all the musical side of the festival. That seemed like a wonderful bonus to all the committee. We couldn't believe our luck."

"I take it you've learned better since?"

The director thought a bit, trying to be fair. "It would be wrong to say that. I think this festival will probably be a great success from a musical point of view. The opera will, too: He makes Donizetti sound as good as mature Verdi. But it will all be a personal success for himself, and to some extent it will be manufactured."

"You mean he brings his own fans, and so on?"

"Well, yes, he does, but I didn't mean that. There are four orchestral concerts, and the third will be given by the Welsh Symphony Orchestra. At the planning stage he insisted that they give *Death and Transfiguration* and insisted, too, that we engage Ernest Petheridge to conduct. Between ourselves, never the brightest conductor, and now, at seventy-five . . . Well, he can be relied on to endow the idea of eternity with new degrees of tedium. They'll be snoring in the aisles. *Then,* two nights later, the final concert, with Gunter Gottlieb conducting *Also Sprach Zarathustra* — surefire popular success, brilliant orchestral showpiece, and of course brilliantly conducted. And don't get me wrong — it will be. But it will *seem* that bit more brilliant by comparison. You get me?"

"Oh, I get you."

"And then, of course, there's the business of next year."

"That was what the row was about in the Green Room, wasn't it?"

"Disagreement . . . Well, yes, row. Except that I did manage not to lose my cool. It would mean changing the whole direction and character of the festival. You probably know what sort of festival Ketterick has had up to now: a festival for families and enthusiasts, with something for everyone. Some of the sillier critics sneer at the operas we do, but they're wonderfully direct and involving — first-rate theater. Gottlieb's is an attempt to change all that and put us in the international league. And, of course, it put us in a cleft stick."

"How?"

"If we say no and lose him, all the arts establishment and all the newspaper people will say we've opted for safeness and provinciality and second-rateness. If we say yes, we hand the festival to him on a plate, the rest of us become ciphers, and we betray our existing audiences."

"Yes, I see. An impossible decision. And I take it an impossible gentleman to work with?"

"Bloody impossible, between you and me. I think we'd be justified in turning him down and letting him go if only because he's obviously using us as a stepping-stone to something else and because it will certainly all end in tears, and pretty soon, too."

"So your view is that he's totally geared to being a success in his professional life and if you hit him there you would really touch him where it hurts? Something along those lines was my conclusion, too. He's a man programmed to succeed. He's to be the next — who's the bee's knees? — Karajan?"

"The comparison has occurred to other people. At the moment, his whole being is intent on two glorious successes: first the opera, then the final concert, where he'll hope to have people standing and cheering, led by his own groupies. Which he almost certainly will. And to be fair to him, which isn't easy, almost all of it will be deserved."

"He is good?"

"He is *very* good. He rides roughshod over everyone, but he is almost always right. And yet there is still . . . somehow — I can't put it simply — a lack. An emptiness. . . . And I wonder whether in the long run music lovers aren't going to find this out. . . . Would you like to see him doing a bit of the opera?"

"There can't be any seats, surely?"

"There's mine. I have to go and see to the interval jamboree for nobs and critics. You've no idea how we butter up the critics from the big newspapers. You can have my seat until the break." He turned to Charlie. "And you can stand at the back, if you don't mind that. It's not usually allowed, but we can explain to the fire people that you're a policeman."

"I'm used to standing about," said Charlie. "I was in uniformed branch for a year."

"I think we'll say yes," said Dundy. "Though I'm not sure that I'm musical enough to understand this . . . this lack that you talk of."

They went back to the front of house, down the staircase, and along the corridor that spanned the back of the stalls. The director

collected programs for Dundy and Charlie
and then, with practiced stealth, opened the
door into the stalls. As the music washed over
them, he pointed Charlie to a place by the
door and then led Dundy down to an aisle seat
three rows down. Then he himself evaporated
to attend to the wants of the important visitors.

Once settled, Dundy found himself cocooned
in a devout attentiveness. This audience was a
totally committed one. Onstage, and close to
the front of the stage, a very personable tenor
was emoting in slow time, sighing his way
towards a close. Iain Dundy had only a smat-
tering of holiday Italian, but he had an awful
feeling that the tenor was boasting about how
much his love had cost him. The cad, he
thought. Then the orchestra hotted things
up, and an attendant or junior terrorist rushed
onstage to deliver an urgent message, of which
the words *Inglese* and *Birckenhead* could be
distinguished. At which the tenor leapt to his
feet and with a skirl of his (unhistorical) kilt
began delivering a martial cabaletta that taxed
his sweet voice to the uttermost. When it was
over, there was polite applause, the curtain
came down, and dimmed lights came up while
changes were made to the permanent set.

In the half-light at the back of the theater
Charlie read the program. He had got a rough

idea of the story from the volume in Des's sitting room: The personable hero, he remembered, would be Robert the Bruce, on the run from the English and about to take refuge, disguised, at *il castello di Birckenhead*, the power base of his rival, who was also the husband of the woman he loved. Well, that was all clear, wasn't it? He turned to the history of the opera and immediately found himself gripped in a way he did not quite understand. He read through the account of the first version of the opera, then the story of the recent rediscovery of the later version. Only when he had finished that did he begin to realize that the break had been rather long. Looking up from his program, he found he was not alone in this feeling. In the Victorian intimacy of the Alhambra Theatre everyone could see everything, and even from the back of the stalls Charlie could see the figure of Gunter Gottlieb, his baton steadily beating on the open pages of his score in patent irritation. No doubt Gottlieb had decreed no more than two minutes for the break, and it had stretched out to four. But then the lights went down, there was a perceptible relaxation of tension in the audience, and Gottlieb raised his baton for the last scene before Interval.

In the previous scene, Charlie, for all his lack of knowledge of opera, had been conscious of a shimmering beauty that Gottlieb extracted from the very simple accompaniment to the tenor aria. Now he began to notice something very different. The curtain had risen on the peasants and retainers of the castle of Birckenhead (all kilted — in defiance not only of historical but also of geographical probability). They were celebrating something or other, probably Hogmanay, in song and dance. The stage picture was supposed to be one of uninhibited revelry, but what Charlie was most conscious of was the *lack* of real spontaneity. What impressed him most was the drilled nature of the performance — the military precision of the drumbeats, the terrified accuracy of the chorus, which at times affected their acting. It was as if — another historical absurdity — the opera was being performed by the soldiers of Frederick the Great for their commander in chief. One might see Gottlieb as the Prussian bandmaster writ large. Charlie did not quite see things in those terms, but he did register to himself: Everyone is bloody terrified.

He stood there, drinking it in, thinking that he might be able to make a habit of this kind of music if he ever got the opportunity. There was a scene for a dreadful comic servant, and then the baritone and soprano arrived to join the merrymaking, exuding manorial gracious-

ness. The baritone found time to snarl something about *"gl'Inglesi"* to a retainer out of the
corner of his mouth, in the way baritones
have. Then suddenly the sound of merrymaking died away. The tenor had arrived. He
stood for some moments at the back of the
stage, commented on by everyone in hushed
tones. Then he advanced to the front in what
Charlie recognized as a clumsy but necessary
maneuver. Soon he was launching into the
great, swaying tune:

Io son pari ad uom cui scende
Già la scure sulla testa.

This was the moment, Charlie felt sure,
that Des had come in on in rehearsal. Standing there in the darkness, letting the music lap
over him and swaying in time to its irresistible
impulse, Charlie thought that he might have
had the glimmerings of an idea.

The Corridors

14

" 'The trivial round, the common task, should furnish all we ought to ask,' " misquoted Dundy under his breath next morning. And in future it bloody well will. Here we go on another load of backstage chitchat, shortly homing in on more accounts of what gives with the Galloways. At least when I rowed with my wife it tore us apart, because we meant it. With these arty people, who knows when they mean *anything?*

And what gives with Peace this morning? His mind isn't on it. And this girl's a perfectly personable little thing. . . . He dragged his mind back to the interview he was conducting.

"As far as the balcony scene is concerned, I inspected them all before they went up the stairs," Susan Fanshaw was saying. "They were all in night gear, so it was quite straightforward. Then I was off hither and yon doing other things. The apprentices were onstage — onstage and off, because it's a very busy scene, and I have to see whether the costumes have suffered in the horseplay, whether they've lost anything, and so on. So though normally I might have noticed when Carston at least came back down the stairs, that night I didn't."

Iain Dundy coughed a dry, diplomatic cough.

"Er, you say normally you might have noticed?"

Susan obviously wanted to get that part of the discussion over with.

"Oh, Carston and I are vaguely sleeping together."

"I see. I had, actually, some idea of this, but perhaps you could put me into the picture. I gather his wife knows?"

"Oh, yes. Everybody knows. It's no great passionate affair. I mean, Carston is nice — " She pulled herself up. "No, not nice exactly, because he's mean as hell, and vain as well. Still, he *is* a wonderful actor, when he's fully stretched, whereas she will never in essence be more than a rep queen, for all her name. So it *is* rather exciting; it is decidedly a pleasant interlude. . . . Not least because of his vast experience."

"Ah . . . You don't mean acting? No. Er, you don't mind being one of a long line?"

"Not at all. It's part of the thrill."

Iain Dundy sighed. He was never going to understand these people, still less like them. His bewilderment was increased when Susan Fanshaw added: "A long, long roster. Both male and female."

He drew his hand along his forehead. "I see. Then Galloway is — ?"

"Predominantly hetero, but he takes it as it comes. He covers the waterfront, like Brad Mallory. It's pretty common in the theater."

"Oh, then Mr. Mallory — ?"

"Must be the same. He doesn't make much secret of being besotted with young Singh — not even from you, I imagine. But I know an actress who had a pretty serious affair with him five or six years ago." She saw Dundy's face and laughed. "It must make it pretty difficult for you."

"All in a day's work," said Dundy bravely. "So you are sleeping with Mr. Galloway, and I gather Mrs. Galloway is sleeping with the producer, and this is all out in the open and talked about quite unashamedly?"

"Yes. What a lovely word: 'unashamedly'! So you think we should be ashamed? Of course, Clarissa uses the situation to launch lethal little barbs against Carston and me, but

228

that's just her nature."

"I find it difficult," said Dundy, trying not to sound prim, "to get a picture of this marriage. Why do they stay together if they're quarreling all the time?"

"Haven't you ever met a soldier who's only happy in action? Or a policeman who couldn't be happy on the beat in a quiet area but is always itching for a bit of action?"

"Frequently."

"Well, then. 'Pleased with the danger when the waves went high/He sought the storms; but for a calm unfit . . .' Dryden. It's quite impossible to imagine either of the Galloways having a *calm* relationship with anyone."

"I see," said Dundy, sighing. "My point in trying to establish how open all this is, is to make the point that there was very little mileage to be got — by Des Capper, for example — out of threatening to reveal the truth of the situation to any of the people involved."

"None whatsoever. We all knew. The whole hotel, down to the kitchen skivvies, knew. The room maids probably had a running bet on as to who would be sleeping with who each night."

"Right . . . Right . . . So if any of you had a grudge against Capper, it would have to be on some other grounds."

"Oh, certainly. Like that he was the biggest

bore, the biggest ignoramus, and the biggest liar in a fifty-mile radius."

"I doubt whether people get murdered for any of those reasons," said Iain Dundy. "And I suppose if there were anything more substantial, you wouldn't tell me. Now, let me get this clear, finally. Your duties in the play never led you to leave the kitchen?"

"Never once. I was there the whole time, even during the interval, checking costumes and props. Jason aims to give the sense of Jacobean bourgeois life, so in the absence of sets, props are very important."

"And the balcony scene we've mentioned is the only time in the play when the upper stage is used?"

"Yes, the only one."

"I suppose you checked that the room upstairs that led onto the balcony was in fact unlocked?"

"Oh, yes," said Susan unsuspectingly. "But well before the performance started. In any case, Carston had a room key in case one of the maids had locked it by mistake."

Dundy nodded his head and mentally wiped Susan Fanshaw from his list of suspects.

"Of course, I'm onstage practically the whole evening," said Ronnie Wimsett, clearly not immune to the same little vanities as

230

Carston Galloway. "Or just off, or just about to go on. So quite apart from the fact that it would be difficult for me to have done it, it's also difficult for me to remember anything that went on backstage."

"Why? Because if you weren't on, you were hovering about around one of the doors onto the stage?"

"That's right. Whereas someone with a smaller part could certainly spend an hour or more in the kitchen just sitting around and noticing."

Wimsett was a very different type from most of the actors, Dundy decided. Apparently open, genial, conversational, but with an overriding reticence, particularly about himself. On essentials he presented a bland front to the world. Dundy was willing to bet that his fellow actors knew little about his character, his private life, his sexual preferences. He kept, in popular parlance, himself to himself. Like many policemen, Dundy thought.

"Miss Geary ought to be ideal," he said. "She was sitting around for most of the play. But for obvious reasons that she makes no secret of, she's not much use. Tell me, during the weeks of rehearsal, who reacted most strongly to Des Capper?"

"Well . . . " Ronnie was either plainly reluctant or plainly acting out reluctance. "I suppose you'd have to say Gillian Soames. She'd been *very* fond of Arthur Bradley, the earlier manager, in a father-and-daughter sort of way. I think anyone would have been a letdown. But Capper she thought the absolute pits."

"Yes, she's been quite open about that," said Dundy quickly. The foot of one of his attendant policemen gave a gentle tap on the ankle of the other attendant policeman. "What about the other people staying at the Saracen? How did they react to him?"

"Oh, in various ways. Carston Galloway with a sort of lordly, amused contempt . . . Clarissa taking the opportunity for a scene. . . . Connie Geary rather relished him. She enjoys the chance of plumbing the depths of human awfulness, and she got that with Des. It's something actors often enjoy — watching dreadful people, to use them afterwards." He thought. "I think some of the people whom he most got under the skin of were the ones he gave advice to." He grinned self-depreciatingly. "That includes me, I suppose. He tried to educate me in the method school of acting. He tried to give Krister Kroll a lesson in breathing techniques, and that riled him."

"Krister Kroll? He is — ?"

"The lead tenor in *Adelaide*. He's not staying in the hotel, but he's been around a fair bit with Peter and Natalya, having a drink in the Shakespeare, and so on. He's sung here before, so he knew the Saracen in better days. He was around after the concert."

"I see. Yes, I saw Mr. Kroll onstage last night. And what about Gunter Gottlieb?"

"Oh, God! Rather an appropriate exclamation, now I come to think about it. Gottlieb resembles the God of our worst fears. Well, I don't think for much of the time Gottlieb was aware that Des existed. I think that was probably worse than ridicule as far as Des was concerned. I mean, if we laughed at his ideas of correct breathing or his cures for the piles, then we were just *wrong*, because he'd read it in *All You Want To Know About Your Innards*, or some such tome, so he *knew*. But if you just ignored his existence, you undermined his whole basis for living."

"And Gottlieb did that?"

"I tell you, I once saw him come into the Shakespeare, where Natalya and Peter Fortnum had been holed up at a table by Des Capper. Gottlieb wanted to speak to Natalya — the usual urge to make sure that she did *exactly* as he demanded at some moment of the score, because he has this need for *total* control and a terrible mistrust of anyone else's creative powers. Anyway, instead of asking Des to go away, he just walked over, pushed against his shoulder, and pointed. Des was in full flood about something or other as usual, but he was so astonished he got up, whereupon Gottlieb simply sat down and started in on whatever he wanted to talk about. And all this was done without a word, as if Des were some kind of intrusive insect."

"Yes," said Dundy meditatively. "One sometimes feels in this case that the wrong person got murdered."

"Oh, don't get me wrong," said Ronnie, putting up his hand. "I had no sympathy for Des. He was quite loathsome, but perhaps in ways that are more difficult to convey."

Dundy turned to another aspect. "You mentioned Mr. Fortnum and Natalya Radilova — "

"Ye-es."

"What's going on there?"

"Search me." Ronnie Wimsett shrugged. "They're keeping very quiet about it, whatever it is. I don't think even Gillian knows, and she and Peter are quite close."

"But you agree there's something going on?"

"Seems so. I know that Peter makes long phone calls involving speaking Russian, and German as well, and that he immediately afterwards likes to report back to Natalya.

Apparently these calls are to Germany. Make of that what you will."

"Why doesn't she make them herself?" wondered Dundy.

"I'd guess because she only speaks Russian. Peter is a great linguist. Also she's very involved with rehearsals. She arrived late and has an immensely demanding part, while Peter has quite a small one. I don't imagine it has anything to do with Des Capper's death."

"Except that Des Capper took an interest in it," said Iain Dundy.

When Ronnie had gone, Dundy sat in thought for some moments, then looked at his watch.

"I'm expecting a Russian interpreter at ten-thirty. I wonder if we could call on the hotel for some breakfast? Just tea and toast would keep the inner man happy. And we *are* investigating the death of their manager, however glad most of them seem to have been to see the end of him."

"I'll go and rustle something up," said Charlie, getting up. "They've got a new body from the Beaumont headquarters here today as temporary manager. I'm sure he'll fall over backwards to keep us happy. He'll want us out as soon as possible."

When he had gone, Dundy remained thoughtful.

"The difficulty in this case," he said, "is sorting out the wood from the trees. I *think* whatever Fortnum and this Russian lady have been getting up to is undergrowth, to be cleared away. And yet it could be the most important thing that Capper was on to. More important than the Geary woman's drinking, obviously, or the Galloways' sleeping around. The trouble with dealing with arty people is, it's like dealing with foreigners. You don't know what they think is important."

"You mean like a Neapolitan would kill to revenge his sister's honor, whereas an Englishman wouldn't care tuppence about his?" asked Nettles.

"Aptly put. Though I'm not sure you're entirely up-to-date with Neapolitan mores." Dundy groaned. "I've just thought: This Radilova woman is *both* foreign *and* arty!"

"Right," said Charlie, coming back from the kitchen, a large tray in his hands. "Very sharp, the young man now in charge. Admits he's been sent from the head office to bring things round. Tea, coffee, toast. Something more substantial if we want it; we've only got to ring. *And* a bit of news to go with it."

"News? What's happened?"

"Literally news. On the news headlines at

ten, and I happened to hear it in the kitchens. Five musicians have defected from the Moscow Radio Orchestra. They'd just completed the last concert on a short visit to Stuttgart."

"Ah! What happened?" asked Dundy, interested.

"Well, the concert had just ended with a performance of Tchaikovsky's *Wet Dreams* Symphony — Would that be right, do you think?"

"I very much doubt it, but it's a happy thought. Go on."

"Anyway, the conductor and orchestra acknowledged tumultuous applause, and by the time it was over, they found they were five members short: two violins, a cello, and two French horns. Ten minutes later the five were asking for asylum in the nearest police station. There's no doubt they'll get it."

"I suspect," said Dundy "that this is going to make our task much easier." He looked at Charlie, who was stuffing toast into his mouth. "And now, young Peace, tell us what's on your mind."

"On my mind, sir?"

"On your mind. Come off it. You've been sunk in thought since you got here this morning. Hardly paying attention. Something occurred to you overnight, or maybe at the opera."

"Well . . ." Charlie stopped eating and looked at Dundy. "It's so fantastic. What's that French word? *Outré*. That's what it is, it's *outré*. Or maybe I just mean sick."

"Come on, man!"

"Well, can I just fetch something from upstairs?" Charlie jumped up and headed for the stairs up to the manager's quarters. A moment later he was back, carrying books. "Look, I'll just put it before you — right? Because if I just explain it, you'll probably think I'm out of my mind. See this book? It was by Des's chair when we first went through the room. It's William Ashbrook's *Donizetti and His Operas*, apparently the standard work borrowed from the local library. Des was wising himself up on the opera, having learned all there was to know about the play. The book was published in 1982. Read what it says about the first version of *Adelaide*."

He laid the book in front of Dundy, who read it, nodded, and handed it on to Nettles.

"Right. Now here's the program the director gave us last night. Did you read it?"

"Skimmed through it."

"Read the account of the *second* version of the opera, which was only discovered, or put together, a year or so ago."

Dundy read it and looked up at Charlie, a

238

light in his eyes that was the beginnings of comprehension.

"Yes?"

"Now look at this. *Heat and Dust.*"

"Why on earth — ?"

"Remember the note in Des's little book? HAD 9? With an arrow pointing to the side. The note *both* belonged on the page about getting Gottlieb *and* referred back to earlier speculations. Look at page nine."

He put the book in front of Dundy. Dundy read it and looked up, aghast.

"I don't believe it."

Charlie stood there silent. He knew that the words meant the opposite of what they said.

"You don't mean — ?"

"Maybe that's how Des intended to 'Get Gottlieb,' " said Charlie.

For a moment there was silence. Then it was interrupted by a knock on the door. The police interpreter had arrived, but he was not really needed. He had met up with Peter and Natalya in the foyer, and both of them were cock-a-hoop, ready to tell all. Peter's exuberance dominated the small manager's office, now decidedly overcrowded.

"Right," he said, rubbing his hands, when they were somehow settled in. "Now we can come clean."

"I suppose it's no good giving you a lecture

about how serious an offense it is, misleading a police officer?" asked Dundy.

"No, because this was a once-in-a-lifetime affair, and there was really nothing else we could do. I promise never to do it again and all the things schoolboys promise, but I'm not going to pretend I'm sorry."

"Who precisely is it who's defected?"

"Natalya's father — one of the violinists. And one of the French horns is a young man she's . . . friendly with. I should say there's no romantic interest between us at all, just so you don't get things wrong."

"Only a very deep friendship," said Natalya in Russian, and in a very Russian way.

"I see. Tell me, was all this cloak-and-dagger stuff necessary? Aren't things much freer, more open, at the moment in Russia?"

Natalya understood that and said something vitriolic in her own language.

"She said, in effect, 'Tell that to the Ministry of Culture,' " put in the interpreter.

"That's it, you see," said Peter. "Glasnost just isn't filtering down. The ministry is run by the same combination of bureaucrats and secret policemen, and they're not changing their ways. Now, Natalya has been allowed abroad before, but there has never been any question of her father being allowed to go at the same time. Natalya has always been adamant in her own mind that she would never defect and leave her father behind. Her mother died young, and they are very close. Her father is with the Moscow Chamber Orchestra, but he deputizes with the Moscow Radio Orchestra when they need a particularly large band or when there is illness. Which there was. Just before coming away on this German tour. Five string players fell ill. . . . I think I should say there may have been a bit of skulduggery, because Natalya somehow hoped her father would be coming before the orchestra even left Moscow."

Peter grinned at Natalya, who smiled mysteriously into her lap.

"Not my business at all," said Dundy.

"I imagine it was something nasty in their vodka at a drinking session," resumed Peter. "Anyway, her father was called on, and for once bureaucracy and the KGB were caught napping: He was allowed out of the country while his daughter was already outside. All this phoning has been to check that he got out, to confirm plans, and so on — all under the guise of innocent-sounding messages from daughter to father. It's as simple as that."

"And these five didn't want to defect until the tour was completed?"

"That's right. The regular members of the orchestra insisted on that. For the honor of the orchestra and so as not to cast a shadow over the whole trip for the others, who would practically have been locked in their hotel rooms. They had a series of concerts in Hamburg, Mannheim, and Frankfurt, then this final one in Stuttgart before flying back. They just got to the end of the *Winter Dreams* Symphony — "

"What an odd name for a symphony," put in Charlie.

" — and *whoosh* they were away. There's no doubt they will be given asylum in Germany. There's so many orchestras there that certainly one or another will want them."

"And Miss Radilova will be joining her father?"

"She hasn't decided where she will live. She's had lots of offers since the concert and last night's *Adelaide*. She's been parrying them with talk of the Ministry of Culture, who normally arrange all this sort of thing, and with a very heavy hand, too. Now she can talk over with Brad Mallory which to accept. A good soprano is never going to starve."

"Was Mr. Mallory in on all this?"

"No."

"That seems odd. He is her agent, isn't he?"

"Yes, but the explanation is simple: He didn't seem to Natalya to be completely reliable. She didn't feel she could trust him not to let something out, say something indiscreet. And I must say I agree with her. So she used me because I could speak German and Russian."

"Right," said Dundy, stirring in his seat. He felt sure that he had now cleared part of the undergrowth away. Was there anything of more vital growth to be revealed? "Well, as far as it goes, that's clear enough. You had no hint that Des Capper was on to all or any of this?"

"No. The phones in the rooms all go through the hotel switchboard, so presumably he could have listened in. Or he could have listened outside my door; he wasn't above doing that. But it was all in German or Russian, and all in coded language, so really I don't think he could have made anything of it. Not anything specific."

"He could have guessed," said Dundy. "It was a fairly obvious possibility."

"Yes, I expect a lot of people wondered," agreed Peter.

"Which bring us," said Dundy, "to what you did on the night of the murder."

Peter Fortnum seemed to lose several degrees of confidence and looked distinctly uneasy.

"Come, come," said Dundy. "You know, I

243

know, everybody knows, that you didn't spend all that time lost in the corridors."

"No," admitted Peter. "Though one can. It wasn't a bad story, and you couldn't have disproved it. Only in fact Connie Geary's room is very close to the main stairwell, so it was comparatively easy to find. I went through the dining room, through the Shakespeare — "

"And Mrs. Capper was there?"

"Oh, yes. Then I went upstairs and fetched the gin. . . . I'd already decided to phone Stuttgart then rather than after the end of the play. Then I could give the news to Natalya as soon as I came off. . . . They put an appalling extra cost on all the calls you make from your rooms here — "

"English hotels are scandalous at that," agreed Dundy.

" — so I went to the pay phone in one of the little alcoves. I am *not* one of the Piccadilly Fortnums, by the way, if they exist, and money is always scarce. That alcove — you can go and look — is a dark little place, and anyone phoning there is not conspicuous. I dialed and then waited while it rang and rang. . . . "

"Yes, go on."

"While I was standing there, someone went past. He didn't see me. He went on — didn't go down the stairs, but went past. You're fa-

244

miliar with the geography up there, are you?"

"As familiar as a day or two's acquaintance can make me."

"The first door after the stairwell is the first-floor door to the Cappers' flat. I'm sure it was there that he knocked. It was not more than a few steps after the stairwell, though I couldn't actually see the door."

"Knocked — and went in?"

"Yes. There was a call; then I heard the door open. Then they answered in Stuttgart, and I didn't pay any more attention."

"You haven't told me yet," said Dundy, "who it was who went past."

"No, I know. I wish I didn't have to. I've nothing against him. But it was Brad Mallory."

Dundy looked at Charlie, then down at the books, and in the crowded little room there was silence.

En Suite

15

When the little office was cleared and the Russian interpreter had gone off to hobnob with Peter and Natalya Radilova in the Shakespeare Bar, the three policemen who were left sat for some moments in thought.

"Brad Mallory is one of the ones I wondered about," said Dundy at last.

"Me, too," said Charlie. "To be honest, there were others, too: I wondered why this American was so often around the Saracen if he loathed Capper's guts. I wondered why Mrs. Capper didn't ring up to the flat to find out what had happened to Des after the interval . . ."

"But both those oddities were probably explicable in terms of character," said Dundy. "The tenor is naturally gregarious. Mrs. Capper is a natural doormat."

"Right. But you can't say the same for Brad Mallory. His actions make no sense in terms of character or of anything else. First of all, he leaves the concert halfway through to flap his way to the hotel, and then he expects us to believe that he was so affected by dear Singh's performance that he had to come back to his room to recover himself. The man's an agent, after all!"

"Wouldn't seem to be much future for him in his own profession," commented Nettles.

"Right," agreed Dundy. "There is Singh enjoying a fabulous success, apparently, with critics and opera directors there to hear him — pressured to come by Mallory himself. And we know for a fact — Singh told us — that offers were made to him of work, future engagements, during Interval and later. But what had Mallory done? Sloped off and left Singh to receive all the plaudits and offers of engagements on his own, holding court in the backstage rooms in the Town Hall. What's an agent for if not to take care of things like that?"

"And it wasn't only Singh," chipped in Charlie. "He was also agent, at least in the West, for Natalya Whatsername. She was a great success in the first half, and she was singing again in the second. He didn't even bother to stay and hear her but left her in the lurch, without translator or any sort of intermediary. If she was any ordinary singer in the West, surely she'd have given him the old heave-ho and got herself an agent that didn't go down with palpitations every time his pet protégé sang."

"One other thing," put in Nettles. "He looked in at the Shakespeare on the way up to his room. If he was wanting peace and quiet to recover in, why would he do that? He was looking for someone, and it's a fair bet it was Des Capper."

"It is," agreed Dundy. "Because look at the sequence of events earlier in the evening when he left the Saracen. He'd been in the Shakespeare, and he came out of the main entrance to go to the Town Hall, immediately followed by Des Capper. Now, let's conjecture that precisely then, on the way out of the Shakespeare and through the foyer, Des came up to him — timing it purposely, Mallory being on his way to Singh's triumph — and said something that showed him his secret had been guessed."

Nettles looked ahead of him, hoping to hide the fact that he was not too sure he understood what the secret in question was. Charlie nodded vigorously, knowing all too well.

"That all makes sense," he said with an enthusiasm born of a love of the chase. "But did you get why he thought he could use Mallory and Singh to 'Get Gottlieb'?"

"I think so. I *think* I sorted it out," said Dundy. "Let's get it clear in our minds. Let's go back to that rehearsal we've heard about from more than one witness. It was a rehearsal with full cast and orchestra, but it wasn't a dress rehearsal. I checked that this morning, by the way, with the director. The tenor, Krister Kroll, was in stage costume. That was because he has to wear that rather camp number in furs and tartan. The rest were in mufti."

"I don't get the point," said Nettles. "Remember I haven't seen the show."

"But you read the program. Anyway, as far as I can reconstruct it, this is what happened. The tenor entered at the back of the stage and launched into his big tune. He's got quite a nice voice, but small, and it was quite ineffective — wouldn't have penetrated beyond the third row of the stalls, even I could hear that. So Gottlieb made him come to the front of the stage, and that totally upset the production. Natalya Whatsit got upset, and Brad went up onstage to calm her down, accompanied by Singh — Brad Mallory being the solicitous singers' agent at this point, you notice. How much he could do to calm her down without a common language I don't know, but he cer-

249

tainly tried. Now, at this point Des Capper arrived backstage to assert his right to go everywhere and poke his finger in everything."

"Yes," said Nettles, still puzzled. "He spoke to Peter Fortnum."

"That's right. Then the staging was altered, the scene played through to the end, then a break was called. We needn't go into that. But what would someone arriving at that point in the rehearsal think?"

"That the Third World War was about to start and the Germans were on the other side as usual?" suggested Nettles.

Charlie jumped up and down excitedly. "No! He'd see Singh up there onstage, in civvies like the rest, and he'd assume that he had a part in the opera. Remember that he made that endearing little joke to Fortnum about the Indians running the corner shops?"

"And not only that," insisted Dundy. "Remember that when Fortnum and Gillian Soames first arrived at the Saracen, he thought they were 'the operatic lady and gentleman.' He not only got the wrong people, but he was wrong about Singh, too. He wasn't singing in the opera, only in a concert."

"I still don't quite see — " began Nettles.

"It means," said Charlie, bubbling on, "that if he wanted to get even with Gottlieb, the best way to do it was through the opera — prestige affair, second big event of the festival, the stepping-stone for Gottlieb taking over the festival as a whole. And Des, getting it wrong as usual, thought he could get at the opera via Singh, who he thought was in it."

"What he thought, I'm sure," agreed Dundy, "was that he could bring the whole thing down around Gottlieb's head by going to the tabloids with a really grubby little story that they'd love. The fact that he'd also destroy Singh's career — and probably Mallory's, too, in the process — wouldn't have worried him. Why would it? He had no reason to love them." He got up and looked at the other two. "Come on. I think it's time that we talked to him."

They got together their things and went out of the office. As they passed the reception desk in the foyer, Iain Dundy pulled out the guest book and found Mallory's rooms. They constituted the Grand Suite — rooms 116 and 117. As they went up the staircase, they threw a glance into the Shakespeare. The new manager, a fair-haired, efficient-looking young man, was coping with the help of Dawn. It was getting on for two, but the bar was very full.

"Ghouls," said Dundy.

Once up on the first floor, the policemen

began to have a renewed sympathy with Peter Fortnum's point about the geography of the place. Yes, this *was* a hotel that you wouldn't necessarily get the hang of in a few days. After a few abortive sallies up dead-end corridors and down stunted flights of stairs that led nowhere, they finally came, almost by accident, it seemed, upon room 116. It was next to room 145. Dundy listened outside the door of room 116, then room 117, and finally knocked on the latter door. There was a moment's pause and then a reasonably confident sounding "Come in."

They went in to what was obviously one of the best rooms in the hotel. It was, in fact, a sitting room with bedrooms leading off from either end and a gleaming bathroom visible through a half-open door. In the sitting room there was a large television and radio, a dining table and chairs, and coffee tables dotted here and there. The furniture was either old or new-old, Dundy couldn't decide which. On one of the coffee tables was a tray with plates and glasses on it. Brad and Singh had obviously just lunched on something sent up from the kitchens. Dundy wondered whether Mallory was becoming embarrassed by Singh or fearful for his discovery. A half bottle of German wine stood on the dining table, and beside it a bottle of Coca-Cola.

Singh was sitting in an armchair on one side of a little table, reading *Uomo*, or perhaps just studying the fashion plates. He looked chubby and satisfied, and Dundy thought there might be a suspicion of makeup on his face. Brad Mallory was sitting on the other side, a cravat tucked airily into his open shirt, suede shoes on his feet. In spite of such old-fashioned dash in his attire, it struck Dundy that he looked very small. As he put his book down hurriedly on the table and bustled to welcome them all in, he looked apprehensive, almost frightened. He was not a good dissembler of fear. Dundy bent down and took up the book.

"Ah, press-cuttings," he said. "I hear you had a great success at the concert, sir." Singh, who had watched the bustle as a disinterested observer, allowed his sallow cheeks to crease into a smile but then let them sink back into handsome repose. "I haven't had time to read the reviews myself, but I hear you gave a very remarkable performance."

"The reviews are *very* good, *very* gratifying," said Brad with a nervous, jerky intensity. "It's the beginning of a brilliant career for Singh. But I don't suppose all three of you will have come to talk about music, Superintendent?"

"No, indeed, sir. I wonder if we could speak to you alone? No reason for bothering

253

Mr. Singh in this instance."

Brad Mallory seemed both nervous and yet glad. "Of course, yes. Do you mind, dear boy? The video is in your bedroom. You seem to have been up half the night with it. I'm sure you have something you'd like to play over again."

Singh smiled again and got up gracefully. He moved as if he had studied deportment with some very aged teacher, possibly with Mr. Turveydrop himself. As soon as he had shut the door, the policemen heard a click, then the opening music of *Mary Poppins*.

When he heard it, Brad Mallory flinched, as if this were a masterpiece with which he was all too familiar. Then his face dissolved into a smile.

"The dear boy," he said, looking round at them. "So faithful to his old favorites."

He waved Dundy and the other policemen to seats, but Dundy waited before he accepted.

"The dear boy seems to have pleased the critics as much as he affected you," he said, tapping the collection of pasted-in reviews. "It must be a disadvantage to you in your job to be so easily incapacitated emotionally."

Brad Mallory looked disconcerted. "It *is*," he said. "But that's one of the penalties one pays for the artistic temperament."

Iain Dundy sat down and gave him a hard

look. "Mr. Mallory," he said. "I'm not going to beat about the bush or get into little sparring bouts with you. And I wish you'd drop this performance."

"Performance?"

"It seems to me you're giving a *performance* as an aesthete, practically a parody of one. You remind me of a character in a not very good detective story from the twenties. You also seem to me to be giving a parody performance of a homosexual."

"Like the chaste apprentice in the play," put in Charlie. "He's doing a parody of the *Carry On* homosexual, and you're doing the quivering aesthete one."

"I really don't think you understand the *feelings* of someone who — "

Iain Dundy leaned forward in his chair. "Come off it, old cock. You're a bloody singers' agent. If Singh was such a triumph at the concert the other night, your job was to remain there and talk to the important people you'd invited to hear him. Natalya Radilova was something of a hit, too, and she couldn't rub more than two words of English together. Your job was to stay down there, and you'd have to be a bloody bad agent not to do it. I don't believe you're that. Why did you come away?"

Brad's voice came feebly, hardly penetrating the pepped-up jollities of *Mary Poppins* from the next room.

"I've told you: Singh is something very *special* to me. His singing affected me profoundly."

"Codswallop! If you were that knocked all of a heap emotionally, why did you look in at the Shakespeare before you went up to your room? You were looking for someone. And I may as well tell you that you were seen knocking on Des Capper's door at twenty past eight."

Brad Mallory's jaw dropped, and he gave out a little squawk, like a strangled chicken.

"No! No!"

"Oh, yes. I tell you, you were *seen*. And I've thought all along your story wasn't worth a bean. I think you came back because of something Des Capper said to you as you left the Saracen on your way to the Town Hall."

Again there was this little squawk, and Brad Mallory writhed in his chair as if he were sitting on hot coals. Then quite suddenly he went still, sagging down into the chair like a half-empty sack of potatoes — small, pathetic, tired. He had dropped the mannerisms, but it was as if the mannerisms had become his self and there was nothing remaining. His eyes stared ahead, the most lively things about him. He was calculating how much he could tell.

"Since you know . . ." he said in a low voice, hesitating as he chose his revelations with care. "Yes, he did say something to me as I was leaving to go to the concert. . . . He'd already said something loaded in the bar about always meaning what he said. Then when I left he caught up with me in the foyer. . . . I won't say what he said. It's not relevant. . . . By the time I got to the concert, my mind was in turmoil! Absolute turmoil!" He caught Dundy's eye and dropped the mannerism. "I was greeting everyone I knew, everyone I'd asked there, and I was casting around in my mind what I could do. I tried to phone him before the concert started, but there was no answer. . . . He was in the courtyard, watching the play, I believe. . . . I went in for the first half of the concert. Luckily I had an aisle seat at the back. I couldn't settle, couldn't concentrate on anything. . . . During the letter scene, Natalya's aria, just before Singh's pieces, I slipped out and rang him again. This time he was in. I said I had to see him, and at once. I said there was an interval coming up in the concert and that I'd come up to the Saracen at about a quarter or twenty past eight."

"What was his reaction?"

"Very genial . . . in his dreadful way. . . . Gloating, really. But before he rang off, he said: 'Not that it will do you any good, Mr. Mallory, but I'm quite happy to have a natter about it.' "

"Right," said Dundy, stretching his legs. "Well, that's clear enough so far. Except, of course, that you've skated over the little matter of what Capper was threatening you with."

"It's not rele — "

Dundy held up his hand. There was no reason why Mallory should be allowed to get off this particular hook.

"There's no way this discussion is going to make any sense unless the whole thing is brought into the open. For the moment, this will be among ourselves. What would need to come out at any future trial I can't possibly say as yet. May I suggest that what Des said to you as you were leaving for the Town Hall — "

"*No!* Please, no!"

" — was something like: 'So you're off to see your little castrato performing, are you, Mr. Mallory?' "

Nettles blinked. So that *was* it! The little bundle in the chair, after a brief spasm of life, collapsed again. He looked like Grandmother Smallweed, needing to be shaken up. At last he said:

"Actually what he said was 'Give my best wishes to your pet castrato.' "

"Right," said Dundy, still refusing to let Mallory off the hook. "I'm sure we're all better off for having that out in the open. Now, I think you'd better explain to us all exactly what a castrato was — *is* — don't you?"

Brad Mallory swallowed and thought. When he spoke, it was very low, as if he were reading to himself from a dictionary of music.

"It was a man who had been castrated just before puberty to preserve his high singing voice. They chose boys with beautiful voices, of course, and as it developed, it became something quite unique — full, brilliant, agile. They used the castrati in the papal choir right up to the end of the nineteenth century, but in opera they more or less died out early in the nineteenth century. The practice had become . . . unacceptable. The castrati were very spoiled, demanding, capricious, vain, and people got tired of their whims. They also became very fat, so they became ridiculous in heroic parts. But a lot of operas *need* that kind of voice: Handel, Gluck, early Mozart, early Rossini. Nowadays they use women for the parts, or countertenors, but it's not right."

"A countertenor, as I understand it," said Dundy, "is a choirboy who keeps his voice high by a big effort, right?"

"Something like that. The trouble is, the castrato roles call for brilliance and volume, and a countertenor voice is too weak; it won't fill a modern opera house. And a woman's voice is quite different, too, and she always looks like a woman in men's clothes." He cast them a look of feeble cunning. "It's a problem nobody has been able to solve."

"Until you came along," said Dundy quietly. "Until you decided to fill a long-felt want."

Brad Mallory sparked up a little. "It's not as though there weren't any eunuchs around! People talk as if you couldn't do that today. That's just ignorance. It's being done all over the world — Turkey, India . . . "

"Yes, indeed: India. How did you come to know about the survival of the practice in India?"

Brad Mallory looked down into his lap and again spoke low. "I went there often when we used to arrange a World Theater Festival in London. I was one of the directors. I got to know all the major Indian troupes and some of the lesser — "

"These would have been some of the lesser, wouldn't they?" Dundy shook his head. "This was something that Des Capper also proved to be expert in, wasn't it?"

"Damn the man! Damn the bloody little know-it-all! . . . Yes, I suppose so. We never talked about *how* he came to know. Part of his

Indian experiences, presumably."

"Yes, it must have been. Of course, he'd never done most of the things he claimed to have done, but he had been there. This is what I think happened. Des came along to the rehearsal of *Adelaide*, and he happened to come backstage at the moment when you and Singh had gone onstage to comfort or reassure Natalya Radilova. He'd always assumed that Singh was 'an operatic gentleman,' in his words, and this confirmed him in his mistake."

"I can't think what part he imagined he played."

"Ah, but remember that the version of *Adelaide* that is being played here is Donizetti's rewrite from the 1830s, which was only discovered last year. When he went to the standard work on Donizetti, all he found was an account of the *original* opera of 1825, written for the castrato Velluti. So he assumed that Singh was playing Velluti's part of Robert the Bruce. What was actually going on onstage during the bit of rehearsal he saw meant little to him, because it was in Italian, and he hadn't then done a great deal of homework on the opera. He was looking for some way of getting revenge on Gottlieb, particularly later, after the scene in the Green Room. He didn't have much luck with Gottlieb's taste in young girls, because his minder was being careful.

So when he got the idea that you had got hold of a *real* castrato for the Velluti part, he got the notion of getting at Gottlieb by turning his operatic triumph into a scandal and disaster that the popular press would seize on like vultures over carrion."

"That's something I don't quite understand, sir," said Nettles. "Would they have been that interested? Opera's pretty much of a minority interest."

"Oh, but they would, they would." Dundy turned to Mallory. "I'm sure you realized that throughout."

Mallory nodded sadly. "Oh, yes. I always knew the public would never stand for a castrated male if they knew. Imagine what the *Daily Grub* would make of the sick tastes of" — his voice took on an Australian twang — "'so-called culture vultures.' Think of the great mountain of pretended outrage and vulgar ridicule they would pile up. They would have a field day. If it were known, Singh could never perform in public again. People would be sickened."

"And Gottlieb's opera would be a disaster. He would be buried in sludge. Except, of course, that unknown to Des Capper, Singh had nothing to do with *Adelaide*. It would have been you who was buried."

"So what we think happened," put in Charlie, "is that Capper saw the rehearsal, went away and read about Donizetti writing the opera for a castrato, and something clicked in his mind, something he remembered from his Indian experiences."

"That's it," resumed Dundy. "India has been in everybody's minds recently, what with *Jewel in the Crown, Gandhi, A Passage to India,* and the rest. No doubt Des bored his saloon-bar regulars with his superior knowledge of the place each time one of them was shown on television. But knowledge he did have, and some reading, too, and when he thought of the subject of eunuchs, he remembered the hijras. He not only remembered them. There was a note in his little book of useful bits of information: HAD 9. He'd remembered that they appeared in *Heat and Dust* and had gone away and looked them up."

"I still don't understand who or what the hijras were," said Nettles. "Or *are.*"

"Are, definitely. Perhaps you could tell him, Mr. Mallory," said Dundy. "I presume it was from them, or through them, that you — what shall we say? — acquired Singh?"

Brad Mallory flinched. His voice was still low, as if he were a great distance away. "They are bands of traveling entertainers. They perform on the streets, at stag parties and suchlike occasions. Probably it would have been at a stag party that Capper saw them. They're hermaphrodites and eunuchs, and their act is scabrous, very sexual, really rather horrible. There is a religious basis somewhere — they have a shrine in Gujarat — but it's not very strong. In fact, for the ordinary Indian they're the next thing to outcasts, though they're very often beautiful, weirdly so, and sometimes talented. Sometimes they buy children; sometimes they kidnap them. Then they castrate them."

"As you knew from your visits to India."

"Yes. I saw a troupe of them the very first time I went there. They fascinated me. They planted a seed in the back of my mind. And when early operas became more and more popular, I thought: *That's* what is needed. Only that sort of voice can really do justice to the music."

"And probably you were right. As we can see from these reviews." Dundy tapped the already pasted in collection of reviews. "They all exclaim how *different* Singh's voice is from the usual countertenor — so much more powerful and brilliant. They guess it's something to do with his being Indian. None of them guesses the real reason. It's interesting that Des Capper did. I wonder what gave him the clue."

"I don't know. I always insisted that Singh was English," said Brad Mallory. "I think I overdid it and gave him the first clue."

"Yes, and I suspect that he was puzzled by your homosexual performance. I suppose you did that to give Singh some kind of sexual identity?"

"Yes. I adopted them gradually, as if I was changing my . . . my sexual orientation. It was a preparation for when I would bring Singh forward, launch him on his career."

"But I suspect that Des learned from the room maids here that there didn't seem to be anything going on between you. 'Where do they do it?' he asked in his little book. . . . But you haven't told us how you procured Singh."

"If you're suggesting that I had him . . . *done*, you're mistaken," said Brad with a brief spurt of fire. "He was twelve when I saw him and had already been . . . operated on. I listened to several of the boys, heard their singing voices, chose the one that seemed most beautiful and most Western. Then I arranged for the boy to be adopted by an Indian couple that I knew in this country. He had no obvious parent or protector, so it was quite easy. From the day he came here he has been having music lessons. Everything has been geared towards his debut. . . . The man who will show us how Handel opera should be sung. . . ."

His voice faded into silence, but then he looked wildly round at the other three men. "I mean, *why not?*" he almost cried.

They didn't tell him. They left a pause, and then Dundy said quietly: "I imagine it hasn't been easy."

Brad Mallory smiled sadly. "Oh, no. It hasn't been easy. As you've seen, he's very vain and childish. It's almost as if he stopped growing up when . . . I'm used to artists who view the world as revolving around themselves. That's usual. And they are *artists*. Singh is a baby. At the center there is . . . a hole. Sweet nothing. And he can be cruel, too. To defenseless things. And he eats sweets. . . ."

"Eats sweets?" asked Nettles, mystified.

"I tell him not to. Already he's getting very chubby. If he becomes grossly fat, he will remind people of nothing so much as the old castrati, and then someone will ask questions. I tell him this over and over, but he takes no notice. . . . He has no gratitude."

"Gratitude?"

"You think he shouldn't have? Maybe. Anyway, he has none. I have this fear that in two or three years, when he has made his name, he will throw me over. All the financial gains will go to someone else. And I'll have nothing to threaten him with to keep him faithful. Any revelation about his ... state would tarnish me much more than it would tarnish him. No, it has not been easy."

"I must say I'm rather glad to hear that," said Iain Dundy briskly. "Now, let's come to the night of the murder, sir. Let's hear exactly what happened?"

"Oh, God." Bradford Mallory went white. "It was a nightmare. It needed all my little ... queer mannerisms to carry it off. ... After I'd telephoned, I went back to the Town Hall to hear Singh's arias. He was brilliant, but I could hardly concentrate. What was I going to do? Was I going to offer him money? If so, how much? Was it possible to brazen things out? Because, after all, I didn't see how he could *know*."

"You left the concert as soon as Singh was finished, did you? When was that?"

"About ten past eight, as I told you before. I was back at the Saracen by a quarter past. I came to this room, put a flannel over my face, lit a cigarette, and put it straight out. It was so *damnable*, after all my work, and just when it was coming to fruition. But I hadn't made up my mind what to do when I went along and knocked at his door. That was about twenty past eight or so, as you said. If only I'd *decided* to face it out or *decided* to pay up. I put up a front, but I think Capper could see from the moment I walked into the room that I was beaten. He behaved as if I was a mouse he'd brought in and was preparing to torment."

"What was he like?"

"Oh — *horrible*. Rubbing his hands with glee, making barroom jokes, leering . . . He was quite disgusting. I tried to face it out, to say there was nothing to it, but the mere fact that I was there told him that wasn't true. He said a medical examination could prove it one way or another. He said he had a good mate on the *Daily Grub*. I could believe it. It's just the paper Des Capper would know someone from. He said it was the sort of story that paper would love, and he was right there: salacious, voyeuristic, anti-art, and the racial overtones wouldn't have come amiss — they could make something of them. I can just see the headlines. They'd have gloated for days over the sick tastes of opera lovers who could watch a nonman who sang like a woman. . . . All this time he was rubbing his hands and leering and making elephantine innuendos. My God, he deserved to die. I shouldn't say that, but he did."

"What happened next?"

"I offered money, of course. That seemed to delight him even more. It was me wriggling on the hook. His hook. He positively chortled. It wasn't money he was after, he kept

268

saying. It was to get even. I was quite bewildered. I asked him why he wanted to get even with me. What had I done? Or was it Singh he wanted to get even with? He said he had one or two little scores to settle against both of us, but it was neither, and so there was nothing in the world I could do about it. I just didn't understand. How could revealing Singh's secret get him even with anyone other than Singh or me? He was rubbing his hands and chortling to himself. I just didn't know what to do. It was like being in a maze."

"What *did* you do?"

"What could I? I kept thrashing around in my mind: Could I explain why I'd brought Singh over, trained him? Would he understand? Was there anything he wanted besides money? He was positively gleeful that there was nothing I could do: 'It's a very unfortunate position for you, Mr. Mallory,' he kept saying, 'caught up in a quarrel that's not your own. I'm afraid there's just no way you can prevent me making a splash of it.' He was loving it, of course. . . . Normally I'm quite tough. You're quite right about my little mannerisms; they've become a cover. If you deal with singers all the time, you've got to be tough, believe me. But this situation was beyond me. In the end, with his standing there grinning at me as I wriggled, I just turned and walked out."

There was silence in the room. "Are you telling me that you didn't kill him?" asked Dundy.

Mallory's face was suffused by a hopeless, beseeching expression. "Of course I didn't kill him. I knew there was no chance of your believing me; that's why I didn't even try to tell you part of the story. I knew I probably wouldn't believe it myself if I were in your shoes. But it's the truth. I'm not the killing type."

"When you left the room, he was still alive?"

"Yes!"

"What time was this?"

"About a quarter to nine. The Interval was still on — I remember hearing talking and laughter coming up from the Shakespeare Bar."

"And you never went back to the flat?"

Brad Mallory swallowed. "I went back to the flat. I never went into it."

"What do you mean?"

"I went back to my room. It's just along the corridor, as you know. I lay down on the bed and tried to think. I was desperate for a way out, but there was none. Even in a maze you know there *is* a way out, but now it seemed as though I'd been put down in the middle of one which had had its way out blocked. But —

270

I don't know — perhaps I'm a congenital optimist; perhaps I don't like admitting defeat. I convinced myself I hadn't pushed the money solution hard enough. Perhaps he was just playing with me, I thought, and was really after money all the time. Everyone responds to money, I thought, if you offer enough — and we hadn't even mentioned specific sums. I decided to try again."

"What time was this?"

"Just about nine. I saw the news headlines, downed a quick scotch, and went along that damned corridor again. My hand was just knocking the first knock at Capper's door when it struck me there were low voices inside. And the moment I finished knocking — "

"Yes?"

"I heard a cry — a grunt — and then a heavy thump."

"What did you do?"

"I ran. I knew then that someone had killed him. I ran back to my room and thought over what the hell I should do. For God's sake, I'm not stupid. I knew then that somebody was going to suspect me of murder."

His face was so agonized that it was almost possible to believe him. From Singh's bedroom came the sound of a high soprano voice assuring him that a spoonful of sugar would make the medicine go down.

The Shakespeare Again

16

The last thing Dundy did before he left the suite was caution Brad Mallory not to leave the hotel without getting police permission first. When the three of them were out in the corridor, Charlie noticed a look of dissatisfaction on Dundy's face, a look of niggling doubt. It disappointed him, but he respected the man's greater experience. Dundy walked on but paused at the little dark alcove where the telephone was. There was a sofa there, and an easy chair. Dundy took the latter and sent Nettles to the kitchens for three coffees. Then he took out a cigarette, lit it — the first time Charlie had seen him smoke — and soon began leafing through his notebook. The three of them sipped strong, hot coffee, and all of them kept silent. Charlie was wondering why Dundy was unsatisfied with Mallory as murderer and what were the consequences for the case if his story was believed. Nettles was somehow simultaneously thinking when his wife and new baby would be home and what would be the ideal side for England to field against the West Indies in the first Test. It was a companionable, not a strained, silence. After twenty minutes or so, Dundy's expression of dissatisfaction began to lift.

"You believe him, don't you?" said Charlie.

The disappointment in his voice was palpable. It had been his brilliant deduction that had led them to Mallory, and it should have been crowned by the coup of his arrest.

"I suppose I shouldn't," said Dundy slowly. "We wouldn't have any difficulty in making one hell of a good case against him. All I've got on the other side is instinct."

"Instinct about — ?"

"Character, I suppose. I just don't feel he has it in him to commit murder. Oh, I grant you he's tougher than he's been pretending. His job proves that. And the motive is there all right. I believe what he says about Singh's career being ruined is true. It would be destroyed by the popular press. There might be a few recordings, because that's closed-door stuff, but a stage career? I doubt it. I suspect that there is one thing Mallory has lied about. I think it may be that he did "choose" Singh, did pick out the boy with the best voice and the best appearance, and then have him "done." And if that is so, he has a motive whether or not Singh's career would be ruined — because sure as hell *his* would be. The papers would crucify him. So there's no doubt whatever about motive. But guts, courage, bottle, nerve — call it what you will. I don't think he has it to the sort of degree that murder demands. I still think he's basically a gadfly, a dilettante. When he shed all those gay mannerisms, there somehow — how shall I put it? — there wasn't much left. I try to square him with all I've ever learned in my life about killers, and all I've ever read about them, and I can't."

"But where does that leave us, sir?" asked Nettles. "Back at square one?"

"No, of course not," said Dundy crossly. "*Think*, man. Surely you can see that if we believe him it alters our whole perspective on the case."

"Time," said Charlie.

"Exactly."

They all three sat thinking about that for some moments. Downstairs, time had just been called. Dundy stubbed out his second cigarette and got up.

"We'll go down."

In the Shakespeare there were a few stragglers left. Newspapers were strewn around on the tables, mostly turned to the arts pages, and a collection of singers and orchestral players were laughing over an article in the *Times* in which Bernard Levin confessed that he was unable to take Donizetti seriously. At the sight of the policemen, they drank up and left. How they knew they were policemen was no mystery: In the Saracen at the time, it was a fair bet. Dundy noted that among the disappearing party was Krister Kroll, the tenor. He let him go and surveyed the rapidly emptying room with satisfaction. Then he went to the bar, where Dawn and the new temporary manager were tidying up the lunchtime debris.

"Ah, you would be the superintendent," said the new manager, coming round from behind the bar, his manner somewhere between the friendly and the ingratiating. He seemed a pleasant enough young man, but people in any way connected with the licensing trade never quite knew how to behave with policemen.

"That's right," said Dundy. "You've been got here quickly. Getting things round?"

The manager's face assumed a serious ex-

275

pression. "Oh, officially, there's nothing to get round. *Un*officially we may admit that perhaps the best appointment may not have been made last time, that there may be a few bridges to mend."

"I think I might like a brief word, eventually, on how that appointment came to be made."

"Of course. I was briefed about that before I was sent over. Oh, by the way, this came this morning from headquarters." He drew from his pocket a Saracen's Head envelope and handed it to Dundy. "We didn't think there was any need to bother about fingerprints since it had been through the postal mill. It's Capper's handwriting, isn't it? Sent the day he died, but by second-class mail."

There was no letter. What Dundy drew out of the envelope was a newspaper clipping. It was the medical column of one of the newspapers they had found in Capper's flat. It dealt, in laymen's terms, with a newly developed treatment for spastics.

"I think you'll find the appointment quite understandable when you know the facts," the temporary manager was nervously saying. "It's far from suspicious. In fact, redounding to the credit — "

"Right," said Dundy, cutting him short. "But before we go into that — "

"Yes? Anything we can do to help, of course."

" — I'd like to try a little experiment with Dawn here."

Dawn looked up, surprised. She was much more alert today, rested and in almost sparkling form. She had, of course, been very much the center of attention both at home and in the hotel. Now she looked puzzled but intrigued.

"I don't see — "

"You don't have to. It's quite simple, and something you're used to doing. Now, I want you to fill a tray with dirty glasses — or clean ones, if you haven't got enough — just as you did on the night of the murder."

"We do generally prefer to wash them by hand, Superintendent," said the fair-haired manager, then seemed to realize the fatuity of this remark.

"I'm sure you do, sir. You can do them later by hand if you like. Did you load up the tray on your own on the murder night, miss?"

"No, Mrs. Capper helped a bit."

"If you could help her, then, sir?"

As he watched them filling a large tray, which it seemed would be all Dawn could manage to lift or encompass the breadth of in her arms, Dundy was conscious that behind him, at the door into the foyer, there was a

277

movement, a presence. He wondered if it were possible . . .

"Now it's full, isn't it? It's now exactly two-fifty. I want you to take it up, go through with the tray to the kitchens, stack the glasses into the dishwasher just as you did on Thursday, at the same sort of rate you did it then, and then set the machine going, do anything else that you — "

"Oh, my God, you know!"

Win Capper, standing at the doorway, seemed turned to stone, her usually sallow complexion turned to an unhealthy white. Dundy held Dawn back from rushing over to her, and after a minute she tottered forward and sat down on a chair. Dundy released Dawn, who swiftly poured a neat scotch at the bar and hurried over with it. She put it to Win's mouth, then sat beside her at the table and put her arm around her shoulders. Win stared down at the table, then took another gulp at the whiskey.

When she spoke, it was in a dull, flat voice. "I overdid it, didn't I? About how wonderful Des was and how he hadn't an enemy in the world."

"It did occur to me," said Dundy carefully, "that the wife of someone like Des Capper might think he was wonderful, but she couldn't remain unaware that other people didn't share the same view. Not in a pub, where she could see people's reactions to him and would probably overhear opinions of him."

Win nodded. She looked up now, and faint traces of color had begun to come back into her cheeks.

"I'm ready to come along with you. It's almost a relief. I was always afraid someone else was going to be charged. Dawn will help me pack one or two things, won't you, dear? I'd just like to say why I did it" — she patted Dawn's hand — "so you won't think so badly of me."

"I don't," said Dawn, only with an effort refraining from saying that she thought Win had done a public service.

"I expect by now you know what Des was really like. He was mean, cunning, and a slave driver. I should have left him years ago, but perhaps I'm a natural slave. Or I'd become one over the years. I was a nurse when I married him. Guess I just went from slavery to matron to slavery in a bar for Des. Seven years ago I got pregnant. I was over the moon. Des was pretty pleased, too. Me not getting pregnant was one of the things he used to throw in my face the ten years we'd been married. Then Kevin was born, and a few days later they told us he was a spastic. . . . It didn't make any difference to me. I only loved him the more. But that was the end for Des. If he wasn't a healthy, normal child, he just didn't want to know about him. He said you couldn't have an idiot child — that's what he called him — growing up in a pub. The customers wouldn't like it. He had to go into a home. So we put him in one in Lancashire, and I went from Carlisle to see him every Sunday. I didn't think I could ever forgive Des for that, but there was more." She put her handkerchief to her mouth and swallowed.

"The director," murmured the new manager.

"That's right. The director of Beaumont Hotels. He's got a spastic son, too. He brought him to our hotel in Carlisle, on his way to the lake district. He's a wonderful father, devoted, always taking the boy places, bringing him out, arousing his interest. Like I would do if I could see Kevin more than once a week. . . . Of course Des was all over his boy. You'd have thought he was Prince William the way he fawned. And he kept saying it made a *bond* — us having a spastic boy as well. The director was the only person I ever remember Des mentioning him to. And Des said if only we had a bigger hotel to run, with room to bring up a family and to get a bit of privacy — "

"The place in Carlisle is not one of our better hotels," put in the manager. "It's very small and inconvenient, with very little residential trade out of the summer season."

"That's right. Des desperately wanted to get somewhere with a bit of prestige. So he went on and on to the director about how he longed to get Kevin out of the home if only he could get somewhere with a bit of space for him to play, somewhere with a good staff, so I could be freer. After the director went, he used to send him anything he read on cerebral palsy and its treatment. Used to cut things out of papers and the like. Said it was so I shouldn't see them. 'Only set you off again,' he'd say. But he always sent them to the director. When Arthur Bradley died, Des heard about it through the grapevine, of course, and bombarded the director with hints of how he'd like the job and what a difference it would make for Kevin's life. . . ."

"That's true," said the manager. "That's how he got appointed. The director told several people at Head office after we began to get hints that the appointment was not turning out well. Naturally he felt responsible."

"I won't say I ever believed Des," Win went on, dabbing at her eyes. "But I thought — hoped — that if we got it he'd have to keep his word. I should have known better. We'd been here a month when he wrote to the director and told him Kevin had had a setback and was hospitalized and it would be dangerous to move him. . . . The lying bastard! Kevin was just as he'd always been. But what could I do about it? That's when I decided he had to die. From then on I was just waiting for an opportunity." She got up, now quite steady, and turned to Dawn. "I'll get my things together now, dear, if you'll come with me. It won't take long. Then I'll be quite ready to come with you." She paused at the doorway. "They won't separate me entirely from my boy, will they, sir?"

Dundy hoped he was speaking the truth when he murmured: "No, I'm sure they won't."

As Win and Dawn went up the stairs, Dundy slipped out into the foyer and detailed a police constable to follow them and station himself outside the room. When he got back to the Shakespeare, the new manager had tactfully taken himself off. The others, inevitably, were wanting a bit of a natter.

"I *think* I can see why Brad Mallory's story changed everything," said Nettles, his forehead creased. "We've been going badly wrong over the times, haven't we?"

"Of course we have. Gently led astray by Win Capper. We put so much weight on Des

Capper's promise to help at Interval and the fact that he didn't turn up that we began to assume that he was dead by then. But there was nothing in the medical evidence to suggest that he need have been. It was slipshod thinking on my part. Once I'd established that Win must have spent the *first* period when Dawn was away pouring nice cold white wine, I began almost without noticing to exclude her — fool that I was! Because the first person you pay attention to when a husband has been murdered is the wife — and *vice*, of course, *versa*."

Dundy sat for a moment in thought. "Actually, there were two things of importance in Brad Mallory's story, if we decided to believe it. The first was that Brad rang Des up from the Town Hall to make the appointment for twenty past eight. That meant Des knew well in advance that he wasn't likely to be able to help in the interval. The second, if we believed him, was that he was *not* dead by Interval — probably not for some time *after* it. That didn't really alter things as far as the play people were concerned, though it let Peter Fortnum off the hook. But it did alter it for others."

"And for Win Capper in particular," said Charlie.

"Yes. I began making an alternative scenario in my mind. You know, people tend to divide murders into premeditated ones and ones done on the spur of the moment. But there is another kind: killings that are *intended* over a long period, the killer merely waiting for a convenient opportunity and then seizing it. That was what we had in this case."

"I think I'm there now," said Charlie. "I think I've got the opportunity Win seized on. Capper rang Win in the bar while Dawn was fetching the snacks."

"That's it, I'm sure. Knowing Des, he might do it, or he might not. But let's assume he did, at about a quarter past eight, when Dawn was in the kitchen getting the nuts and the cheese dainties. I suspect he did it because he wanted to gloat. He told Win she'd have to cope or get someone else from the kitchen, because he'd be holding someone over a slow fire. He may even have named him. We don't know how much he told Win about his activities and the people he wanted to 'get.' Anyway, she decided then and there that now was the time. As she said, she'd intended doing it for some months, and while the festival people were here was obviously a good time, since Des had put up so many backs. The fact that there was now going to be an interview of murderous potential made this an irresistible opportunity. She was getting ready the drinks for the interval, which gave her a marvelous alibi for *this* period on her own. As she poured them out, her mind must have been working furiously."

"And she decided not to mention Des's phone call to Dawn when she returned," suggested Nettles.

"That's right. So that when he failed to turn up at Interval, the presumption would be later that he was dead by then. And even if the plan misfired — say, Des came down after his interview with Mallory — well, forgetting a phone call was no great matter. The plan could be put on ice."

"I did wonder," said Charlie, "why she didn't ring up to the flat after the interval. I thought it must be because she knew he was dead."

"No, it was because she knew that he was alive. So, during the interval she commented on Des's nonappearance to Dawn, and doubtless within the hearing of customers as well. Then, when Interval was finished, she had to make herself an opportunity. She packed Dawn off with glasses for the big kitchen dishwasher — an unusual procedure but easy to justify. Then she was off through the manager's office, up to the flat. She was just talking to Des — *making* conversation, by the table with the knife on it, perhaps about the problems at Interval — when there was Brad Mallory's knock on the door. Des turned, she took up the knife she'd all along intended as the implement, and she shoved it in his back."

"Come to think of it," said Charlie, "that knife was always a pretty unlikely murder weapon for Brad Mallory."

"Right. It was Indian. It directed too much attention to Singh."

"Another thing," said Charlie. "That damp patch on the cover of the sofa in their flat. It probably came off her apron; she'd been washing up pretty well nonstop all evening."

"Yes. I think she leaned against the sofa to give herself purchase as she stabbed. When I thought about it, there was nobody else, other than Dawn, likely to leave that sort of wet patch."

"And provided she was back in time, she could wash off any blood in the sink in the bar."

"That's it. She went back into the bar, and she acted as usual for the rest of the evening. She wanted the body found as late as possible, of course, so that the *time* of the murder would be reasonably open. So she expressed no great worry about Des's nonappearance, and Dawn, and all the regulars in the bar, knew that Des was just the sort of person who would say he'd turn up and then not do so."

"He hated working in the bar," said Charlie.

"Yes, and it was only his wife who was inconvenienced. He treated her like a skivvy, and he didn't care who knew it. By closing time she thought it would be all right for the body to be found, so she talked to Frank and began to express worry. For a plan that was largely improvised at short notice, it was extremely cunning. It could very well have worked — except that I rather think that if we had charged anybody else, Win would have come forward and confessed. I can't see her letting Brad Mallory take the rap for her."

"Interesting question," said Charlie: "Would we have believed her confession?"

"That's rather a frightening thought," agreed Dundy.

The fair-haired head of the new manager appeared at the dining room door.

"Sorry to intrude. I've just been on the phone to head office. They're glad it's all cleared up, though the fact that it's Mrs. Capper does tie it in rather unpleasantly with the chain. But they've told me to make it plain that they'll do everything in their power in the matter of legal advice, defense, and so on. The director was very insistent on this. Blames himself a lot, as I said before. Feels that if he hadn't pushed for Capper's appointment none of this would have happened. And of course he feels very cut-up about the boy. . . ."

"I can't see the police pushing very strongly for a heavy sentence," said Dundy. "It would be hard to argue that she'd be a danger to anyone else in the future. The courts take a surprisingly lenient view, sometimes, these days, especially in cases of domestic murder."

They heard a sound from the stairs, and the policemen went out into the foyer. Win was coming down the stairs. Dawn was following, carrying a small suitcase. Win needed no help now. She was quite composed. As Charlie and Nettles went out to usher her from the door to the waiting police car, Dundy went forward to take her arm. She smiled at him, a smile he had not seen before, with some faded prettiness in it.

"I feel much happier now," she said.

The Webster

17

Much later that day, after a long interrogation of Win Capper, the policemen came back to the Saracen. The play was just over, and the audience was streaming out of the great gates or into the three bars. It had been full, of course. If it had been booked solid before, the murder would have seen to it that it would be now. Rumors that an arrest had been made had rather disappointed most playgoers as they arrived. Secretly many of them had cherished the unlikely hope that at some point in the evening a uniformed cop would stride onstage and arrest somebody, preferably one of the Galloways. Now *that* would be something to tell one's grandchildren!

The policemen collected up their papers and anything they thought might conceivably be used as evidence at the trial. They told the temporary manager that the flat would be available to him in a few days, but he said he didn't fancy it and would use one of the hotel bedrooms. Then there was really nothing more to be done. Yet Charlie and Nettles felt that Dundy was oddly reluctant to be gone. He surely wasn't getting a taste for arty people, was he? Awkwardly they made conversation.

"You'd better be booking your ticket sharpish, hadn't you, sir?" asked Nettles.

"Ticket?"

"For *The Chaste Apprentice*. You'll want to see a performance, won't you, after all we've heard about it?"

"I suppose it might be an idea. I expect they'll let me in if I say I need it to set the seal on my case. As a Ketterick man I can't think why I've never seen a play here before."

"Personally I wish Singh was giving another performance," said Charlie. "Someone might guess the truth at any time, and that will be the end of his career. It would be something to boast about to the sort of girl from London University who fancies a black boyfriend: 'I'm one of the few people in the world who's heard a real castrato.'"

"You have a twisted sense of humor." Dundy's head jerked round. "Oh, I say, excuse me for a moment. Or actually you two can push off home."

But they didn't push off home. They made themselves discreetly scarce and watched while Iain Dundy walked up to Gillian Soames, who had appeared down the stairs from the upper rooms, having changed into civvy clothes. If the superintendent had been a younger man, they would have said that he was chatting her up. It must be said that Dundy got somewhere in a remarkably short time. Indeed, it was almost as if she had been waiting for him to make a move.

"I did wonder if you'd care for a drink," they heard him say after two or three minutes.

Charlie's foot moved for the last time to tap Nettles's ankle.

"I'd love one." Gillian glanced toward the Shakespeare.

"Or even a late supper?" said Dundy, moving towards the street door. "There's a place I know — little Indian place — where they'll still be happy to serve us."

"That would be lovely," said Gillian, following him out into the High Street. "After a performance I always feel I could eat a horse."

Charlie and Nettles looked at each other.

"It has been known," said Nettles. "Policemen marrying actresses."

"Hope for me yet," said Charlie cheerfully. "Drink?"

"What else?"

"The Shakespeare?"

Charlie looked towards the Shakespeare Bar and seemed to see the ghost of Des Capper leaning familiarly over the shoulders of his guests with his quack remedies, false information, and real threats.

"The Webster," he said firmly.

THORNDIKE-MAGNA hopes you have enjoyed this Large Print book. All our Large Print titles are designed for easy reading, and all our books are made to last. Other Thorndike Press or Magna Print books are available at your library, through selected bookstores, or directly from the publishers. For more information about current and upcoming titles, please call or mail your name and address to:

THORNDIKE PRESS
P.O. Box 159
Thorndike, Maine 04986
(800) 223-6121
(207) 948-2962 (in Maine and Canada call collect)

or in the United Kingdom:

MAGNA PRINT BOOKS
Long Preston, Near Skipton
North Yorkshire,
England BD23 4ND
(07294) 225

There is no obligation, of course.